OPERATION DRAKE
VOYAGE OF DISCOVERY

OPERATION DRAKE
VOYAGE OF DISCOVERY

Written & edited by Andrew W. Mitchell

SEVERN HOUSE

To the 57,586 young people who applied to join us but whom we could not take

British Library Cataloguing in Publication Data
Mitchell, Andrew W.
  Operation Drake
  1. Operation Drake (*Expedition*)
  I. Title
  910. 4'1 G419
  ISBN 0-7278-2007-9

Published by Severn House Publishers Limited
144–146 New Bond Street
London WIY 9FD

Text © The Scientific Exploration Society 1981
Artwork illustrations © Severn House Publishers Limited 1981
Editorial: **Ian Jackson** and **Diana Levinson**
Design: **Rob Burt**
Artwork: **Eddie Botchway**

Filmset by Tameside Filmsetting Limited, Ashton-under-Lyne, Lancashire
Printed and bound in Great Britain by Fakenham Press Limited, Fakenham, Norfolk

BUCKINGHAM PALACE

Over the past two years I have watched the progress of Operation Drake with interest. I think that we can all feel well satisfied that the expedition has been an outstanding success.

I have been particularly pleased to see how the Young Explorers have been able to make a genuine contribution to the many scientific projects. I hope that this can be an example to others of how simple scientific studies can be completed by young people, even though at the outset they may have been lacking in any specialist knowledge.

Much of the expedition's programme has been concerned with conservation studies. I am hopeful that in due course the results will make a modest contribution towards encouraging the conservation of our natural resources. The work of Operation Drake in Indonesia has been a fine example of how an expedition comprising teams of scientists and Young Explorers from many different nations and cultures can work in harmony together towards a common goal - in this instance, the survey and preparation of a management plan for a nature reserve.

Operation Drake has provided opportunities for a great many Young Explorers to work and live amongst people of other countries and contribute towards a better understanding of one another. Often projects have been conducted in remote areas and under arduous conditions, which have provided both adventure and an opportunity for the Young Explorers to stretch themselves mentally and physically. If, as I hope will be the case, these young people transmit their enthusiasm to others and seek to put their experience to use in service to the community - then the aims of Operation Drake will truly have been fulfilled.

The expedition would not have been possible without the wonderful measure of support afforded by governments, commerce, industry, the armed forces and many individuals throughout the world who have given freely of their time, energy and resources. I am most grateful to all those who have contributed to provide this wonderful experience for the Young Explorers.

Author's note

This book is about the largest and most complicated expedition ever to leave Britain. It is therefore impossible to mention everyone who took part or name the thousands of generous sponsors without whom it could not have begun. It is to the hundreds of people who tirelessly worked unpaid and unknown around the world ensuring the smooth running of the expedition that we owe great thanks. Another book written by John Blashford-Snell entitled *Operation Drake* portrays the expedition through the eyes of the young people who took part. Together they tell the story of Operation Drake.

In particular I would like to thank those who contributed to this record of our exploits: Hussein Adan, John Blashford-Snell, Trish Holdway, Mark Horton, Chris Sainsbury, Hugh Savill, Richard Snailham and Ian Swingland. Thanks is also due to the many people who supplied material for the illustrations and photographs. Finally, a special thank you to Ian Jackson and Diana Levinson who so expertly saw the book through all its stages.

I have written about more than Operation Drake alone for *Eye of the Wind* embarked on a voyage of discovery with far-reaching implications when she left Plymouth 400 years after Francis Drake. I hope to have painted a picture of some of the remarkable discoveries we made and have tried to examine the projects we undertook and the unique wildlife we encountered in their environmental and, in some cases, historical contexts. Operation Drake was intended as a stimulus to think about the world about us. So too is this book. If *Eye of the Wind* were to circumnavigate the globe 400 years hence, would she still find a world so abundant in varied forms of life and magnificent wild places?

Andrew Mitchell

Contents

Contributors

Hussein Adan Isak BSc
Ornithologist
National Museums of Kenya

Dr Patricia Holdway
Researcher, Marine Biological Association
of the United Kingdom

Mark Horton MA
Department of Archaeology
and Anthropology
University of Cambridge, England

Dr Hugh Savill
Leader of Medical Research
Papua New Guinea

Christopher Sainsbury
Watch Officer and Photographer
Eye of the Wind

Dr Ian Swingland
Zoologist
Department of Biology
University of Kent, England

Foreword

When Francis Drake sailed from Plymouth in 1579 he took with him a number of young people motivated by a spirit of adventure and exploration. Today there seem to be few outlets for young people providing such a challenge.

Operation Drake was much more than just a sailing adventure around the world. It was an opportunity to give service in an ever growing field of scientific exploration. It brought together young people, institutions and scientists of many nations in a common aim of research and endeavour. Together they learnt much that will help us in the conservation of our natural resources.

In addition the Young Explorers had the unique opportunity of working in environments and amongst cultures very different from their own which gave them a new perspective with which to judge themselves and their attitudes towards their fellow man. They went as ambassadors for their countries and returned as focal points for future projects of their own making and as part of a unique fellowship from which to build their own qualities of leadership. Operation Drake affected a great many more people than merely those who went on it and I hope that Young Explorers with their increased knowledge of their own capabilities and the magnificence of what they have seen will inspire greater awareness of the world in others.

Introduction

In the late sixteenth century Sir Francis Drake composed a prayer which begins: *O Lord God, when thou givest to thy servants to endeavour any great matter* ... During his action-packed life Drake was involved with many 'great matters', amongst them the raids on Spanish treasure in Panama, the defence of England against the Armada and the circumnavigation of the globe. When the Scientific Exploration Society (SES) were considering a 'great matter' of their own in the mid-1970s it was fitting that they should liken it to Sir Francis's journey round the world and call it Operation Drake.

The idea first came from one of the society's members, Major Bill Kingston, Managing Director of Borodin Communications in York. We were discussing what the SES might do after its successful four-month scientific survey of the Zaire River in Africa in 1974–5. Bill suggested that a two-year voyage round the world in a sailing ship, with eight or nine expeditions taking place for two or three months at a time at various ports of call along its route, might very effectively be carried out on the 400th anniversary of Drake's circumnavigation of 1577–80.

It seemed an ironically appropriate anniversary to mark. The times were as out of joint in the late 1970s as they had been in 1570s. Inflation raged. Britain was racked by grave economic and social problems. Soviet Russia presented the same kind of ideological threat as Spain had done. Some fillip to national morale was sorely needed. Drake's achievements did much to deflect the Spanish menace, as well as bringing home to England much needed silver and gold and giving a boost to the nation's self-confidence. Perhaps Operation Drake, in its own different way, could make a small impact on the world for Britain?

Of course, there was much that was dissimilar in the two enterprises. When he set off, Drake never intended to circle the world whereas we consciously planned to sail from Plymouth in October 1978, heading westwards across the world's oceans to return there in December 1980. Drake aimed to attack and plunder the Spaniards in the South Sea but we envisaged wholly peaceful scientific and community projects designed to involve and help the local people and bring together men and women from as many diverse nations as possible in a spirit of friendly cooperation. Drake's raids were spectacularly profitable, whilst I knew that to mount and carry through such a protracted and multi-faceted operation we should have to call on the generosity of many sponsors and supporters. Drake was a chauvinistic Englishman and a staunch Protestant, but – while none can doubt the great patriotism of the British organisers – Operation Drake was developed on a truly international basis, committees being set up in sixteen countries with participants coming from another eleven. And a small point: Drake in the *Golden Hind* had to battle his way round the southern tip of South America and round the Cape of Good Hope, whilst our ship *Eye of the Wind* could avail herself of the canals at Panama and Suez and she sailed mostly in tropical waters. She had her share of storms, but they were never as bad as those that beset Drake off Cape Horn.

There was one further major difference. Drake's original venture was carried out by him and his long-suffering men solely for their nation and their faith. What they themselves derived from it was of less significance. The commemorative journey of 1978–80, on the other hand, was primarily designed for the benefit of its participants. Those who sailed on *Eye of the Wind* and those who flew out to the major points which the ship visited and where work was to be done were to be the main beneficiaries. Who were they?

Sir Francis Drake

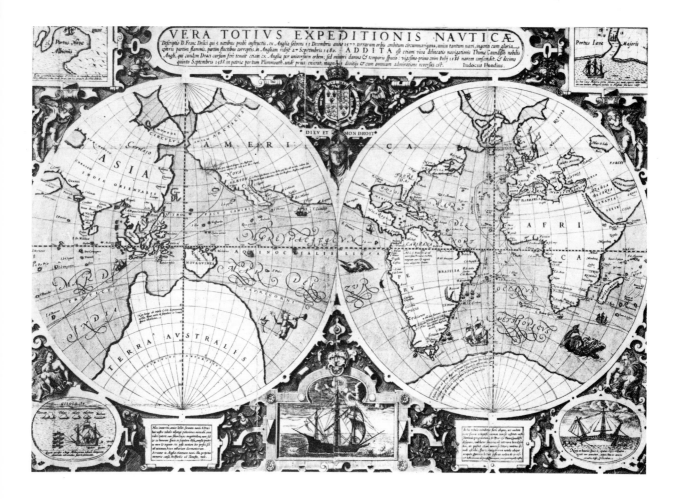

VERA TOTIVS EXPEDITIONIS NAVTICÆ

Jodocus Hondius produced this map in c.1595 depicting the voyages of Sir Francis Drake (1577–80) and Thomas Cavendish (1586–88) with insets showing incidents from Drake's voyage. **In the bottom right the** *Golden Hind* **lies stranded on a reef in the Spice Islands.**

At a very early stage in the planning we decided that they were to be young people between the ages of seventeen and twenty-four, of both sexes and from many nations. After all, Sir Francis had had three or four youngsters among his 164 crew, including his page John Drake and John Hawkins's nephew, William. On the Zaire River two young men from the island of Jersey, Richard Le Boutillier and Peter Picot had formed part of the team. They had been sponsored by local companies and had played their part most successfully in the scientific work of that expedition. This principle could easily be expanded. Sponsors could be found, world-wide, who would finance the participation of not just two, but large numbers of Young Explorers (YEs) who would form the core of the whole operation. The experience they would get, at an impressionable age and in a new, challenging and often remote situation, would surely represent a milestone in their lives.

To be a beneficiary in this sort of exercise, however, you have also to be a contributor. This was never to be merely a subsidised jaunt. As members of a particular phase of the operation, the young people would tackle, under direction, whatever work was planned for that phase. The aims of Operation Drake's activities at sea and in the field were manifold: scientific work was to be carried out, community projects were to be completed and many straightforwardly adventurous pursuits were to take place. All the nine phases offered an amalgam of these three ingredients.

But I anticipate. Before we could embark on the first phase we had to begin the long, time consuming and often frustrating business of setting up a big expedition. Just as Francis Drake had had to depend on wealthy sponsors like the Earl of Leicester, Sir Christopher Hatton and Sir Francis Walsingham, so we first got the backing of our friend and supporter, Mr Walter Annenberg, lately American ambassador in London. In Britain and overseas various concerns offered their help – the Ministry of Defence, British American Tobacco, Gestetner, BP, many airlines, Capital Radio, Esso, Unilever, The Hanson Trust, Inchcape and Stewart Wrightson – to mention just a few of the 4,000 sponsors.

Under the aegis of the SES several committees and sub-committees were formed. I ran an Operations sub-committee, whilst administration was initially under Mervyn Price, a retired company director, and later controlled by a most resourceful ex-Royal Marine, George Thurstan. A suitable sailing ship had to be procured and a Ship sub-committee, chaired by Maldwyn Drummond, set about this task. Freddy Rodger, a leading ophthalmologist and senior scientist on the Zaire River Expedition, presided over a Scientific sub-committee which began to harness the interest of the scientific world. The chairmen of all these sub-committees were also to meet regularly in the company of other influential figures as members of an overall Executive Committee and we asked my former commander at the Royal Military Academy Sandhurst, and long-term aider and abetter, General Sir John Mogg, to chair this important body. The General had just retired from the Army and having been Deputy Supreme Commander in Europe, his experience and international circle of friends were to prove of enormous value to the venture.

Certain key people such as Ruth Mindel, Andrew Mitchell, Christopher Sainsbury, Val Roberts and a number of others became, one by one, full time staff of Operation Drake. In subterranean premises below the pavements of Whitehall the nerve centre

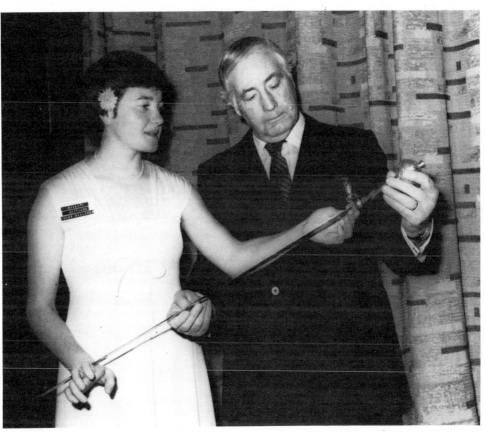

Barbara Shopland, a Canadian YE, presents Walter Annenberg with a replica of Drake's **sword. It was carried right round the world aboard** *Eye of the Wind.*

of this great undertaking began to burgeon and expand. Hundreds of other experts volunteered to help in their spare time, including my old friend Richard Snailham who became our invaluable historian. Another key member was ex-Royal Engineer Captain and veteran explorer, Jim Masters, who had the unenviable task of arranging all the logistic support and the movement of personnel.

The greatest power behind Sir Francis Drake's expedition to the South Sea had been the throne. Queen Elizabeth I, hovering as she often did between placating Philip of Spain and squaring up to him, was moved by events in the Netherlands to take up a more hostile stance in mid-July 1577. Drake's plans, which she had known about for some time but ignored, now seemed to offer a fine chance of striking at Philip by clandestinely sending an armed fleet through the Straits of Magellan to raid Spanish ports and shipping in what he regarded as his private lake. The Queen saw Drake at Greenwich and while the real objectives of the expedition were agreed verbally, a charter for an innocent seeming trading mission to South America was drawn up. The Queen became his biggest investor.

The parallel between all this and Operation Drake's involvement with Buckingham Palace is thinner but nonetheless significant. The Prince of Wales's interest in schemes for the encouragement of young people is well known. Operation Drake would be likely to appeal to him and in a series of meetings with him I outlined our plans. Prince Charles agreed to become Patron of Operation Drake and thereafter personally supported three young people who took part in it. He came on board *Eye of the Wind* at Plymouth in October 1978 and took the helm as the brigantine moved off for the first time down the Tamar and past the Hoe. At the end of the historic voyage in December 1980 he visited her again in St Katharine's Dock at Tower Bridge. His steady support was to prove invaluable.

With royal patronage and widespread backing from the services, the media and sections of the commercial and industrial worlds the enterprise could forge ahead. Capital Radio made frequent mention of the forthcoming venture and there was a keen response from London and the home counties. In the end the Operation Drake offices worldwide had 58,000 bids for what were, at first, only 216 places, although we later expanded and were able to accept a total of 414 YEs.

Sadly, some kind of stringent selection process had to be inaugurated. It was impossible even to interview all those who filled in the initial form, so a great many quite suitable young people were inevitably disappointed. What were we looking for? We laid down four simple criteria: the Young Explorer must be compatible, be able to understand and speak English, be fit and able to swim. Thousands would be able to meet these requirements. So, for a few young people who looked to be good prospects, a series of rigorous selection weekends were arranged throughout 1978.

It is said that Drake chose with care the seamen who were to man his own ships, the *Golden Hind*, *Swan* and *Christopher*. How he did this we do not know. Plymouth in 1577 was seething with unemployed, and the seafaring life, though dangerous and often fatal, could be spectacularly lucrative. He had to choose prudently. Operation Drake's problems were different – it was more a question of *embarras de richesse*. Vast numbers of those who were tested in all countries, could have done well and have benefited. There was much heart-searching among the selectors when they had to discriminate between the absolutely first-rate and the merely excellent. But each successful candidate was to be sponsored to the tune of £2,300, so the judges owed it to the benefactors to do a good job. They had to pick, as fairly as they could, those whose resourcefulness, enthusiasm, public-spiritedness and good humour was the more shiningly apparent.

Had Drake been setting off in the 1970s he might have taken some of his potential crew up onto Dartmoor for their selection tests. But his main problems were to come not from the crew so much as from the ten 'Gentlemen Adventurers' whom he invited to come down from London to join the enterprise as officers. Although Drake was the 'General' he was their social inferior. There was also bound to be friction

John Blashford-Snell working at an Operation Drake Signals Centre in the field.

between them and the rough crew. It was on the bleak shores of Patagonia that he laid it down that: 'the gentleman should haul and draw with the mariner, and the mariner with the gentleman', and camaraderie began painfully to be forged.

Operation Drake suffered none of this in the egalitarian 1970s; directing staff and Young Explorers buckled together. The selectors' judgment of compatability proved to be acute. The administration and logistics of the enterprise were largely run by members or ex-members of the Armed Forces on rather gentle military lines. The military content of the expedition resulted from immensely helpful backing from the British Armed Services and those of many other nations. This was provided under the 'Adventurous Training Scheme' which enables British servicemen to participate in worthwhile projects of this kind whilst still on duty. Research projects were directed by the scientists who had devised them. No special abilities were demanded of the YEs. Where specific scientific or other skills were required they would have to be learnt on board *Eye of the Wind* or in the field. As it happened quite a few were highly qualified as, for example, nurses, photographers, underwater divers and archaeologists. This was useful, for scientific work was an important aim.

One of Drake's crew, Lawrence Eliot, was a botanist of sorts and he contributed to the collection of descriptions of plants seen on the voyage, published at Antwerp in 1582. This collection, by the botanist Charles de l'Ecluse, is probably the first expedition scientific report. The drawings of animal life made by the chaplain, Francis Fletcher, are also notable. These were just by-products, however, of what was essentially a warlike venture. In Operation Drake's case there were clear, prearranged objectives. The scientific work was to be biological, archaeological and medical.

The biological research was primarily into the ecology of the tropical rainforests – one of the earth's most precious, dwindling resources. This was to be a comparative study in Panama, Papua New Guinea and Sulawesi and was to be given a new, astonishing dimension by the construction of high-level, aerial walkways to enable scientists to study comparatively in the jungle canopy for the first time ever. The success of these aerial walkways was such that more are planned for future research projects. Andrew Mitchell, the expedition's Scientific Co-ordinator, was one of those who pioneered this idea. He explains the use of the aerial walkway in greater detail in the book as indeed he does the other multifarious biological programmes – amongst them, the collection of minute marine organisms living close to the surface of the sea along the 30,000 mile path that *Eye of the Wind* sailed, the gathering of sufficient zoological information in Sulawesi to enable a plan for a nature reserve there to be submitted to the Indonesian Government and the carrying out of a survey of the wildlife in the Masai Mara Game Reserve in Kenya.

On the archaeological front, Mark Horton, from Cambridge, supervised teams of YEs who did important work. They discovered the sixteenth-century 'lost' Spanish city of Acla on the Caribbean shore of Panama, which was the second settlement ever to be planted by Europeans in the New World and, together with the National Museums of Kenya, opened up the overgrown ruins of Moslem towns on islands off the Kenyan coast, dating from the tenth century.

Medically the results seem as if they will be just as exciting. (It takes so long for scientific seeds actually to bear fruit that at this stage I can only hazard a guess.) Typical projects were comparative studies of the visual acuity of young children in Panama, Papua New Guinea and Sulawesi to show their degree of vitamin A deficiency which causes 100,000 children to go blind each year.

Time has proved that all this work could be efficiently carried out by enthusiastic, if relatively untrained, groups of Young Explorers.

Like the *Pelican* in 1577 (later renamed the *Golden Hind* after one of Drake's sponsors), Operation Drake's *Eye of the Wind* made a false start, but eventually got over to Jersey and thence, via Tenerife in the Canaries, to St Vincent in the West Indies. Here the Phase I Young Explorers climbed the volcano of La Soufrière and examined the relatively recent and still growing island in the water-filled crater. This visit was fortunately timed: three months after the YEs moved off to the mainland La Soufrière erupted. The timely warning given by Operation Drake helped to avert a greater disaster. Four months were then spent at Caledonia Bay on the isthmus of Panama before *Eye of the Wind* slipped through the canal and up the Pacific coast to Costa Rica. Here a monument was unveiled to commemorate Drake's brief visit to Isla de Caño in March 1579, and the expedition then travelled on to the Galapagos Islands, that Ecuadorean treasury of unique species, followed by the long haul westwards across the Pacific. *Eye of the Wind* passed through the Tuamotu Archipelago and Tahiti on her way to Fiji where useful community projects were completed and thence to Papua New Guinea. This was Operation Drake's second major region of concentrated study and several months in 1979 were spent in and around this vast, relatively unknown island lying to the north of Australia.

The expedition crossed Sir Francis Drake's path again when it moved to Sulawesi where it carried out a multi-discipinary survey to draw up a management plan for a nature reserve in possibly the most remote and wild of all the areas in which it operated. Here the results, zoological for the most part, were rich indeed, and the sense of achievement experienced by the Young Explorers was the most marked.

The *Eye of the Wind* moved on (it was now 1980) across the Indian Ocean, via the

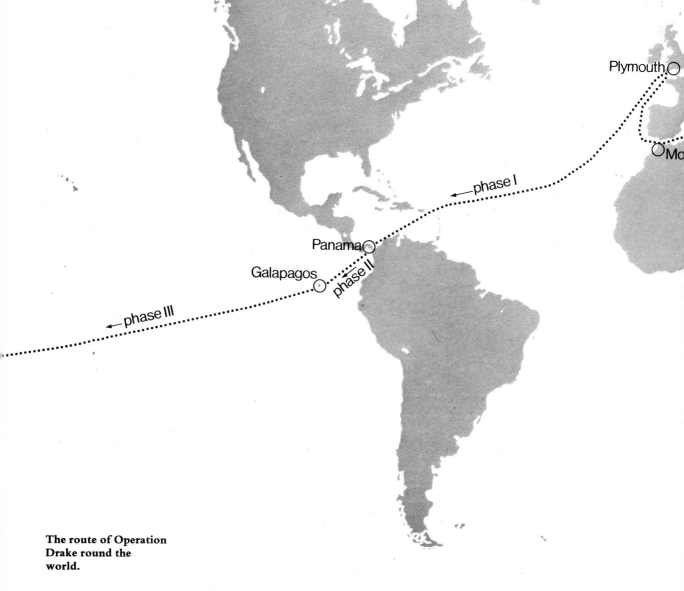

The route of Operation Drake round the world.

Chagos Archipelago and the Seychelles, to the coast of Africa and to Kenya's major port, Mombasa. Here Phase VIII disembarked and the YEs were scattered throughout Kenya on various projects until they were relieved by Phase VIIIA. For two months activities of a mixed character – scientific, constructional and simply adventurous – were undertaken, during the course of which Phase IX YEs had sailed north from Mombasa to the Red Sea and the Gulf of Suez. Some trees were planted in Ismailia before the ship passed through the canal on her way to do some interesting pollution studies, in conjunction with the Goodyear airship *Europa* off Alassio in the Gulf of Genoa. There was still time for the YEs to climb a few peaks in Morocco's Atlas Mountains before returning, via Jersey, to Plymouth on December 9th 1980. The culmination of the whole great enterprise came on December 13th when *Eye of the Wind* passed up the Thames and under the upraised arms of Tower Bridge into the Pool of London, and on the 19th when our Patron, Prince Charles, inspected the vessel in St Katherine's Dock and talked to a gathering of 212 YEs (over half of the total) and organisers who had travelled from many countries specially for the occasion.

Sic Parvis Magna was Sir Francis Drake's motto: 'Great things have small beginnings'. From the experience of two young Jerseymen in Zaire in 1974 and a conversation in York with Bill Kingston so many great and good things were to flow.

Outward bound

The whirring rotors of a rapidly moving helicopter announced the arrival of HRH The Prince of Wales, Patron of the most complicated and far-reaching expedition the world has ever seen, and brainchild of the tall, rounded figure of Royal Engineer Lieutenant-Colonel John Blashford-Snell. The Prince began his royal address by saying that participation in the expedition would be rather like banging your head against a brick wall – jolly nice when it was all over. As it had not yet begun, one wondered what lay ahead on the *Eye of the Wind*'s two-year voyage of exploration and scientific discovery to far continents and islands around the globe.

Stepping briskly aboard, Prince Charles was warmly welcomed by General Sir John Mogg, Chairman of Operation Drake, a former Deputy Supreme Allied Commander in Europe. To his right he met Kirsty Henderson formerly a woman police officer in Plymouth and now a Young Explorer on Operation Drake, and to her left, Mohan Limbu a British Gurkha soldier from Nepal, another Young Explorer.

HRH The Prince of Wales chats to Captain Patrick Collis as he helms the ship at the start of her two-year voyage.

They were part of the full complement of twenty-four young people sponsored by industries, charities and trusts for the first three-month phase of the voyage.

As *Eye of the Wind* moved from Plymouth dockside amidst an impressive flotilla of hooting and cheering boats she was ceremoniously towed to the mouth of the Tamar to begin her magnificent voyage, only to return later that night, creeping into Plymouth Sound under the politely averted eyes of those celebrating her departure in the inns along the waterfront. Owing to unavoidable delays during the refit she was not yet ready to face the Atlantic and as Drake had done 400 years before, returned to port before commencing her circumnavigation of the globe.

Eye of the Wind, a 150 tonne brigantine, had been chosen to act as the expedition's flagship, the base from which a series of scientific and adventurous projects would be undertaken in Panama, Papua New Guinea, Indonesia and Kenya as well as a host of islands in between. The voyage was split into nine three-month phases. On each of these twenty-four Young Explorers, or YEs as they became known, aged between seventeen and twenty-four, were to act as ship's crew and to assist the scientists and explorers in the field anywhere in the world; in short the adventure of a lifetime.

When Operation Drake was announced on December 13th 1977 it caused little excitement in the world's press but amongst many young people the effect was explosive. Letters began pouring into the expedition's office at Gestetner House in London's Euston Road as 58,000 people from all over the world applied to compete for a place on the voyage. Selection committees were set up in Canada, the United States,

Eye of the Wind **sails past Drake's Island in Plymouth Sound to begin her journey across the Atlantic.**

Monty provided plenty of surprises for the YEs as Wiz Gambier found out on her selection weekend in England. Wiz later found herself facing up to the real challenges of Papua New Guinea.

Australia, New Zealand, West Germany, Iceland, Papua New Guinea, Nepal, Hong Kong and Great Britain to process the applications and a lucky few then went forward to a selection weekend.

Some Young Explorers said later that their selection weekend was the hardest thing they ever did on Operation Drake. The first one in Great Britain took place at St Augustine's Priory in Kent on two freezing February days deemed suitable for testing the bold and the nervous for tasks in the tropics. After twenty-four hours of constructing rafts, plucking pigeons, nocturnal map reading, and wrestling with a 4 metre reticulated python, both the judges and the Young Explorers were exhausted and the winners were declared. The first was Christine McHugh, a police cadet in the Kent constabulary. The judges looked in the main for compatability whilst under stress as the cramped accommodation aboard and the rigours of the tasks ahead were likely to test the patience and strength of the most seasoned explorer. In the end, far from a group of blue-eyed Vikings and Amazon women a remarkable cross-section of people from all walks of life emerged. A steel-plate worker from Wales, a medical student from the United States, a trawlerman from Iceland, a journalist from Korea, a barman from Hong Kong to name a few. In all, 414 Young Explorers were chosen from twenty-seven nations.

In October 1978 the first eager Young Explorers began arriving at Plymouth to begin their voyage bearing tales of their selection adventures in the canyons of Colorado

Sail training was a vital part of the voyage and everyone soon became adept at climbing the ratlines up into the rigging.

or the deserts of the Australian outback. On reaching the ship they discovered that a month's back-breaking work lay ahead to complete the refit and prepare her for her ocean voyage.

Only five months before the expedition was due to depart, it was without a ship, the originally chosen vessel having been bought by the Sultan of Oman. A frantic world-wide search revealed the brigantine *Eye of the Wind* in Australia returning from her first voyage around the world. She was chartered by Operation Drake for her second. *Eye of the Wind* was built in 1911 at Braca on the river Weser near Bremen in Germany by C Leuring and Company to carry salt to the Argentine, from there to carry hides to Cornwall, finally returning to Germany with a cargo of English clay. Two trips were made each year. She was one of the last vessels to be built for this purpose before steam put paid to the days of sail. Her movements in the war years are largely unknown but she reappeared in 1958 as a cargo vessel in the Baltic in the winter, drifting for herring off the coast of Iceland in summer. Here disaster struck. In the late sixties, whilst trapped in the ice off Iceland, she was gutted by fire and towed, a burnt-out hulk, to Gothenburg where she remained until 1973.

Tiger Timbs was a panel beater from East Finchley in London and a fanatical square-rig sailor. He and like-minded friends had searched for years to find their own vessel when they discovered *Eye of the Wind* in Gothenburg. Six months later they had purchased her and patched her up sufficiently to make the journey from Sweden to Grimsby where final plans were drawn up and the money raised to refurbish the ship. In April 1975 she was moved to a berth at Faversham and eighteen months of hard labour began. Materials were gathered from all over the country. Church pews formed the benches in the galley, a magnificent oak floor from a dance hall became the deck of the lower saloon, beautiful walnut panelling was salvaged from a demolished bank, an Australian minesweeper due for the breaker's yard provided teak for the deckhouse and the ship's compass came from an old trawler. The spars were made from carefully selected English larch trees, felled and shaped by adze and spokeshave as craftsmen would have done in days gone by. Remarkably, the combination of inventiveness and skilled workmanship produced a beautifully authentic square-rigged sailing ship which left for Australia in September 1976 to return two years later as the flagship for Operation Drake.

On her arrival in Plymouth an immense amount of work was needed to prepare her for the voyage ahead. The first part of the job was routine. The ship was slipped and all the marine life that had taken a free ride on her hull removed. The Royal Naval dock-yard of HMS Drake could not have been more apt a place for the remainder of the refit designed to refurbish the vessel which was to commemorate Sir Francis Drake's epic voyage. A mixture of servicemen and civilian volunteers together with the YEs toiled all hours of the day and often well into the night converting her from a passenger charter vessel carrying twenty-four into a research and sail training ship with a full complement of thirty-eight.

A second after-deckhouse was built containing the laboratory and radio room, whilst below, cupboards were replaced with folding bunks to accommodate the Young Explorers. The structure of the ship was altering visibly and deeper down inside her even more dramatic changes were in progress. Originally without an auxiliary engine, *Eye of the Wind* had been fitted with a massive two-cylinder Skandia. This had plenty of character but was not capable of ensuring that the ship would keep to her two-year timetable or forcing her through headwinds and heavy seas. Prince Charles came to the rescue and enabled us to buy a reconditioned eight-cylinder Gardener, complete with feathering propeller, gearbox and a powerful auxiliary generator.

The Young Explorers' first impressions had been of a sailing ship without any sails, let alone spars, apparently half submerged by swarms of people trying to push different pieces of wire through the same small holes. Now the naval ratings dance hall that had housed the mass of yards and spars was empty and the master rigger had completed his work. At last *Eye of the Wind* was ready to go and at 6.51 on the morning of November

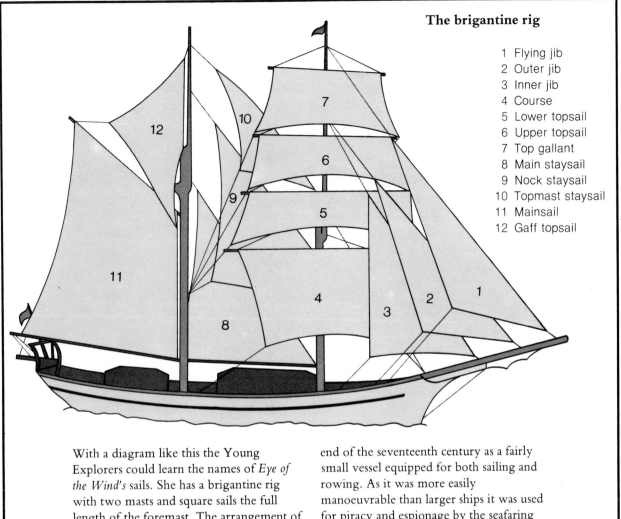

The brigantine rig

1 Flying jib
2 Outer jib
3 Inner jib
4 Course
5 Lower topsail
6 Upper topsail
7 Top gallant
8 Main staysail
9 Nock staysail
10 Topmast staysail
11 Mainsail
12 Gaff topsail

With a diagram like this the Young Explorers could learn the names of *Eye of the Wind's* sails. She has a brigantine rig with two masts and square sails the full length of the foremast. The arrangement of the sails is ideally suited to trade wind sailing.

The brigantine originated towards the end of the seventeenth century as a fairly small vessel equipped for both sailing and rowing. As it was more easily manoeuvrable than larger ships it was used for piracy and espionage by the seafaring nations of the Mediterranean. This form of rig was popular and used throughout the last hundred years of sail.

8th 1978 she slipped quietly out of Plymouth Sound and headed out towards the Atlantic.

St Helier, Jersey was the first and last British port of call. With sacks of fresh vegetables donated by island farmers and a plaque of Jersey granite presented by the Constable of St Helier, the crew set all plain sail and headed for the Azores. Sasha Campbell, the first of ten Young Explorers sponsored by the island community, through no fault of his own, missed the boat and had to be rushed out after her in the States of Jersey launch to meet the wrath of Captain Patrick Collis angrily pacing the poop.

The crew were truly green. They had spent nearly six weeks working on board but very few of them had ever been to sea in their lives and two Nepalese Young Explorers had never even seen the sea before coming to England. All soon became inanimate bundles of red oilskins, struggling on downhauls or clinging to the pinrail, learning about life at sea.

At every hour of the day or night, whether in port or on the high seas, there was always somebody awake keeping a watchful eye open on board the ship. The watch at sea was composed of a helmsman, a lookout and a messenger, the rest of the watch

Eye of the Wind **ploughs
into a heavy sea in the
Bay of Biscay.**

**All hands on the main sheet as Tiger Timbs
and the YEs prepare** *Eye of the Wind* **to go
about.**

either helping with the deck work or performing one of dozens of other regular daily
tasks. Every hour rounds would be made to ensure that the ship was safe and secure,
that no fires were smouldering, that everything was securely lashed in case of a sudden
squall, and that if running, the engine was not overheating; fuel had to be constantly
pumped by hand into a header tank. If under sail continuous checks had to be made to
ensure that no lines were chafing; any change in the weather meant that sails would be
trimmed, set or handed. Every six hours a detailed meteorological report would be
compiled and sent back to the Meteorological Office at Bracknell in Berkshire providing otherwise unobtainable information from the middle of the world's oceans.

Regular turns or 'tricks' at the wheel were one of the more popular tasks on watch
for it was then that the Young Explorers really had the feeling that they were sailing a
square-rigged ship. Everyone immediately discovered that standing behind the wheel
and trying to steer a steady compass course was not as simple as it first appeared.
Depending on the force and direction of the wind, the size and period of the swell and
which sails were set, the handling characteristics of the ship could change dramatically.
Some people became more adept than others in wandering only a degree or two off
course. There were others though who found their concentration wavering, especially
in the middle of the night when their hands and faces were numbed by rain and cold,
and they would often suffer the wrath of the watchkeeper when he noticed the wake
bending behind the ship or the sails flapping. The most difficult and dangerous time to
be at the wheel is when the wind is coming from directly behind the ship and a large
swell accompanies it. At times like this a ship can literally surf down the waves and the
helmsman has very little control. Reactions have to be instinctive and instant to avoid
the danger of being dismasted. At least the helmsman has his back to the approaching
waves and is spared the awesome sight of vast mountains of black water bearing down
on him; all he feels is the ship being lifted up under his feet as the bowsprit points
further and further down into an ever deepening trough.

Being on lookout had its moments of excitement. There were occasions when it was
physically exhausting just trying to hold on as the bow slammed up and down into a
nasty, short, choppy sea. Some of the most memorable moments were during the quiet
hours of night when the chipping hammers had been put away, the generator was no

longer running and the lookout felt like the only person left alive on board. This was one of the very rare moments when, on a ship of this size, it was possible to have a little peace and quiet and a few private, undisturbed thoughts, undisturbed that is, unless a school of dolphins appeared and started racing the ship on the bow wave, their trails of phosphorescence following them. At other times the lookout could not allow his concentration and vigilance to relax for a second. Perched high up aloft he might be looking for a lighthouse or land at the end of an ocean crossing or, if in busy shipping lanes, be constantly making sure that he is able to tell the watchkeeper exactly which direction every vessel he can see is going in and, as soon as one of them alters course, predicting whether it will pass a safe distance away or not.

One of the first impressions every member of the crew had was of the maze of rigging and numerous belaying pins, realising uncomfortably that he would have only a day or two in which to learn the function of each and every one to enable him to find any specific one even in the middle of the night. There were always bewildered looking people equipped with the pin diagram wandering the decks at the beginning of a voyage trying to remember the difference between a halyard and a sheet or which pin the devil's purchase was on and which one the topping lift was on. Even under the watchful eye of the mate or bosun there was invariably chaos during the first sail training lessons, but soon most of the crew were beginning to feel as comfortable as monkeys in the rigging when they were sent aloft to furl and gasket or just overhaul the buntlines.

For Martin Browne, life aboard *Eye of the Wind* was very different from being a Welsh Guardsman. One of the YEs' many chores was learning to cook in the galley for 36 people, three times a day.

Which line is it to trim the topmast staysail? Irwin van Asbeck from New Zealand begins to learn the ropes.

The huge ocean swells presented little problem to *Eye of the Wind* **although they did make for exciting sailing.**

The ship's company was divided into five separate watches and these rotated every week. The three sailing watches were on duty for four hours and then off for eight. The galley watch and the bosun's deck watch worked a normal daily routine. The bosun was responsible for organising all maintenance on board and from 08.00 until 17.30 the tranquility was disturbed by the almost endless banging of chipping hammers, the buzzing of power tools and the noisy drone of the generator. Under the direction of the mate, the bosun or watch leaders, members of the crew who showed some aptitude for the more skilled maintenance jobs had plenty of opportunity to become adept in splicing, sail making and carpentry.

The constant battering that a sailing ship gets whilst plying across thousands of miles of ocean means that the continual round of painting, varnishing and mending can never be relaxed. Visitors on board a well maintained ship are often awed by the shining woodwork and unblemished paintwork and fail to appreciate that it is not for purely aesthetic reasons that wood is varnished and metal painted, but to prevent it from cracking, rusting or rotting.

In past days of sail the bosun was responsible for discipline on board and he was in fact the ship's executioner. His symbols of office were the bosun's pipe and the cherriliccum (a cane sheathed in the cured penis of a bull), the 'bosun's come along' with which he used to encourage the crew to work harder. The equipment used by the bosun on board *Eye of the Wind* has changed little from the earliest days of sail but today he has also to be adept at sail mending and rigging which once upon a time were skills practised by specialised craftsmen.

Under the watchful eye of a member of the permanent crew, the galley watch was not only responsible for catering for thirty-eight people but also for keeping the communal areas of the accommodation spick and span and hygenic. Many a male Young Explorer returned home with plaintive tales of cleaning the heads.

Special dinners became a custom on board and YEs of different nationalities frequently produced traditional dishes from their home countries. Meals were influenced by the availability and range of food on board; the storage space was limited and fresh food would run out after a week or two at sea. Some YEs became expert at bargaining in markets where they would hunt through local produce trying to find some vegetables or fruit they recognised. Sometimes the only fresh meat available was still alive and kicking and everyone would join in, quickly becoming practised butchers. On board they all had to put their hand to baking the daily bread as well, some with a greater degree of success than others.

Probably one of the least enjoyable parts of the morning was 'happy hour' when all hands were employed with a variety of chores around the ship, both above and below decks. The four-to-eight watch had the unenviable task of scrubbing the decks every morning and evening and by the time 'happy hour' came along the next watch would be busy polishing the brass which never seems to stay bright in salt sea conditions for more than a few hours. Other watches were hard at work below sweeping and polishing or scrubbing out the heads, all tedious but nonetheless important jobs. With so many people living in such a confined space it took only a few hours of thoughtlessness before the ship became a slum, with wet clothes everywhere and not a place to sit down because of the books and personal possessions that seemed to have overflowed out of the cabins; dirt accumulated in all the dark corners and the inevitable cockroaches thrived. Some members of the crew were surprised to discover that, whereas they could live in their own mess and chaos at home, they suddenly became meticulously neat and tidy on board and would chase their own cabin mates if they failed to wash their socks or make their bunks.

In order to ensure everyone on board got as much out of their sea-time as possible, a daily lecture programme was instituted. The subjects covered varied widely but there were always instruction periods in navigation, marine biology, photography and radio communications. Often a member of the crew was quite an expert on countries the ship would be visiting and would give talks about them. At other times when the YEs were to be involved in scientific projects they would receive a grounding in the work ahead. Most of the Young Explorers also had the opportunity to discuss their own interests which varied from butterfly collecting to learning the language and customs of the Maoris.

Although life on board the *Eye of the Wind* was carefully designed to ensure every hour of the day was filled, not to mention those of the night, the YEs always found time to relax and enjoy themselves. Despite the problems of overweight baggage, hardly a phase went by on the voyage without someone bringing along a guitar or some other musical instrument. The mellow sound of a flute drifting around the decks never caused a moan, but the slightly more rasping notes of a bagpipe turned a few heads.

By the time the *Eye of the Wind* docked in Tenerife on November 26th, the Young Explorers had every right to feel that they had left their landlubber's habits behind. Most of them were using nautical terminology without thinking; floors had become decks, walls bulkheads and left and right had long ago become port and starboard. The weather across the Bay of Biscay had been variable, providing plenty of opportunity to learn the ropes. Tacking into the wind on a square-rigged ship is hard work and even more so for an inexperienced crew, who seem to have to pull twice as hard on a line to hoist a yard or sheet in a headwind. The Nepalese YEs were still looking desperately green but most of the crew had overcome the *mal de mer* and instead of having soup for every meal appetites were growing. A pair of half-frozen and sleepy lookouts had quickly learnt the hard way that the safety of the ship and the lives of all those on board were in their hands when a small cargo ship failed to alter course early one morning. As the *Eye of the Wind* bore away to avoid a collision, a few sharp blasts of the ship's horn produced a pyjama-clad figure rushing up to the bridge.

When dolphins were sighted for the first time everyone hurried on deck, braving their cameras against the flying spray and tried to freeze the motion of these beautiful creatures on film. Later most of them would search their developed prints trying vainly to distinguish mammal from blurred waves. Soon the cry of, 'Dolphins off the bow', would hardly produce a stir from the crew but a pair of killer whales close to the ship had everyone climbing the rigging for a better view.

There was a calmer air on board when the ship began the 2,700 mile passage across the Atlantic. Even the most reluctant sailors amongst the crew were conditioned enough by then to realise that every ounce of patience they possessed would be required to stop tempers becoming frayed and keep the *Eye of the Wind* a happy ship.

One of the most fascinating distractions during the long crossing was learning about the marine biology of the ocean. Whilst the great ocean deeps are still unexplored, the life living on the surface of the sea is, surprisingly, becoming a major new field of research. The foundations of marine scientific research were laid down in the days of sail. The father of marine studies was probably the sailor William Dampier, an unlikely candidate since he was a buccaneer rather than a scientist. Despite such an improbable background, his late seventeenth-century publication, *Discourse on Winds*, was based on many years of meticulous research. Subsequent to Dampier, the work of Humbolt, Darwin, and the scientists on the *Challenger* and *Discovery* expeditions has led us to appreciate the vast diversity of organisms which inhabit the oceans.

Nowadays it is unusual for a research vessel to spend a protracted time at sea, two or three weeks being the norm for a scientific expedition. A two-year scientific circum-navigatory voyage was thus a unique opportunity to undertake marine research. Dr Patricia Holdway, a specialist in marine plankton from the University of East Anglia, joined *Eye of the Wind* at Plymouth as the ship's marine biologist. She originally intended to stay only for the two-month voyage across the Atlantic but enjoyed it so

The ship's laboratory was well equipped giving the YEs an ideal opportunity to learn about the marine life in the ocean under the direction of Dr Patricia Holdway.

The sled behind Dr Holdway was designed
to tow the neuston net through the sea
collecting a multitude of marine
organisms specifically designed to live at the
air/water interface.

much that she remained for two years and sailed right round the world with Operation Drake, carrying out her own research into pollution on the sea surface as well as teaching the Young Explorers about marine life.

For a modern scientist the experience of sailing on the *Eye of the Wind* demonstrated both the joys and frustrations which must have been felt by marine scientists of former days. Those gentlemen however would not have missed the sophisticated electronic equipment which is now available. Due to limitations of space and in the electric power supply, *Eye of the Wind*'s laboratory was equipped in the same fashion as laboratories of past centuries. Plastic replaced glass, but the basic equipment of collection nets, preservatives, specimen jars and microscopes remained unchanged.

Studying on a sailing ship rather than a powered vessel, the crew was very much more at the mercy of the whims and moods of the elements. On a calm day, jellyfish and other marine animals floated past 2 metres below the sea surface, whereas in rough weather they would appear uninvited on the deck of the laboratory as a wave broke through the door. The peace and serenity of sailing in good weather contrasted dramatically with experiences in squalls and storms when looking down a microscope became an impossibility and any loose articles crashed from one side of the laboratory to the other with each roll of the ship. Trish Holdway, and the entire ship's crew, came to appreciate the ease with which the speed of a motor vessel can be adjusted to the correct rate for collecting scientific samples, when as many as fifteen sails sometimes had to be handed to achieve the same end on the *Eye of the Wind*.

It rapidly became apparent that the *Eye of the Wind*'s laboratory was suited to the collection of organisms from the sea surface and observations on their behaviour. Sophisticated chemical analysis would, of necessity be left for land-based laboratories. Decanting concentrated nitric acid or similar tasks, integral procedures for analytical work, are best performed when the visible world is not veering alarmingly from sky to sea and both hands can be used for the job rather than for maintaining one's own vertical stance.

Despite these physical obstructions for scientists under sail the benefits outweighed the difficulties. It was possible to rediscover the basic delights of simply observing and describing a wide range of animals in their natural habitat, a practice which was the absorbing work of the early naturalists but which has now become unfashionable as biological sciences are channelled into numerous specialist activities. Unlike the nineteenth century, the twentieth does not normally produce natural historians, men who have an interest in and enthusiasm for every branch of biology. This is not the fault of the modern scientist, since for a successful career he has to specialise if he is not to become an unemployable Jack-of-all-trades and master of none, and it is mainly left to the enthusiastic amateur to maintain the traditions of natural historians of past centuries.

Although scientists on modern research ships normally pursue their own particular line of research, such a restricted approach was not feasible on *Eye of the Wind*. A very wide variety of animals and plants, all of which required identification, were caught in the nets and the members of the crew assumed that the marine biologist would be equally knowledgeable about whales and plankton, seabirds and seaweeds. For Trish as a zoologist it came as something of a culture shock to be launched into a situation such as this, but having adapted, the experience was very rewarding with a constant stream of different creatures coming into the laboratory every day.

Eye of the Wind was equipped with both plankton and neuston nets. Plankton consists of small animal and plant organisms which drift with the ocean currents, appearing like dust in the water column. Neuston is composed of animals which float either on or just below the sea surface. Plankton were caught in cone-shaped nets which were towed behind the ship and sometimes weighted with lead in order to trap the organisms living at greater depths. The gauge of the nets used varied, from those which were extremely fine and used for catching minute planktonic plants, the phytoplankton, to the coarser nets for trapping zooplankton, the planktonic animals.

A mid-Atlantic plunge from the bowsprit. It is almost 3 kilometres to the bottom.

30

Even the coarsest of plankton nets had to be towed at a slow speed, usually less than 2 knots, as the net would otherwise filter inefficiently, pushing a cone of water in front of it. Ultimately, at a greater speed it would rip, in which case all that remained was a brass ring festooned with tatters of net, and a marine biologist feeling rather silly and extremely annoyed.

In contrast, the neuston net could be used at speeds of up to 6 knots. Since it was designed to catch animals living at the air/water interface, half of the mouth of the net was out of the water whilst collecting, unlike the plankton nets which were wholly immersed, thus reducing the pressure of water within the mesh. To increase further the speed at which they could be towed, the neuston nets were constructed from two different gauge meshes. Around the mouth, very coarse netting allowed excess water to escape, whilst the main body of the net which was made of finer material, filtered off the neuston. The animals were washed down into removable collecting pots fastened to the tail of the net. The majority of collecting work undertaken utilised neuston rather than plankton nets as it was not practical to slow the ship down to a speed suitable for plankton hauls unless the sea was very calm.

The neuston net was regularly streamed in the daytime and at night from the ship's boat boom, fishing for about twenty minutes, after which it was hauled on board creating much excitement as to the contents. On one occasion, shortly after leaving port, strange orange forms were discovered in the nets which defied explanation until Trish Holdway pronounced them to be pieces of carrot. It was only then that somebody noticed one of the Nepalese YEs being violently ill over the bow. Another time Spider Anderson, one of the ship's watchkeepers, planted a plastic squid in the net as it was being hauled over the side. In shaking hands the glistening red beast was transported to the laboratory where a keen Young Explorer, convinced a species new to science had been found, subjected it to the closest examination. It was not until *Made in Hong Kong* was discovered printed on its belly that the hideous truth was revealed!

Many different projects were conducted concurrently utilising the biota caught in the nets. The major study investigated the distribution and speciation of neustonic organisms around the world. Everyone on the ship became involved to some extent, with the marine research. The YEs undertook projects which varied according to their individual interests and scientific background. Some examined plants and animals which are bioluminescent (capable of emitting light), while others identified the marine mammals and seabirds seen during the voyage. The dissection of fish and analysis of their intestinal contents yielded information on marine food chains and in contrast, an examination of the development of fouling organisms on the ship's hull supplied data on the efficiency of various anti-fouling paints under different climatic conditions. Since the introduction of VLCCs (very large crude carriers), goose barnacles *Lepas* sp. have become a problem for the oil industry. VLCCs move more slowly than their smaller relatives and goose barnacles, whose larvae float freely in the sea, attach to their hulls more easily. They grow in profusion slowing the tanker's speed still further. The difference in turn around time can cost millions of pounds in lost revenue. The cost of protecting one VLCC with anti-fouling paint is between £20,000 and £30,000, so the search for an effective paint is vital. The neuston collected on the expedition is now being identified and counted so that it will be possible to compare the distribution and concentration of the different animals in the oceans which the ship crossed. The findings will augment the limited information which exists on neustonic distribution.

The surface of the world's oceans contains an ecosystem of great interest to biologists as many of the creatures upon which all life in the vertical water column depends live there. Chlorophyll within the minute phytoplankton photosynthesises the sun's energy into sugars which can then be ingested by zooplankton which are themselves eaten by larger animals. Planktonic creatures migrate up and down at different times so that hauls in the net would vary a great deal between night and day as well as in different parts of the ocean. Phytoplankton are major contributors of oxygen and the

Goose barnacles grow on anything they can find in the ocean, even lumps of tar. With their fans they filter plankton from the sea.

Life at the surface of the ocean

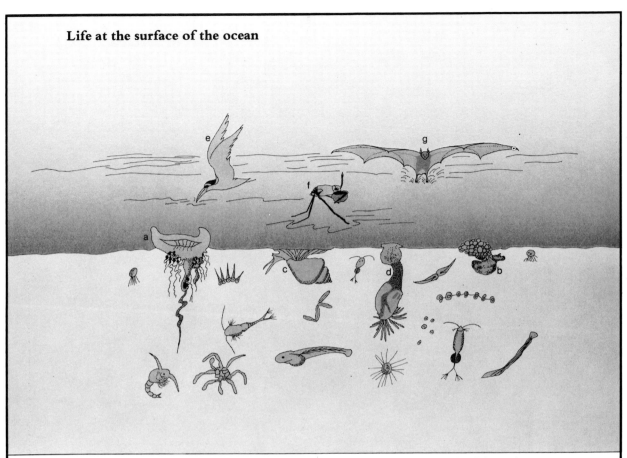

Right at the surface of the ocean there is an extraordinary variety of animals and plants specially adapted for living there collectively known as neuston. Some have specialised structures enabling them to float on the surface film. *Physalia*, the Portuguese man-of-war (a), employs a large blue, gas-filled chamber from which tentacles, which contain stinging and feeding polyps, extend into the sea below. *Janthina* (b) captures air bubbles and attaches them to its 'foot' as does *Hydrobium* (c), another marine snail. *Lepas*, the goose barnacle (d), hangs from the surface on a small blue float, filtering food from the sea. Beneath them live a multitude of minute copepods, euphausids, fish larvae, fish eggs and larval crustaceans. These all provide food for birds like the skimmer *Rynchops* (e) or insects like *Halobates* (f). There are even neuston-feeding bats, Noctilionidae (g), which detect their prey beneath the surface by ultrasonic sound, snatching it up with specially clawed feet. With the nets on board *Eye of the Wind* we could filter off this surface layer and study the fascinating life it contained.

ocean itself absorbs carbon dioxide. As the sea water filters off the sun's energy, phytoplankton are forced to live in the euphotic zone near the sea surface. Myriads of crustaceans, jellyfish, hydroids and fishes feed on the planktonic broth and themselves provide food for the next level up the food chain or sink in death to accumulate amongst the nutrient rich ooze of the ocean floor.

Food chains provide a pathway for the accumulation of potentially poisonous trace metals in the ocean, particularly those known as 'heavy' metals. These are arbitrarily defined as being five times heavier than water and include copper, cadmium, mercury, lead vanadium, cobalt, molybdenum, nickle, tin and manganese. Many heavy metals are essential to life, although they occur only in minute amounts in body tissues, but they can be toxic if their concentration exceeds their optimum level. Since they are not excreted from the body they become concentrated up food chains, and therefore small amounts in the sea can eventually become fatal to a top predator such as a bird, a seal or perhaps man. To investigate levels of heavy metals in the ocean, certain organisms collected from the neuston were sent to laboratories in the United States and Britain for analysis.

If you look closely at the sea you might observe a tiny insect skipping across the surface looking not unlike the pond-skater of freshwater streams and ponds. It is in fact a marine gerrid belonging to the genus *Halobates* and is the only insect group to have colonised the open ocean. It has four long spindly legs and one short pair for grasping prey. The 5 to 6 millimetre-long body has a silvery appearance due to a layer of air trapped by a covering of velvety micro-hairs on the body surface so that if the insect is accidentally submerged it will not drown. Eggs are laid on any floating detritus such as feathers, wood, balls of tar or even on each other. Of the forty-two species so far described, only one, *Halobates micans* is circumtropical and widely distributed in all three major oceans in the world.

Dr Lanna Cheng at the Scripps Institute of Oceanography in California has discovered that these tiny insects concentrate cadmium in their bodies which could provide an indicator to the distribution of metals in the ocean. Those caught aboard *Eye of the Wind* were sent to her for biological studies and heavy metal analysis. Other animal species may also act as indicators of heavy metals. *Janthina* is a tiny marine snail which produces a bubble float to keep it at the surface. Those caught in the neuston net were sent to Dr Philip Rainbow at the University of London as were samples of goose barnacles from the hull of *Eye of the Wind*, to see whether they too contained heavy metals in their bodies.

'Invisible' pollutants such as heavy metals and PCBs (Polychlorinated Biphenyls) are more insidious and dangerous to the environment than oil, tar, plastic and sewage which, being visible, immediately arouse public concern. Tar and plastic were frequently collected in the neuston nets and a quantitative and qualitative survey of the distribution of these pollutants was undertaken throughout the voyage. Many animals colonised these seemingly unattractive floating habitats, hydroids, isopods, goose barnacles and small anemones to name but a few. *Halobates* also used tar and plastic as a convenient substrate on which to lay it's eggs.

Tar, which is a degradation product of crude oil, was found in very large quantities in the Atlantic. Although normally regarded as a man-made pollutant, it can originate from the natural leakage of oil seams. The majority, however, originates from oil tanker disasters such as the ill-fated *Torrey Canyon* and *Amoco Cadiz* or routine cleaning of the tanks or from marine oil well blow-outs. In terms of visible pollution the Pacific appeared far cleaner although numerous small plastic pellets of unknown origin were found in the Western Pacific. The Indian Ocean, Red Sea and Mediterranean all contained high concentrations of tar and plastic near land. The contents of the neuston haul frequently resembled a rubbish tip rather than a scientific sample, and twenty years ago few, if any, of these things would have been found. (Further Operation Drake projects in the polluted waters of the Mediterranean are discussed in Chapter 9.)

The day to day routine of life on board was now running like clockwork and as one day blended into another, the joys of trade wind sailing were appreciated by one and all. Fresh water conservation was an aspect of life that most people had not thought about before and there were some horrified looks when it became necessary to scrub greasy pots and pans on the decks and heave bucket after bucket of sea water up. The distinctly unpleasant feel of clothes that had been washed in salt water was there to stay and during the make-and-mend period on Sundays that replaced 'happy hour' most of the crew were seen doing their 'dhobey' while others were more intent on personal hygiene. On the calmer days it became a real pleasure when the ship was hove-to and the order for hands to bathe over the side given, although a good masthead lookout was always kept for sharks.

During their off-watch hours, while some members of the crew were happy to sit

The warmth and calmer waters of the Caribbean provided a welcome contrast to the Atlantic storms.

and read or write up their logbooks, others were constantly engaged in the more creative arts of seamanship. Traditional sailing ships used to set studdingsails in light winds giving them several hundred extra square metres of sail area. Retractable studdingsail booms had been fixed onto both ends of the course yardarms on *Eye of the Wind* and the sails were being made out of parachutes. All the work was done by hand and hours of patient stitching were required to complete the job. At last, one mid-December afternoon in a gentle force 4 breeze, the booms were extended and the sails hoisted. As they were broken out of their stops, rather like a yacht's spinnaker, the wind filled them and all those who had been involved with making them imagined they could feel the great surge in acceleration. This was in fact purely wishful thinking, but when both the course and topsail studdingsails were set they did add half a knot to the ship's speed.

There was a great air of excitement on board when the lookout was sent aloft to look for land and just before last light on December 20th, the dramatic and exaggerated cry of 'Land Ho', was heard. Barbados had been sighted. A few days were spent on this beautiful island to fuel and re-victual the ship before she set sail again.

The next port of call in the Caribbean was the tiny island of St Vincent where the YEs were to carry out the first of their land-based tasks. The whole of the northern part of the island is dominated by the 1,171 metre-high volcano of La Soufrière. This is one of a chain of active volcanos in the Lesser Antilles, caused by the meeting of the American plate heading westwards from the mid-Atlantic ridge with the Caribbean plate, which slides beneath the former to melt in the earth's mantle. A deep oceanic trench has formed as the plate disappears into the earth. Volcanos caused in this way can produce particularly violent eruptions. On May 8th 1902 an incandescent aerosol of red hot particles and high temperature gasses (a *nuée ardente*) was ejected from Mount Pelée on Martinique and within minutes it had wiped out St Pierre and all but two of its 30,000 inhabitants. On the day before, La Soufrière, only 160 kilometres away, had claimed 1,565 lives on St Vincent. La Soufrière's earliest recorded eruption was in 1718 and four times this century it had erupted deadly *nuées*. In 1971 it erupted again producing a small island inside its crater lake. Now, in 1978, monitors inside the crater indicated that temperatures were rising again. The question was, what was going to happen next?

Operation Drake was asked to carry out a biological, physical and chemical survey of the crater lake and island. The results would be sent to the Seismic Research Centre of the University of the West Indies, in Trinidad, to assist them in predicting the volcano's active state. Trish Holdway reorganised her thoughts from marine biologist to vulcanologist and led by Captain Patrick Collis, set off with the YEs carrying an Avon inflatable boat up the steep jungle-clad slopes of the volcano and then down into the crater. It was Christmas Eve.

The view from the crater rim was magnificent, the steep slope down into the crater terrifying. With much heaving, sliding and swearing, the inflatable was finally launched. In patches the water was so hot that we feared it might melt the glue holding the boat together. The YEs were deployed to collect plankton using the ship's nets and to survey the island, whilst others took temperature measurements around the lake. Scrambling over the huge lava boulders and amongst the sinister, spiralling steam vents they found extensive growth of lichens, mosses and some clumps of ferns, a few spiders and even a frog that had colonised the island since the whole crater area had been sterilised by the 1971 eruption. PH and oxygen readings were taken all over the lake. In places the water was discoloured a sulphur-yellow and reached 47 degrees Centigrade, much hotter than expected. Their work complete, the team spent the night on the crater rim and as dawn broke on Christmas Day they could look down on the beautiful blue-green lake encircling its smoking island. They were the last people ever to see that scene again.

At midnight on April 18th 1979 St Vincent was shaken by a massive explosion. La

Climbing down the steep inner wall of La Soufrière's volcanic crater was dangerous work. The island in the centre looked deceptively small from the crater rim; no one knew it was a time bomb.

Following the 1979 eruption, the lake vanished leaving only a smouldering chasm.

Soufrière had erupted. 20,000 people were evacuated from the northern area of the island. The super-hot gas clouds incinerated the forest that the YEs had walked through and the huge lake on which they had paddled their boat all but boiled dry. Fortunately few people were injured but it served to remind us at Operation Drake's headquarters in London of the inherent dangers in some of our projects. The awful consequences of what might have happened sent a chill down everyone's spine.

Oblivious of what was to come, the YEs rejoined the ship and departed from Kingstown, capital of St Vincent. Under full sail with excellent fair winds *Eye of the Wind* headed for Panama where she was due to arrive on New Year's Day. Meanwhile in England, feverish plans had been in progress to launch the first land phase of Operation Drake deep amongst the jungles of Darien.

Darien disasters

Some of the greatest tragedies and the most heroic exploits in history have been enacted on the short stretch of battered Atlantic coastline known as Darien. It is perhaps one of the most unpleasant places in the world, where the north-east trade winds bring six metre waves crashing against the granite shores and drop over 700 centimetres of rain every year into the hot, humid jungle. The region is bounded by the precipitous *cordierra*, dividing the two oceans and the swamps of the Gulf of Uraba. Most of the killer diseases known to man are endemic here, malaria, yellow fever, tuberculosis and rabies being the commonest. Yet it was to this coastline that Columbus led his small fleet on his fourth voyage in 1503. As it was one of the first areas of continental America to have been discovered, for a few tempestuous years, it accidentally became the capital of the Spanish mainland empire.

In 1508, a small town was established amongst the swamps and named Santa Maria la Antiqua de Darien. Soon the first cathedral in the Americas was built there and the townsmen had elected their leaders. One, a merchant, who had arrived as a stowaway, was soon to prove the first conquistador of the New World. Vasco Nuñez de Balboa set out to explore and pacify the country and in 1513 crossed the *cordierra* to discover the Pacific Ocean. The unhealthy backwater of Darien suddenly became a region of immense strategic importance. The route it provided to the South Seas meant that from

The hostile Darien shore where the Scots
built Fort St Andrew and New Edinburgh.
The remains of their ill-fated settlement can
still be seen today amongst the palm trees.

here the great campaigns of conquest set forth: Pizarro to Peru, Cortés to Mexico and Pedrarias Davilla to Nicaragua. Soon Panama became the funnel of gold, as the riches of South America were brought by mules over the mountains to the waiting ships at Nombre de Dios, to be taken back to Spain.

It was to this lure of gold that Sir Francis Drake was attracted. In four voyages, between 1570 and 1595, his fleet sailed up the coast, attacking the treasure towns of Nombre de Dios, Cartagena, Chagres and Portobello. The area was the scene of some of his greatest successes as well as the end of his remarkable career. Like so many others, Drake fell ill with fever and died at Portobello on January 28th 1595. He was buried at sea in a lead coffin.

Without doubt the most bizarre episode of all happened exactly 100 years after the death of Drake when the noble 'Company of Scotland Trading to Africa and the Indies' tried to colonise this remote piece of land. A small group of Scottish merchants, led by William Paterson, one of the founders of the Bank of England, saw the commerce of Scotland declining, with increasing English and Dutch protectionism forcing her to trade only in the North Sea. Paterson believed that a share of the lucrative Indies trade would create wealth and prosperity in an economy ravaged by poverty and famine. So in 1695 an 'Indies Company' was founded by an Act of the Scottish Parliament, (the Union with England was still twelve years away). The company had free rights to trade, establish and defend colonies in any part of the uninhabited world and was to be exempt from duties for the first twenty years of its life.

Soon potential investors were storming the offices in Milne Square, Edinburgh, demanding to place money in the company. Forecasts of fantastic yields were coupled with a patriotic zeal to participate in this panacea for Scotland's ills. Some 50 per cent of Scotland's national reserve was invested in the project. By 1698 four ships had been fitted out, not only with brandy and pitch, flour and biscuits, blunderbusses, gunpowder and shot, but also with less well-tried trading commodities – bagpipes, cartridge paper, blue bonnets, clay pipes, guinea goods, 'mungie mungies' and garden seeds (especially leeks and cabbage) – in fact everything that was sold in Scotland at the time. Ships were sent to Stockholm to buy salt, to La Rochelle to buy vinegar and wine, to Amsterdam for raisins, nutmeg and white Spanish soap. Merchants travelled down to London for Mercator charts and books of navigation 'bought of Mr Thornton' the most famous map maker of the day.

On July 4th 1698 the first ships, the *Unicorn*, *St Andrew*, *Caledonia* and *Endeavour* under the command of Captain Pennyquick left Leith Roads, with 1,500 colonists, men, women and children. All were totally ignorant of which part of the uninhabited world they were going to settle in, but certain that they were going to a land that would bring wealth and prosperity to an ailing nation.

Only one of the 'planters', apart from the captain, knew their destination. William Paterson, now disgraced due to a scandal concerning the financing of the expedition, wished to see the dream that he had conceived if only as a humble settler. Darien, which had been abandoned by the Spanish, would be the 'key to the Universe' and a 'mart where ships might freely pass'. His plan was to build a colony where goods could be transhipped across the isthmus, thus avoiding the difficult sea route via Africa. His proposals were more far-reaching than simply an earlier version of the Panama Canal; he planned to use the colony as the means to establish a new economic system, whereby the prosperity it engendered would initiate free trade between nations. He could not know that his dream would end in disaster and that few of the colonists were ever to see Scotland again.

The Atlantic crossing was uneventful and though seventy colonists died this was considered normal for a sea voyage of that length. Anchored in the lee of Golden Island, the legendary rendezvous of pirates and buccaneers roaming the Spanish Main, the Scots saw a long, natural and sheltered harbour now called Puerto Escoces. They sailed in believing that they had discovered one of the best harbours in the world. In his journal entry for November 3rd 1698 Captain Pennyquick wrote:

Herman Moll published this map of the Scots' Colony in 1735. He incorrectly placed New Edinburgh outside the fort.

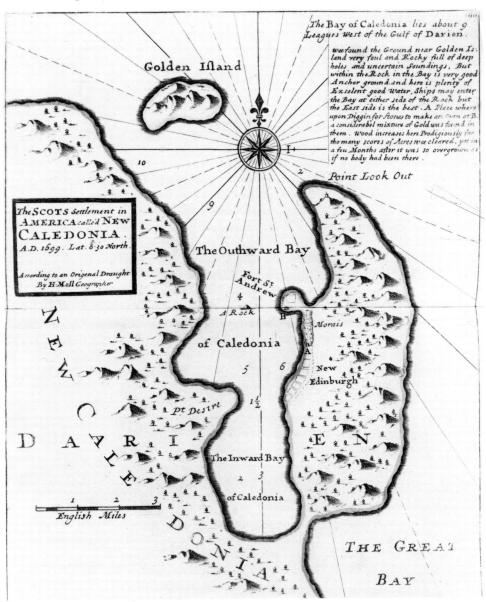

The Bay of Caledonia lies about 9 Leagues West of the Gulf of Darien.

wee found the Ground near Golden Island very foul and Rocky full of deep holes and uncertain Soundings, But within the Rock in the Bay is very good Anchor ground, and here is plenty of Excelent good Water, Ships may enter the Bay at either side of the Rock but the East side is the best. A Place where upon Digging for Stones to make an Oven at B. a considerabel mixture of Gold was found in them. Wood increases here Prodigiously for tho many scores of Acres wee cleared, yet in a few Months after it was so overgrown as if no body had been there.

Golden Island

Point Look Out

The SCOTS Settlement in AMERICA call'd NEW CALEDONIA. A.D. 1699. Lat. 8:30 North.

According to an Origenal Draught By H. Moll Geographer.

The Outward Bay

Fort St Andrew

A Rock

of Caledonia

Morais

New Edinburgh

Pt Desire

The Inward Bay

of Caledonia

English Miles

THE GREAT BAY

This harbour is capable of containing 1000 sail of the best Shipps in the World. And without great trouble Wharfs may be run out, to which Shipps of the greatest Burthen may lay their sides and unload.

In fact the harbour was a trap from which their ships could not escape because of the prevailing north-east winds which blew continually down it towards the land.

Almost 281 years later to the day, it was a moving experience to sail *Eye of the Wind*, her journey across the Atlantic complete, between the same forest-clad headlands described by the optimistic settlers. After a brief reconnaissance expedition in 1976, John Blashford-Snell had decided that the survey and excavation of the Scottish colony of New Caledonia would provide the perfect task for the Young Explorers. The first Operation Drake base camp was set up on the shores of what the Scots had called Caledonia Bay.

The Scottish settlers were initially delighted by their new home and letters went back to Edinburgh describing their 'earthly paradise'. A paper was even read before the Royal Society detailing the strange and beautiful flora and fauna. Mention was also made of 'monstrous adders', probably a pit viper *Lachesis muta*, the deadly bushmaster, which is still common in Caledonia Bay. Their first job was to clear the bush and decide where to build the huts. William Paterson wrote later:

> *The first thing fallen upon was a place of landing, but the sea councellors were for a meer morass, neither fitt to be fortified, nor indeed for men to ly upon. We were upon clearing and making hutts upon this inproper place near two months, in which time experience, the schoolmaster of fools – convinced our masters that the place now called Fort St. Andrew was more proper for us.*

The first of many bitter arguments had started that continually divided the colony and spelled doom for the new settlers.

Attempting to consolidate their position, the Scots laid a series of fortifications but it soon became obvious that the land, far from being an 'earthly paradise', was in fact a hell hole. In April of the following year the rains began and with them the mosquitos came bringing malaria and yellow fever to the settlers, already weakened by starvation and unable to survive on their rapidly spoiling rations. By June half the colonists were dead. King William III, incensed that the Scots should embark on this diabolical scheme without informing him, issued a proclamation prohibiting any English ship from having anything to do with the settlers and declaring the colony illegal. No vessels came to trade and in desperation a sloop, the *Despatch*, was sent to Hispaniola to gather fresh supplies. She returned with nothing other than the news of King William's wrath. In December the Scots learnt that the Spanish were mounting a huge force to attack them. It was the final straw. Panic spread through the small unfinished town of New Edinburgh and in July the settlers fled. Only one ship out of the four, the *Caledonia*, returned home; the others were sold or lost at sea.

In those days news travelled slowly. Scotland was full of the success of the noble 'Company of Scotland' and three more ships, brim-full with supplies and 1,302 settlers eager to begin a new life in the famous colony, sailed for Darien oblivious of the disasters that had befallen the whole enterprise. A letter from the councillors to the Directors in Scotland described the scene:

> *On our arriveal, we found all the hutts within Fort St. Andrew (and without it yr were never any built) burn'd to the ground and the principall batteries of the Fort which guarded the enterance to the Bay quite demolished; and whereas there were full accounts given of ye Colony's haveing cutt all the wood on the neck of the Isthmus, wee found no such thing, but on the conterary on the side within the Bay, imperviable mongrove and mossy ground; and on the side without the Bay for the most part inaccessible rocks and the middleway mountainous and full of trees, whereof there are not six cutt.*

The new settlers were forced to start again. They rebuilt the huts and extended the fortifications but soon they too were struck down by the many diseases, 'all manner of distempers such as head and belly aches, fevers fluxes etc.' although they added optimistically 'but all this not withstanding the place was very wholesome'.

However a new threat loomed; this time the Spanish were not to let the Scots escape so easily. As the famous nineteenth-century historian Macaulay put it:

> *To imagine that (Spain) would tamely suffer adventurers from one of the most insignificant kingdoms of the Old World to form a settlement in the midst of her empire within a day's sail of Portobello on one side and of Carthayena on the other was ludicrously absurd.*

A massive build-up of Spanish forces had been planned for over a year. The Spanish fleet sailed from Cartagena under the Governor, General Piamenta, and an army marched from Panama. On February 29th 1700 they landed at Caretto and slowly marched towards the now miserable colony. The Scots courageously beat off the first

Spanish attack at the neck of the isthmus, but soon had to retire inside the fort, venturing out only to collect water.

Unfortunately, there were two major flaws in the Scottish defence. There was no water within the fort and the seaward side was left totally undefended. Soon the Spanish army had placed a battery on Pelican Point and bombarded the fort from the sea. The misery of the colonists was described by Reverend Francis Borland, one of the Presbyterian ministers who accompanied the expedition:

> *There was much consternation of heart among us at this time . . . sinking fears and little Faith and Hope, our Condition now seeming most desperate like Death on all hands stared us in the face, and indeed most of us had the Sentance of Death in ourselves. many amoung us believed there was not a people in the world in more calamitous and deplorable circumstances than we were at this time.*

On March 31st the colonists concluded a treaty with the Spanish as with the rains approaching, Piamenta had decided to end the campaign quickly. A bastion of the fort was given up to the Spanish garrison and the colonists were to have fourteen days in which to wood and water their ships so that they might be in 'readiness to sail' when the 'wind should present fair'. Two weeks of loading took place but when the appointed day came the Scots were too weak even to sail out. Piamenta immediately ordered his navy to help tow them out to sea and so finally on April 12th they set sail for America. But their troubles were not over; on September 3rd the last two ships sank in a hurricane off South Carolina and most of the survivors from the unfortunate colony were drowned.

Mark Horton, an archaeologist from the University of Cambridge, had spent many months researching into the colony amongst archives in the libraries of London and Edinburgh and even in the vaults of the Royal Bank of Scotland. He then travelled to

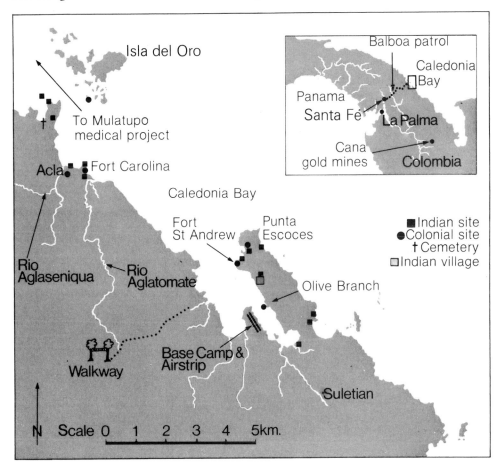

A map of Caledonia Bay showing the main Operation Drake project sites.

**The base camp in Darien. The airstrip had
to be cleared of bush by hand. Behind lies
the harbour where Scottish ships once lay
at anchor.**

Panama with Operation Drake to direct the archaeological excavations. The Patrimonio Historico, the State Antiquities Service of Panama, had kindly agreed to the
survey of the colony and provided three of their archaeologists, Hacinto Alimentra,
Fernando Martinez and Marcella Noriega, to assist in the work as well as the full
facilities of their museum in Panama City. Now Mark and the rest of the archaeology
team were on the shores of Caledonia Bay, weighed down with maps, copies of
manuscripts, machetes, trowels and brushes ready to discover what remained of the
colony and even the truth behind the strange happenings leading to its failure.

The expedition established a camp on the old airstrip which had been built by a
Dutch company seventeen years before trying to export bananas from the area –
another Darien disaster. It took an immense amount of effort to clear the airstrip of
bush which had grown up over the years of disuse, but once serviceable it provided the
expedition's lifeline to the outside world. The Panamanian Guardia Nacional supported
the expedition throughout providing immense assistance with aircraft and helicopter
flights for there were no roads in this part of Darien, no telephones and no towns. The
camp resembled a small village with a stores tent, radio shack, accommodation tents,
cook tent, medical tent and even a bar constructed of bamboo and built on the shore.
There was no drinking water on the site and just as the Scots had done before us, we
were forced to send a boat full of jerry cans to the 'Watering Bay' where a small

Hacinto and Mark Horton clear water from
the well dug by the Scots in the last days of
the colony.

stream flowed into a tiny semi-circular bay. Twenty minutes boat ride away across
Caledonia Harbour, lay the site of Fort St Andrew on the neck of land that was known
as Punta Escoces.

At 7.30 a.m. each day, after a breakfast of porridge and baked beans, the Young
Explorers and local Panamanian YEs jumped into the Avon rubber boats and motored
through huge, oily swells, entering the bay at the site of the fort. It was difficult to
imagine the palisades which had surrounded Fort St Andrew amongst the tall coconut
palms which now covered the site of the large coral platform on which it had been
built. Picking amongst the undergrowth however, here was a piece of old pottery,
there a mound, and was this deep trough cut into the coral the moat which the Scots
had built? The local Cuna Indians who farmed the site gave their permission for the
clearance and excavation to take place. Machetes in hand, the YEs set to work, cutting
down the bush just as the Scots had done. Swathes 10 metres wide were cleared
traversing a rectangular grid through the fort. Slowly, the plan of the colony came to
light.

The bastions and full extent of the moat were first to be seen. Soon the placing of the
rampart with its cannon positions, fighting platform and gates could slowly be
understood. Gun batteries had been built on the seaward side and their distinctive
polygonal shape was soon recognised. Inside the fort area sherds of pottery, brandy

bottles, clay pipes and iron and bronze objects littered the ground. The surface that the Scots had lived on remained unchanged. Nothing was buried and little had been disturbed since the last Scot left in 1700. Here indeed was an archaeological paradise where much of the fort could be revealed simply by clearing back the jungle rather than digging deep beneath the earth.

Some excavation was, of course, necessary in order to learn about the Scots' existence in greater detail. A letter written from the colony described the building works:

> We have been as busy as possible since our arrival in getting hutts built whereof we now have 72 for planters each 12 feet long and 10 feet broad and 15 for officers, 30 feet long and 16 feet broad. Also we have built two storehouses and otherwise repaired the guard house.

Traces of these huts soon came to light. The soil was carefully cleared by the Young Explorers under the direction of Mark Horton and Andrew Hunter, a Canadian archaeologist. It soon became evident that the dark soil shades which appeared marked the holes dug into the ground to take posts for roof and walls. Discarded animal bones, including the bones of sea turtle, pieces of broken pottery and glass, buttons, Scottish coins and shoe buckles littered one hut floor. A well was found, the water still brackish. In it, preserved because the earth was still wet, were the seeds of fruits that the colonists had been eating to supplement their salt beef and dry biscuit. The well had been built in the last days of the colony when the water supply had been cut off by the attacking Spanish forces. Its water had been brackish and foul, causing discomfort and disease to the men already fighting for survival.

All the buildings of the fort were made of wood with one exception. It seemed a stone building had also been constructed. Circular, with an outer wall of granite (quarried nearby and containing much iron pyrite or 'fool's gold', which had led to the rumour that the colony had discovered gold), with a floor of compacted coral and a domed roof of imported Scottish bricks, it was the gunpowder store. Careful excavation showed it to be very well preserved, despite the fact that it had provided bricks for the bread ovens of many generations of local Indians.

Investigations of the defences showed how inadequate they had been. An earthen rampart was surmounted by a timber palisade; four bastions survived, each with cannon positions. The moat which flanked the rampart was cut through the natural coral. Overlying the fortifications were discarded weapons: sword blades, hilts, musket fragments, lead shot, canister shot and cannon balls. One of the cannons left behind may be that which lies in a nearby village. Had the seaward defences been improved, the Scots might have withstood the Spanish attack.

The intense heat made the work exhausting and mosquitos and scorpions added to the discomfort. Great care had been taken when cutting back the bush as the 'monstrous adders' still inhabited the ruins. Ripening coconuts were an added danger. Falling 25 metres from the top of a palm tree, they were capable of killing with ease and after several near misses, those working under them took to wearing protective helmets.

Some of the YEs were trained to survey the site with theodolite and tape while others painstakingly sifted through the soil, marking the position of each find with one half of a numbered cloakroom ticket, the other being placed in a plastic bag with the potsherd, glass trading bead, or coin that had been found so that the archaeologist would know where it had come from. The scatter of pottery and boulders was carefully plotted onto a grid so that foundations and the distribution of household goods could be determined. At the end of each day the picks, shovels and trowels were collected and the rubber boats boarded for the journey back to camp and a wash in the sea, leaving the Indians to wonder what on earth was going on.

On the white coral sand of the shore near the boat jetty was the 'finds' tent. Inside, Maria Mabee, an osteologist from the Museum of Urban Archaeology in London, and Debbie Fulford, a draughtswoman with the Department of the Environment, were in

Maria Mabee marking the position of glass trading beads found inside the fort. Modern beads are still a popular form of decoration amongst the Indians.

charge of the mass of archaeological material being recovered from the site. Every item was carefully recorded, drawn and any conservation measures necessary to aid its survival immediately taken. Many of the finds could actually be found recorded on the old cargo manifests detailing the Scots' supplies. All helped to build up a picture of life in the colony years before. The most exciting discovery, however, was yet to come.

Shortly before Christmas Day 1698, two ships were sighted off Golden Island. The spirits of the colonists immediately rose as they thought that these might be the first ships that had come to trade with them. One of the ships was a French merchantman of '42 guns' that was loaded with church plate and 60,000 'pieces of eight' that had apparently been looted in a raid on Cartagena a few months previously. The Scots invited the French ship into the harbour. The captain, Duvier Thomas, readily accepted because his ship was 'very leaky' and the Spanish Bartliovento fleet was patrolling the coast, attacking all the foreign ships and pirates.

On Christmas Eve the French captain entertained the Indian chiefs. The next day, with a crew still drunk from celebrations the night before and in appalling weather conditions, against all reason the captain set sail and made for the 'sea gate'. A heaving swell was bombarding the harbour and as the ship tried to sail out, the wind suddenly dropped and she began to drift dangerously near the reefs. After valiant rescue attempts by the Scottish commodore which included taking personal command himself as the captain was in his cabin unable to stand up, the ship was wrecked on an 'iron shore'. With bags of gold hung about their necks, many of the crew perished in the violent seas as they swam vainly for the beach. Duvier Thomas being 'unable to sweeam' owing to his drunken state, was floated ashore on a raft where he was hung up by his legs so that the water 'ran out of him'.

There is a strange twist to the story. While the events are not in dispute, the Scottish records give conflicting names for the French ship. Some describe her as the *Maurepas*, others as the *St Anthony*. Anna Richards, a Young Explorer from Canada had read of the fate of the *Maurepas* whilst preparing for the expedition. She wrote to the French Maritime Museum in Paris and they replied with the extraordinary news that a ship of the same description and called the *Maurepas* was still sailing around the Peruvian coast fourteen years after the sinking in Caledonia Bay. Moreover, the *Maurepas*, the museum said, had been launched in November 1698 at La Rochelle and could not possibly have reached Caledonia Bay by Christmas when the sinking occurred. The *St Anthony* had also been built in Brittany some years before and, like the *Maurepas*, she had joined the East India Company before sailing to South America, after which records were lost. It seems therefore that the ship was the *St Anthony*, but where had she sunk and was the confusion in names merely a cover up, as bitter letters from the colony suggest that some of the officers made themselves rich with gold that they salvaged from the wreck?

To solve this question a ten-man Royal Air Force diving team led by Flight Lieutenant Michael Cameron and Corporal Brian Ranner, both highly experienced divers on ancient wrecks off the English coast, began the search for the *St Anthony* in Caledonia Bay. A grid survey of thousands of square metres of the sea bottom was fruitless: the wreck was more than likely covered in mud or coral. Modern electronics had to be employed. Anthony Lonsdale, an electronics expert from England, had some years before developed his own proton magnetometer for locating potentially oil-bearing rocks in the North Sea. Different stratas of rock distort the earth's magnetic field producing a 'signature' on the instrument's data record which can later be interpreted to show the probability of the rock configuration containing oil. Metal, such as ship's cannon, also produces a signature so that the instrument can be used to search for ancient wrecks concealed beneath the sea bed. Anthony flew into Caledonia Bay with his boxes of electronic instruments, wire, graph paper and two crates of claret.

Captain Pennyquick's description of the sinking suggested a reef marked on the 1856 Admiralty Chart as St Anthony's reef and lying just off our base camp, but here nothing was found.

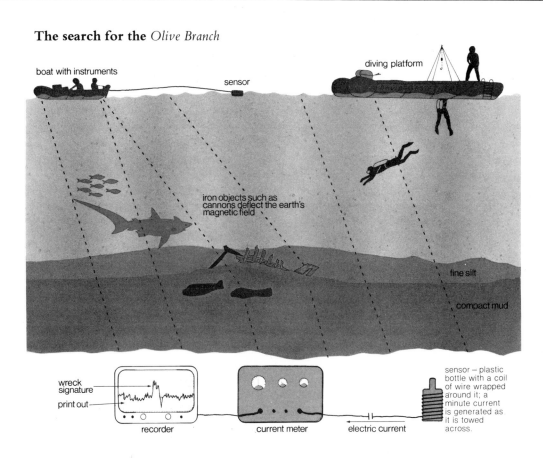

The search for the *Olive Branch*

boat with instruments

sensor

diving platform

iron objects such as
cannons deflect the earth's
magnetic field

fine silt

compact mud

wreck
signature

print out

recorder

current meter

electric current

sensor – plastic
bottle with a coil
of wire wrapped
around it; a
minute current
is generated as
it is towed
across.

A magnetometer is not a true metal detector since it will detect only iron objects. As it relies on the earth's magnetic field it can work over great depths of water. An ordinary metal detector, although very accurate over short distances, would not detect a ship one metre away. Magnetometers are also used in the search for oil-bearing rocks as the structure of the earth's crust can be determined by examining the magnetic field it produces.

Weeks of searching in other areas only produced a barge full of old railway lines, sunk seventeen years earlier by the Dutch banana company. The Young Explorers carefully recorded the read-out as the instrument was painstakingly towed backwards and forwards across the harbour. Then, close to the Cuna India village of Sukunya, a major anomaly was found, spread over about 50 metres and close to the fringing coral reef. The water was only 6 metres deep but 2.5 metres of mud had to be removed before the timbers which lay beneath were revealed. There was tremendous excitement in the camp as Meredith Sassoon, the marine archaeologist in charge of the conservation of marine finds, announced that the timbers were indeed of seventeenth-century construction consisting of a sandwich of pine and oak with tarred felt in between. But they did not seem to belong to the *St Anthony*. The oak on the inside was severely burnt. Charred holes where nails had been bore witness to the intense heat. There was only one ship known to have sunk by fire in the Bay – the *Olive Branch*.

Research into the archives revealed how the sinking had occurred. A few weeks after the first abandonment of New Caledonia, the *Olive Branch* and the *Hopeful Binning* had sailed into the harbour bringing long overdue supplies to the now deserted colony. Their troubles were not at an end:

Corporal Brian Ranner slips beneath the *David Gestetner* anchored above the *Olive Branch*. Behind him Chris Lothian, another RAF diver, pays out line to keep him supplied with air from Hookah pumps while he works on the bottom.

These two ships brought over 300 men Captain Jamison's ship being loaded with provisions and Brandie, while some were drawing Brandie in the Hold of the Ship, having a lighted candle with them accidentally the fire of the candle catched hold of the Brandie which forthwith flammed so terribly that it set the ship on fire and in a little time destroyed both ship and provisions. The wrack of this ship is yet to be seen in Caledonia Harbour.

The words, 'yet to be seen in Caledonia Harbour', suddenly took on a new significance. The *Olive Branch* was the only Scottish ship to have sunk in the harbour itself; she seemed to have gone down with all the cargo and it was likely that little attempt had been made to salvage her. The original manifest for the *Olive Branch* still exists and would enable us to trace directly the origin of all the stores. This Scottish disaster was a unique possibility for marine archaeology.

The 12 metre inflatable raft, *David Gestetner*, formerly used to navigate the giant rapids of the Zaire River on a previous Scientific Exploration Society expedition, was now positioned above the work site. It had been converted by the Royal Engineers into a diving platform. A battery of petrol driven pumps provided air to the divers working below and above a hole in the centre of the raft a gantry was rigged enabling heavy objects to be winched to the surface. The pumps also provided pressure to the 'air-line' which sucked mud away from the wreck. The work was dangerous as visibility was down to centimetres. Nobody expected sharks to be swimming nearby until we put a protective net around the site and caught five in one day including a 3 metre-long hammerhead.

With time rapidly running out there was little that could be done other than establish the configuration of the wreck and excavate a small exploratory trench. At the very bottom of this, fragments of burnt ship's timbers, some still in position, with barrels and ship's fittings clearly showed she was a merchantman but how could we prove she was the *Olive Branch*? Little was lifted or disturbed but a number of concretions were brought up from the tops of the barrels. One of these contained clay pipe fragments. They were identical to those recovered from the fort. From the cargo manifest of the *Olive Branch* we knew she was carrying 30,000 clay pipes for the colony and from initials on one pipe bowl we could trace it to its seventeenth-century maker in Scotland, James Colhoun. She was indeed the *Olive Branch*. When the diving phase was concluded the excavation was sealed again with mud, until a future team could continue the work. Of the *St Anthony* no trace was found. Perhaps she had been salvaged or perhaps she still lies somewhere in the bay waiting for future archaeologists to discover her.

Proof that we had unearthed the *Olive Branch*. **On the left, a clay pipe bowl found inside the fort bearing the initials 'PG' matches one recovered from storage barrels in the wreck. The** *Olive Branch* **was the only ship to have sunk in Caledonia Bay carrying** clay pipes for the colony. **On the right an invoice for pipes and tobacco bound for the colony aboard the** *Rising Sun* **in 1699. Some of those discovered during the excavations were possibly from this shipment.**

Artifacts from the Scottish colony included a cannon ball, musket shot, knife blades and decorated pottery.

Whilst work continued within Fort St Andrew, Mark Horton turned his attention to another piece of Darien's history, further back in time. Just behind the base camp there was a large hill and beyond this a valley containing two rivers. Between these a final archaeological mystery remained.

In 1513, Vasco Nuñez de Balboa set out from the Atlantic coast in the region of Careta and crossed to the Pacific. This great discovery shifted the direction of exploration southwards away from the Atlantic coast. A new base was required and Pedrarias Davilla, Governor of Panama decided to establish a town in the region controlled by the chief 'Ponca' at a place that the natives called Acla. This was in late 1515 or early 1516.

Little is known of this early foundation. It was initially shortlived and the lieutenant and his followers who had been ordered to build the town, were all killed by the Indians. In 1516 however Balboa returned to supervise the rebuilding of the town personally. The building programme proceeded quickly, and the houses were favourably compared with those in Seville. The real purpose behind this venture was to create a navy for the South Seas. Ships were carefully taken apart at Acla and carried across the isthmus piece by piece to the Rio Balsas on the Pacific. The project was not particularly successful, with only two out of the four ships completed. Notwithstanding, here were the first European ships to sail on the Pacific, four years before Magellan discovered the Straits and sixty years before Drake sailed there.

At this stage Acla must have been a thriving town, with as many as 300 inhabitants. But in January 1519 events took an unpleasant turn when Balboa was imprisoned by the jealous Pedrarias Davilla and tried for treason. With four companions he was executed in the main plaza. In the same year the town of Panama was founded in an area of healthier climate and soon the pattern of trade shifted away from the earlier settlements in Darien. But Acla lingered on as a mining town, producing small quantities of gold until 1560 when the last four inhabitants were moved to Conception, further up the coast. As the remains of Acla, with its buildings, houses and church, were covered by the thick jungle, so nobody thought to record its position. The second 'city' in the Americas, perhaps the first one ever laid with streets and a plaza, the site of

Married Cuna women cut their hair short
and wear gold rings in their noses. Their
beautifully patterned 'molas' are made of
different layers of material cut through to
reveal the colour beneath. Fine beadwork
adorns their wrists and ankles.

the first great exploration of the mainland of the New World, passed into folklore and eventually oblivion.

The possibility existed that by closely studying historical documents, clues could lead us to the site's identification on the ground. All the evidence pointed to a small area some way inland, north of the Scottish colony, where today the Aglatomate River flows into the sea. John Blashford-Snell in his reconnaissance of the area in 1976 had made some interesting discoveries here. As he approached the coast from the sea in a dugout canoe, there did not seem to be any way in through the line of raging white surf as huge waves broke onto the coral reefs. Then the Cuna Indian guide headed straight towards the waves, at the last minute zigzagging through a gap that could not be seen from the open sea and beached the canoe on the shore. Moving inland John and his team met a Cuna Indian who explained that he had recently burnt some forest to plant a new coconut grove only to discover that the place was bisected by a low wall and he would have to find somewhere else. The guide led the group to the site and there on the ground to their great excitement were the remains of what appeared to be some stone walls. Now, two years later, Operation Drake's archaeology group moved from Caledonia Bay and set to work to discover what they were and if they could have belonged to Acla.

Ann Smith from Canada negotiating a swamp on the Balboa trail. She joined Denise Wilson and Cathy Davies from Britain in becoming the first women ever to make the crossing from the Atlantic shore of Darien through the jungle to the Pacific.

Whilst all this work was going on another group of Young Explorers, under the watchful eye of an ex-Marine and deputy leader of the Caledonia Bay project, George Thurstan, set off to follow the route taken by Balboa to cross the isthmus with his boats in the early sixteenth century. Careful excavation can be tedious, even for archaeologists, and the intention was to provide some adventure for those who had worked so hard scraping, brushing and picking amongst the soils of the coastal sites. In fact it developed into a dangerous challenge which four of the party were never to complete.

On arrival at Caledonia Bay all the Young Explorers had been sent on jungle survival courses run by Guardia Nacional soldiers and Chris Lawrence, a Captain in the Scots Guards. They disappeared into the forest for a week at a time to learn how to navigate, build bashas, filter and sterilise water and live off the fruits and animals around them. The Guardia jungle experts taught their amazing art of making waterproof shelters from leaves and vines, preparing owl and rat pie, or searching for freshwater crayfish by torchlight during night time prowls along streams and rivers. At the end of their week most YEs were thinner, exhausted and footsore but knew the rudiments of survival in the jungle. Now some of them had a chance to put it to use.

George led his group of twenty-one YEs past the toiling archaeologists hoping to uncover Acla. All went well for the first week during which they climbed the mountain divide of the Serrania del Darien and descended onto the Pacific side. Ahead lay 186 kilometres of flat, featureless forest, swamps and rivers leading to the Chucunaque River and La Palma on the coast.

Due to an unusually dry period there was very little water between the river and the coast and five days after crossing the Chucunaque the group began to run out of water. They were forced to take water from muddy, wild pig pools and despite precautions one of the party contracted dysentery. Rick Gustavesen, a member of the film crew, was becoming seriously ill through loss of body fluids which, due to the lack of water, the patrol was unable to replace adequately. George decided that they had to get him out.

He called the expedition's HQ in Panama on the radio they were carrying and requested a rescue operation. In Panama City everyone bounded into activity. John Blashford-Snell contacted the Guardia Nacional and the US Army in the Canal Zone who instantly agreed to despatch a helicopter. The problem now was how to find them in the mass of rolling green forest 100 kilometres away.

On the ground the Young Explorers summoned their last reserves of energy and began cutting down the trees to form a helicopter landing pad. It was backbreaking work using only machetes but an area had to be cleared before darkness came when a landing would be impossible. They could hear the helicopter but it could not find them. They had brought a marker balloon with them designed for just such an emergency. Without water to mix with the calcium carbide powder, however, they could not make the acetylene gas with which to inflate it. Attempts to use urine also failed. By late afternoon three Young Explorers had collapsed from heat exhaustion brought on by lack of water. Just as dusk was approaching the helicopter located them and Rick was winched to safety and flown to hospital. There was no time to return for the other three or to bring water, which incredibly had been overlooked.

The following morning once again the helicopter pilot could not see the patrol. A second helicopter was despatched but with no better success. Then a high altitude US Air Force spotter plane got a fix on the heli-pad cut in the forest and guided the helicopters in. The three YEs with heat exhaustion were lifted out and water dropped in allowing the other members of the team to continue on their way. Five days later they reached the coast exhausted but elated. They were the first group to cross the isthmus through the Darien since Balboa had done so nearly five centuries before.

On returning to the base camp at Caledonia Bay they discovered that the work at Acla had met with major setbacks. By systematically clearing and searching the thickly covered area near the Cuna Indian farm, substantial stone foundations had come to light. Walls and mounds suggested that traces of a sixteenth-century settlement had been found but stratified beneath one of the walls were fragments of an eighteenth-century bottle. The walls could not then have been those of Acla but must instead have been part of the eighteenth-century Spanish fort of St Fernando de la Carolina discovered in 1953 by the Venezuelan archaeologist Cruxent. Exciting new finds of pottery nearby proved to be entirely of local manufacture: beneath the eighteenth-century fort was a large pre-Hispanic Indian settlement. To confuse the strong minded even further, next came up quantities of nineteenth-century Willow Pattern pottery, all made in Staffordshire and probably left by a survey party in the mid-nineteenth century looking for a route for a sea-level trans-isthmian canal. (This extraordinary scheme had proposed excavating a route to the Pacific by blowing up the hills and mountains with atomic devices but it was fortunately abandoned in the face of widespread opposition.) The search for Acla seemed to have failed.

In the closing days of Operation Drake's Panamanian projects a Young Explorer came into the finds tent at the Fort Carolina site clutching a piece of white pottery with a characteristic tin glaze on the surface. Mark Horton was jubilant for its significance was clear. It was sixteenth-century pottery similar to that made at Seville in Spain at the time of Balboa's great crossing. The find had been made inland from the site on which they were now working and the archaeology team now moved there and began to search with renewed interest. More pottery soon came to light, along with iron and glass as well as distinct earthworks on the ground. Acla had been discovered. Final confirmation had to wait until potsherds were examined by Dr Florence Lister at the University of New Mexico who identified some of the pottery as Isabela Polychrome, a ware only produced in the early sixteenth century. It now seems certain that this is the site of Acla. Dr Reina Torres de Arauz, Director of the Patrimonio Historico was delighted with the news and with the huge array of finds from the Scottish colony as well as Acla which now forms the basis of a major new collection at the historical museum in Panama City.

During this time and in all our projects in the area we were under the watchful eyes of the Cuna Indians. They were the first tribal people the Young Explorers had come into contact with and some of the most colourful and interesting that we were to encounter on Operation Drake. The Scots too had spoken of Indians living on the coast when they settled in Darien and the Cuna there today may be descendants of those earlier tribes. The settlers entertained them aboard their ships to gain their confidence and friendship.

A gentleman living in Darien at the time described the Indians wearing:

> . . . an Ornament in their Nofes of an Half-Moon, which when they drink, they hold up with one hand while they lift up the drink with the other. The Men paint themfelves fometimes with Streaks of black, and Women with Red. The Women have in their Nofes a pretty thick Ring of Gold or Silver and cover themfelves with a Blanket only.

The description is fairly close to that of the Cuna today but there was another comment in the old accounts which originally defied explanation:

> I saw feveral fairer than the faireft in Europe, with Hair as white as the fineft Flax. Tis reported of them, that they fee better in the Dark, than in the Light.

We were later to discover that these white-skinned Indians are still to be found in the San Blas Islands, where the Cuna now live.

Today the Cuna lead lives dependent upon the sea as well as the land but it has not always been so. In time past they lived away from the coast competing with the more primitive Choco Indians and after years of fighting most moved, in the nineteenth century, to the many islands of the San Blas Archipelago on Panama's Caribbean coast. Of the 20,000 Cuna living today a mere 1,200 live inland on the Bayano River on the Pacific side of the central divide as custodians of the original tribal lands. Progress has now dealt them a final blow. The advent of the massive Bayano Dam has provided the Panamanian Republic with much of its electricity but has also displaced the Cuna to lands which they consider unsuitable, further upstream.

The Cuna on the coast are thriving, leading an independent life almost as a separate nation. Years of contact with marauding buccaneers and pirates have taught them to mistrust strangers. Outsiders are not encouraged and for many years were not allowed to remain in the settlements overnight. By living on the low, flat coral islands, some only a metre or so above sea level, the Cuna avoid the mosquitos and sandflies which plague the coast often only a few hundred metres away. There is little water on most of the islands so a major task of the women, dressed in colourful 'molas' and yellow and orange head scarves is to paddle to the shore in dugout canoes to collect it in round calabash gourds.

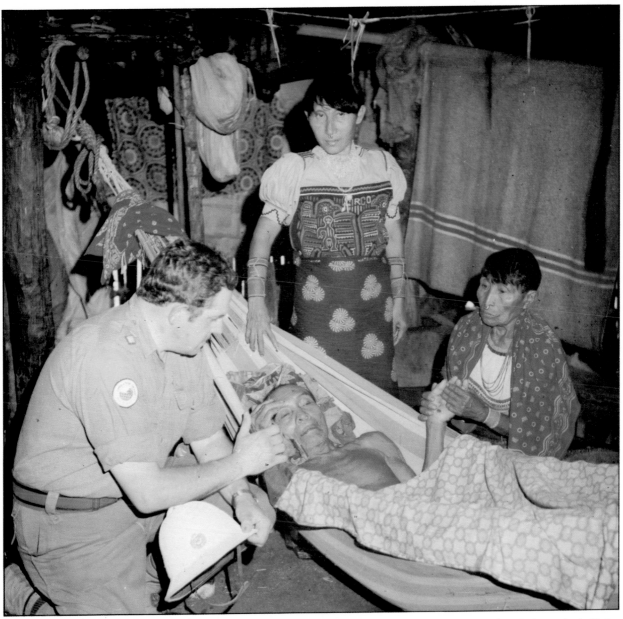

John Blashford-Snell comforts a dying man on the island of Mulatupo. Suspicion of modern medicine often prevents patients being moved to the local hospital until it is too late. This serves to reinforce the belief held by many of the Cuna that once admitted they will not emerge alive.

The Cuna live in a close cluster of palm-thatched huts built around a central 'congress' hall. Whilst the men fish from canoes off the coral reefs, the women are ashore collecting plantains, cassava and cocoa. Fish cooked in coconut juice is a favourite and with eggs or the occasional iguana and monkey ensures that they receive protein in their diet. Inland the forest is cut down to make farms which last for a number of seasons before fertility trails off and a new area is selected. It was amongst these people that the first of our comparative medical projects was to begin directed by Dr Nigel Pearce and his team of Young Explorers and nurses.

The Cuna's independence is not accidental. They are politically very proud and nothing can be achieved without the consent of the 'sailah' or chief of the relevant island or, in more important issues, of the whole archipelago. It was essential that we had their support and so, at the suggestion of the Guardia Nacional, our hearty moustachioed camp commander, Major Alan Westcob, agreed to initiate the great Cuna Indian sports day!

Invitations were sent out to all the important chiefs nearby and on the appointed day hundreds of canoes began heading towards Caledonia Bay. The airstrip was soon bustling with Cuna women with thick gold rings in their noses and clutching pretty, giggling children. The sailahs, in sombre trilby hats, embroidered shirts, and grey flannels moved with statesmanlike precision around the camp exchanging disapproving glances. Flags were lowered and raised and important speeches made before the signal was given for the games to begin. John Blashford-Snell took on the Paramount Chief of the Islands for a game of bowls played with coconuts which, if struck too hard, split and sprayed milk in all directions. Volleyball and football were followed by canoe races in the bay, whilst the Cuna women danced to the sound of pan pipes and Drake's fair maidens twirled in Scottish reels. The event was an enormous success and permission was given for us to work on the island of Mulatupo.

Visiting Cuna Indian chiefs from the San Blas Islands pose with members of the expedition prior to giving their approval for the medical projects to begin.

Dr Nigel Pearce arrived there with Scots' Guards Piper Robbie Little who wheezed and wailed his way around the village with an ever growing band of screaming, delighted children. In the daunting congress hall that night Nigel explained through interpreters what the project was about whilst old men coughed and spat in approval from the comfort of their hammocks and Cuna women stitched patterns into their 'molas' by the light of a hundred small paraffin flames. Working from the new clinic on the mainland and greatly aided by the Panamanian Ministry of Health medical staff, Nigel set the YEs to work gathering children from the village and carrying out questionnaire surveys on diet, later visiting farms inland.

To start with each child had an exhaustive physical examination which revealed that tuberculosis and gastroenteritis were common and almost all had worm infestations. The children's vision was tested as was their ability to see in the dark as this is related to vitamin A deficiency. Next a solution containing sugars was drunk and the urine later collected for analysis. The amount of the sugars recovered indicated the efficiency of the intestinal tract in absorbing food. Many types of samples were obtained to uncover the presence of blood, urinary, and intestinal disease, all potential malnutrition-inducing factors. (A fuller account of the expedition's medical projects and the results obtained is given in Chapter 5.)

Most of the children had smooth, coffee-brown skin and jet black, long straight hair but occasionally individuals would appear with almost white skin and reddish tinted, fair hair. These were the 'moon children' mentioned earlier, so called because they avoided the harsh sun of the day preferring to walk at night thus preventing blistering of their sensitive skin. In the past, adults with the same characteristics had given rise to the belief that there was a tribe of white Indians, possibly descendants of the Scots, living on the coast of Panama. This was not unreasonable, when one considers that the Cuna have one of the highest rates of albinism anywhere in the world.

As two other doctors had dropped out at the last minute Nigel was responsible for medicare back at base camp as well as the medical project. He did a magnificent job shuttling between Mulatupo and Caledonia Bay where many members of the expedition were suffering from skin infections aggravated by the almost continuous presence of biting sandflies. The Young Explorers then had to cope on their own assisted by Nurse Naomi James, who had lived amongst the Cuna for some ten years. Travelling by canoe to the mainland they journeyed into the forests and quickly learnt how dependent the Cuna were on the forest and also how they had over generations, learnt to live with it, carefully balancing what they needed with what the forest could provide. Here were medicines for cataract, stomach-ache, strained muscles, and even good luck and food grew in abundance providing for all without shortage. It is this balance, however, which is increasingly being destroyed all over the world as the pressure of growing populations undermines the system of agriculture practised by forest dwellers for centuries. Further in from the coast the Young Explorers found themselves in primary seasonal rainforest, largely untouched by man and one of the richest natural systems in the world. Here, concealed in their small camp on the banks of the Aila River was another group of scientists exploring the unknown and extraordinary world in the roof of the rainforest.

Walking in the treetops

Imagine a world with no tigers, no orang-utans, no birds of paradise, no coffee, no car tyres, no cocoa, no contraceptive pill. All have originated from tropical rainforests and the rate at which new things are being discovered is increasing; yet the final disappearance of these forests has never been closer nor the potential consequences so devastating.

Take a large piece of land, shower it with not less than 1,200 millimetres of rain per year and ensure that not less than 100 millimetres falls in any one month. Then set the temperature at a mean of 25 degrees Centigrade with a diurnal variation greater than the annual variation, add a few million years and you will have a tropical rainforest. Within it will be the richest diversity of animals and plants on earth. Although covering less than 10 per cent of the earth's land surface, tropical forests are believed to contain 40 to 50 per cent of the earth's five or ten million species. A temperate forest may have sixty species of tree for example compared to 210 in an equivalent area of tropical forest.

To walk beneath a tropical rainforest is unforgettable. Massive vine-tangled trees reach up, the branch-patterned sunlight filtering through their huge interlocking green crowns, 50 metres or more above. These massive trees are merely the matrix in which the rest of the rainforest lives. Light, temperature, humidity and wind all change in the journey from the forest floor to the canopy and at each level animals and plants are adapted to live within an ecosystem so complex and so little understood that it will take years of detailed research to unravel it.

A rainforest is not a quiet place. Throughout the day and night a multitude of avian, arthropod and amphibian players chirrup, wheeze and scrape their way through their respective love songs in an ever-changing synthesis of tropical sound. As dawn approaches the night frogs pipe down, the scraping cicadas begin and the throaty roar of the howler monkey reverberates through the Panamanian forest. Iridescent birds flit between flower and fruit whilst ants scurry about upon the brown leathery leaves of the forest floor. Standing amongst the leafy greenness, the Young Explorer sees nothing at all apart from motionless bushes, giant trunks and nodding drip-tipped leaves. If he sits and waits however, the animals of the forest will begin to move. A small red skink crawls from under a leaf, an emerald hummingbird materialises in front of a flower and in a flash is gone again, chestnut-headed oropendolas leap from suspended nests and if he is very lucky he might glimpse a giant anteater tearing at a rotten log scooping ants onto its sticky tongue and into its toothless mouth. Being unable to see very far in such a forest gives rise to a tingling sensation of anticipation as to what might be around the next bush: a puma, a pit viper and a hairy black spider all too readily spring to mind. These are the subjects of dreams, however, for one rarely sees them in the forest – man is too noisy for that.

It has taken millions of years for these forests to evolve, yet if exploitation whether for energy, agriculture or timber revenue, continues at its present rate, man will have destroyed the world's accessible forests within about twenty years. Montane forests are not yet at risk but as timber prices rise, extraction by helicopter and even by helium-filled airship will become more economical so that these areas may also be felled.

Many developing nations desperately need foreign exchange and the stripping of their national assets is often the quickest way to get it. The consumption of tropical hardwoods by the developed nations has increased enormously since the 1950s, from

Andrew Mitchell with a pair of three-toed sloths *Bradypus tridactylus*. The mother and baby were rescued when their treetop home came crashing to the ground as part of a forest clearance scheme. Surprisingly, they had escaped the experience unhurt. They were later released into one of Panama's nature reserves.

4.2 million cubic metres to 66 million in the United States alone. This massive upsurge in demand is reflected by the rate of deforestation in the developing world of the 'south' which contains them. Modern logging equipment can remove 1,000 tonnes of trees and the attendant wildlife in just one hour. The raw logs are exported at a fraction of their final value when fashioned into furniture and veneers and so provide less revenue and employment to their countries of origin than would be the case had this been done prior to export. Forestry departments seem to want annual increases in export figures rather than a potentially sustainable yield in future years. At present it is not sustainable. Peninsula Malaysia will have exhausted its timber supplies within ten to twelve years and others will follow, so losing one of their major sources of revenue for ever.

Timber exploitation is highly selective. Of Amazonia's many thousands of tree species, only fifty of the 400 estimated to be commercially valuable are used. In South East Asia the bulk of exports consist of a mere twelve species. However, the extraction of these few species per hectare unavoidably results in the felling of many more in the removal process creating an imbalance in the forest ecosystem. An alternative but equally unsatisfactory method is clear felling. Modern pulping equipment can now cope with a full range of hardwoods so that all trees, regardless of size or value, can be bulldozed to the ground and converted by the mills into woodchips and later paper. As much as 20,000 tonnes of woodchips are exported from Madang, a small port in northern Papua New Guinea, every month. They have been clear felled from the once magnificent forests of the Gogol Valley, now a wasteland laid open to the ravages of soil erosion.

Rainforest clearance in Malaysia. Tracks formed by heavy logging equipment can cause serious erosion problems.

Advertisements like this one from a logging company illustrate well some attitudes to tropical forests. It is to this dilemma that we must address ourselves.

Scattered throughout tropical lands there are estimated to be 200 million 'slash-and-burn' cultivators; semi-nomadic forest farmers growing crops for one or two years on a cleared piece of forest and moving on when its soil fertility is exhausted. According to the United Nations Environment Programme (UNEP), they clear 8.5 million hectares of forest annually from South East Asia alone, out of the total 17.5 million they clear from the whole of the world. This problem is exacerbated by an increasing population utilising a decreasing area of forest so leaving less time for the forest to regenerate.

Another new factor is the influx of subsistence peasants from inadequate agricultural land outside the forest. These 'pioneer' foresters make little attempt to adapt to the environment and often move in along logging tracks which provide access to the otherwise impenetrable forests. It has been estimated that in the Ivory Coast in West Africa, for every 5 cubic metres of logs extracted by the timber exploiter, 1 hectare of forest disappears at the hands of the follow-on cultivator. Firewood is also needed by these people for cooking and keeping warm in the sometimes cold tropical night. Their fires are minute however when compared to the massive infernos of Central America designed to turn the rainforest into beef cattle.

Since 1950 the area of man-made pasture land in Central America has more than doubled, almost entirely at the expense of natural forests. Virtually all the beef raised on it finds its way into the American hamburger and frankfurter trade. One leading manufacturer needs 300,000 head of cattle to produce the 3,000,000,000 hamburgers it sells each year.

Ironically, car tyres the rubber for which originated from rainforest trees, are used to ignite the giant fires which destroy them on a massive scale in Latin America. Thousands of hectares of forest are burnt off each year to convert the forest into pasturage for cattle. Enormous profits can be made but only in the short term. The few species of grass upon which the cattle rely for food are gradually eaten out and replaced by less palatable and even poisonous species. In addition, the surprisingly infertile soils of the rainforest ecosystem are soon exhausted and the pasture lands become useless within six to ten years. The rancher maintains his profits by merely moving on to a new patch of forest. In Brazilian Amazonia, the 350 large ranches established up until 1980 under the Superintendency for the Development of Amazonia (SUDAM) has resulted in the clearance of 80,000 square kilometres of forest.

Putting all these disturbing statistics together reveals a frightening picture. At worst it seems that the overall annual loss of tropical rainforest is approximately 30 million hectares, an area the size of Italy each year; at best about 20 hectares a minute. The consequences are extremely difficult to assess; nothing like this has ever happened before. Some effects are immediate and recognisable but others are more sinister and slow acting.

One of the most noticeable effects may be on climate. Rainforests act like a giant sponge regulating the distribution of water around their ecosystem. Approximately 50 per cent of the rainfall which falls on them is returned to the atmosphere by being drawn up through the roots and evaporated from the leaf surface, a process known as evapotranspiration. They therefore act as a source of their own moisture. Remove them and there could be a steady regional reduction in rainfall which may affect the forest remaining. In twenty-five years Haiti's forests have declined from 80 per cent of the national territory to just 9 per cent; since 1977 there has been severe drought and the country's single hydro-electric dam, providing 99 per cent of its energy needs, now receives so little water that cities are routinely without power for half of every day.

As well as producing oxygen, tropical trees also absorb carbon dioxide. Since the industrial revolution there has been a constant increase in carbon dioxide levels in the earth's atmosphere; in the last twenty years by as much as 5 per cent. Much of this is thought to originate from the burning of fossil fuels and the release of carbon stored in trees when forests are burnt. Carbon dioxide is relatively transparent to incoming short wave radiation but long wave radiation, re-emitted from the earth's surface, is both absorbed and reflected back into the lower atmosphere. A rise in carbon dioxide levels will trap more long wave radiation in the atmosphere and could cause the global atmospheric temperature to rise. Mathematical models have suggested that a rise of 1.5 degrees Centigrade would produce climatic changes in rainfall distribution, wind patterns and snowfall all round the world. A rise of just 2 degrees Centigrade could de-stabilise or melt polar icecaps so raising sea levels; changing rainfall patterns could affect the productivity of the great American wheat belt. All this is speculation but at current rates of increase carbon dioxide levels will have doubled the pre-industrial figure within seventy years. The very unpredictability of the effects makes them important to study. If the models are right, it could be the greatest environmental challenge man has yet had to face.

Removal of the rainforest has many consequences of much more immediate impact. Up to 80 per cent of the nutrients contained in a tropical forest are above ground in the forest biomass. A rapid recycling system operates whereby decaying matter is quickly overgrown by fungus which transfers the nutrients into the trees via a close association with their roots enabling the forests to flourish on poor soils. Once the vegetation has been removed, little else remains. As most of the nutrients have been taken away or burnt off, soil fertility will only sustain crops for a few years, after which ever increasing

amounts of fertiliser are required. Without roots to bind them, the soil is easily eroded by the intense rainfall and the remaining nutrients which have increased solubility in the high temperatures are easily washed away. Hydropower installations become less efficient as reservoirs silt up, waterways become clogged and landslips destroy roads and bridges. The giant Mississippi River carries half a tonne of eroded soil per hectare of its watershed annually. President Marcos has recently declared deforestation to be a national emergency which indicates the level at which concern is now being felt.

Approximately 1,000 years ago temperate forests still covered Europe and much of North America. Now, little remains in its original form. Far from devastation, immensely productive agricultural land has resulted, because the forests of temperate lands were totally different from those of the tropics. Here the soils were much deeper and more nutritious. The removal process was much slower and the soils were not

The banks of the Aila River provided a perfect setting for the walkway camp.

laterised or eroded. Very few forest species appear to have been eliminated as they seemed to adapt to the changing conditions. On the rich soils remaining agriculture flourished.

The benefits of tropical forests are legion and many have only been realised in the last decade. The extraordinary diversity of species they contain provides us with a bank of genetic material which may be drawn upon for our future benefit. One of the most important areas will be in food production. Already the forests have given us many staple foods: rice, millet, yam, cassava, banana, pigeon pea, pineapple, mung bean, taro and sugar cane to name but a few. At least 1,650 plants from tropical forests offer highly nutritious leaves and thousands of other plant species remain to be investigated for their food potential. The successful food crops of today often result from careful genetic engineering but in order to maintain high productivity they need constant infusions of fresh germ plasm to resist disease, pests and environmental changes. In this century vital crops such as coffee, sugar cane and bananas have been saved from disaster by cross-breeding with genetic resources from tropical forests, the wild forms remaining resistant to diseases threatening their more specialised relatives. Recently a new form of perennial corn was discovered in the tropical forests of Mexico. If hybridised with existing annual forms it could produce a variety which would eliminate the need to plough and sow seed each year. The savings would run into billions of dollars.

One of the most exciting advances in the use of tropical forest products is in the field of medicine. A quarter of all prescription drugs are of biological origin. Curare, used in heart surgery in our hospitals, came from the poison used by the Amerindians of South America on their blow pipe darts and powerful anti-cancer drugs are also being discovered. Two drugs developed from the pink and white flowers of the Madagascan rosy-periwinkle have given leukaemia sufferers a four in five chance of survival.

It is difficult to put a price on the value of tropical forests. Their products produce vast revenue in the form of timber, tannins, oils and dyes. Tragic loss of life and 2,000,000,000 dollars' worth of damage was caused by the 1979 floods in India's Ganges valley; deforestation in Northern India and Nepal was thought to be a major cause. Many hundreds of tribal groups are totally dependent upon rainforests for their survival and now they are disappearing as fast as the forest. A major problem is that the environmental benefits cannot be identified as easily as can the revenue from timber sales or the desperate need for agricultural land which are more important in the eyes of the politician, economist and peasant. The forests provide another value, at present almost untapped, for which man in his diminishing world is increasingly craving. They remain one of the last truly wild places on earth still unexplored, unmapped and unknown. Man, with all his modern technology, is still forced to travel on foot through the forest in just the same way as Livingstone, Wallace and the other early explorers. The swamps and mosquitos are still there to cling and bite, as are aching limbs and sweat-stained clothes to spike on serrated, razor-sharp vines. But for the time being the forests will continue to fall and the race to find a compromise will intensify. All over the world scientists are desperately trying to answer one question – how does the rainforest ecosystem work? If we can understand the ecosystem, we may then learn how to manage it more effectively. Suspended 30 metres up in the jungles of Darien, Operation Drake's biologists were helping to supply another piece of the jigsaw puzzle.

Two hours' walk inland from the expedition's base camp on the shores of Caledonia Bay was a small basha made of leaves and sticks precariously constructed on the shingle bank of the Aila river. This was the laboratory and concealed amongst the vegetation along the river bank were the scientists, botanists and zoologists engaged in the first of Operation Drake's rainforest projects. There was no other shelter. Sleeping was done in a hammock suspended between the trees under a plastic sheet to keep off the downpours. Securing a roof over a hammock is quite an art. There are few more ghastly moments than litres of collected water splitting the plastic and cascading down onto the snugly sleeping occupant below whose hammock is by then 10 centimetres deep in water.

Whilst the camp was simple, the project was not. One of Operation Drake's main objectives was to study tropical forests in different parts of the world and gather information that could be used in their conservation. To achieve this aim it is vital to discover more about them, how they work, what they consist of and how one animal relates to another. By visiting three areas of undisturbed forest in Panama, Papua New Guinea and Sulawesi it was hoped that interesting observations on the least known part of this unique ecosystem, the living upper canopy formed by the leafy crowns of the tallest trees, could be made.

It is in the upper canopy that the trees convert the sun's energy into sugars through photosynthesis in their leaves and a large part of the life processes occur, the flowers, fruits and growing shoots. Also living in the canopy are many animals, from insects and frogs to birds and monkeys, all dependent to a greater or lesser extent on the forest layers around them but seldom seen and little studied. This continuous leaf layer was far out of reach above the ground supported on trees of 50 metres, as high as Nelson's Column. How could we get into it?

Surprisingly, the first Englishman to climb into the canopy of a tropical forest was none other than Sir Francis Drake. The year was 1573 and Drake was preparing to raid the Spanish royal treasure road through Panama. An unlikely story of a huge tree from which it was possible to see two oceans diverted him into a four-day march inland, west of Nombre de Dios on the Caribbean coast. Pedro, the Cimarron chief who had guided Drake and his men, finally led the stout Devonshire captain up steps cut into the side of a giant tree on the mountain divide. It was true. From the top Drake gazed out over the rolling, green canopy and first laid eyes on the Pacific praying that he:

> *... survive their present hazardous enterprise with profit and in due time be given leave to be the first man to sail an English ship upon that far-off, forbidden sea.*

The idea for his great voyage was born.

Almost exactly 400 years later Dr Stephen Sutton, an ecologist from the University of Leeds and I were puzzling on the canopy problem over coffee in London, when the idea of constructing portable aerial walkways in the field between the treetops which could be dismantled and transported on to the next country was conceived. Earlier designs had been bulky and taken years to build; methods for winching oneself into the canopy did exist but this would be impracticable for a team of scientists together with Young Explorers as assistants. Hank Mansley, a Regimental Sergeant-Major in the Royal Engineers of the British Army, came up with a design that he thought would work. Mike Tyndall, a director of Package Control Ltd, provided special man-made fibre tapes to support strips of galvanised steel factory flooring to make the base of the walkway. He even watched the first test construction amongst the pine trees of the Wiltshire countryside when it was used as an obstacle on one of the selection weekends. In the end however it was trial and error in the field that finally produced the perfected bridge.

Sergeant Mike Christy hangs in space as he builds the aerial walkway for the first time. The angled Dexion strips were later replaced with galvanised steel factory flooring in Papua New Guinea and Sulawesi.

On the banks of the Aila River Sergeant Mike Christy, a Royal Engineer, and Claire Bertschinger, the nurse who had, it turned out, a remarkable capacity for hanging upside down in the treetops for long periods of time, prepared to climb their first tree. Often, local people could do it in about three minutes needing only a stout vine on which to cling. It took Mike three and a half hours using rock pitons, a sledge-hammer and plenty of rope to reach the tree crown. Infuriated hornets and scorpions helped to make the experience entertaining but the greatest danger was from falling. Once there he and Claire set about constructing the walkway helped by the Young Explorers. In five weeks it was complete. In the tallest emergent trees observation platforms were built, the highest at 43 metres. Three looping sections of walkway, totalling nearly 125 metres in length were suspended from tree to tree forming an inter-connected bridgeway 30 metres above the ground. Not a single branch had been cut.

On later phases in Papua New Guinea and Sulawesi the system was perfected. The polypropylene main cables stretching from tree to tree were replaced by lighter 4,540 kilogram breaking-strain fibre tapes from which lightweight steel flooring was hung from smaller suspender tapes. To enable the main tapes to be pulled across, Mike Christy originally used a water-filled shampoo bottle with string attached which was thrown from one tree crown to another. This was later replaced by the more sophisticated crossbow and monofilament line which was fired between the tree crowns. Tirfor jacks tensioned the walkway adding stability as the trees swayed back and forth causing the bridge to rise and fall rather disconcertingly. The ingenuity of the army engineers was a wonder to behold as they worked for hour after hour in the mosquito-infested heat, swaying in their harnesses as they tied, banged and bolted with sweat-slippery hands piecing things together high above the ground.

The result was magnificent – a highway in the trees. Multicoloured macaws and toucans flew overhead. Squirrel-monkeys and arboreal anteaters approached unafraid and birds hopped about, only a metre or so away. The animals seemed less frightened of man in the trees. Once a hummingbird settled on the binoculars of the person trying to study it. From the walkway, botanists, zoologists, entomologists and ornithologists were able to examine the ecology of the canopy in an entirely new way for the very first time in three different countries. From any point, dozens of vines, epiphytes and trees were accessible, many of which had never been studied in their natural state before. Over the two years a multitude of different projects were carried out supported by the universities of Oxford, Leeds, York, Swansea, Colorado and Queensland. Years of work lies ahead on the thousands of plant and insect specimens collected but it is as well to explore some of the things that were found in the extraordinary world of the canopy and the forest beneath.

One-hundred-and-fifty years ago pollen was thought to be a waste product produced by flowers which had ingeniously adapted themselves to having it blown away by the wind. No one realised then that, contained in this fine yellow dust, was the genetic information needed to build everything in the plant kingdom from the most delicate daisy to the giant trees of the tropical forest. The reproductive biology of the rainforest is immensely complex. A strong evolutionary potential exists for its trees to ensure that their pollen is safely carried from one flower to another, whether it be male, female or hermaphrodite, on the same tree or on different trees of the same species. Once the nucleus of the pollen grain has united with that of the egg, a seed is produced and furnished with food for later development and a protective casing is added. The seed is then removed from the tree by an extraordinary variety of dispersal mechanisms so maximising chances of survival. The answer to how these huge trees pollinate each other lies up in the canopy where most of them have their flowers and it was one of the pieces of the jigsaw puzzle that the walkway could help with.

As she balanced herself carefully on the gently swaying platform, Hazel Preston gazed through her binoculars at the bright yellow flowers in the dense foliage. Iridescent bees buzzed between the petals, sending clouds of pollen into the warm humid air. Turning to make another entry in her notebook she discovered some leaf-

High observation platforms provided a
magnificent view of the forest and the
walkway. A second span can be seen leading
off to the right.

Layers of life in the rainforest

Different animals are found at different levels in the forest. Using the aerial walkway, Operation Drake studied the life in the upper canopy of tropical rainforests in Panama, Papua New Guinea and Sulawesi. This diagram shows the position of the walkway and some of the traps that were used. Larger animals such as tapirs and leopards obviously live at ground level, but even iguanas will ascend into the treetops where the climbers such as primates and arboreal anteaters live. Birds and many insects were also found to have their own favoured position in the forest.

cutter ants busily chewing their way through the paper. She paused briefly to wonder what a secretary from Yorkshire was doing walking in the treetops of a central American rainforest. She was, in fact, studying the yellow strings of flowers belonging to *Swartzia panamensis*, a member of the bean and pea family or Leguminosae, which is found in the lowland forests of Panama, Costa Rica and Nicaragua. These trees produce hanging inflorescences about 30 centimetres long, containing some fifty bright yellow flowers, 3 centimetres across. A few flowers emerge each day in the early hours of the morning. We were lucky as at this time of year the canopy was full of them. The question was, who were the pollinators: birds, insects, bats, or just the wind? This is quite easy to predict as both the shape and colour of a flower is carefully adapted to attract its specific pollinator. This is best developed in the orchids which even fashion themselves to mimic their insect pollinators.

Every twenty minutes Hazel and the other Young Explorers were busily writing down the numbers of each bee species alighting on each flower on the inflorescences they were watching, and recording what the bees did when they got there. Each of the thirteen species noted had its own behaviour pattern and needed close examination in

order to discover which the pollinator was. There was the 'black bum bee' which turned out to be *Trigona nigerrima*, the 'iridescent bee' and the 'huge bee', a species of *Eulaema* almost 3 centimetres long which came whirring across the canopy like a miniature helicopter scattering pollen and insects before it as it alighted on the delicate flowers in a clumsy embrace. The names had to be invented until captured specimens could be examined in Oxford and their taxonomic names revealed.

Of the 7,019 bees recorded in this way, 76 per cent landed on a haphazard collection of stamens in the upper section of the flower and only about 11 per cent on a lower section of stamens shaped like a landing stage. This lower section contains the stigma on to which pollen grains from another *Swartzia* tree must stick to ensure fertilisation goes ahead. In fact most of the bees visiting the flowers were 'robbers' interested only in taking as much pollen as possible from the upper stamens before moving on to the next flower. Of those visiting the lower stage, and therefore possible pollinators, the majority (76.5 per cent) consisted of *T. nigerrima* but this little bee did not seem to be the pollinator either. It lived in exposed nests high in the canopy and was extremely aggressive. On finding a rich source of food such as a *Swartzia* tree in flower it tended to

Pollination in the tropical rainforest

Rainforest plants have evolved a number of specialisations in flower structure to promote the transfer of pollen for fertilisation. *Brownea rosa-de-monte's* bright red flowers attract hummingbirds which feed on its copious supplies of nectar (a). As their long beaks reach into the flower their feathers become dusted with pollen. *Swartzia panamensis* (b) produces large quantities of pollen to satisfy the bees attracted to its colourful strings of yellow flowers. Other trees produce strongly scented flowers that open at night to attract bats (c). The petals are often thick and strong, providing a grip for the bats which in turn have very long tongues to reach into the flowers. Strong protruding stamens deposit pollen onto the bats' fur.

The bright colour of *Brownea rosa-de-monte* **flowers helps its pollinator to find it.**

Tree frogs are some of the most colourful creatures in the world. This species, *Agalychnis callidryas*, inhabits the forests of Panama north to Mexico. Bromeliads and palm fronds are its favourite resting places. Powerful legs and adhesive pads on the tips of its feet enable it to creep about the canopy and leap from branch to branch.

stay there without visiting other trees. This is of no use to the *Swartzia* tree which needs pollen to be carried from one tree to the next in order to fertilise its flowers. It seemed that the 'huge bee' was in fact the pollinator. This powerful bee flew frequently between trees whilst foraging for pollen and could thus carry the agents of fertilisation from one tree to another.

Another question remained. Why should the flowers put so much energy into making large amounts of pollen available merely for 'robbers' to seize? Careful observations provided a possible answer. It emerged that the upper pollen-laden stamens act as a lure to draw the non-pollinating 'robber' bees away from the vital landing stage below, so leaving plenty of pollen for the occasional visits by the 'huge bee', *Eulaema*. As it plunges the upper part of its body into the bountiful pollen supply at the top of the flower, *Eulaema*'s abdomen is both collecting pollen from the lower stamens and then depositing it on the stigma concealed amongst them. Pollination thus occurs.

Whilst all this was going on in the canopy, a different story was unfolding on the ground. Dotted around the forest were the beautiful bright red flowers of the *Brownea rosa-de-monte* tree. Overnight and on alternate days this sub-canopy species produces a starburst cluster of red spiky stamens and tube-like flowers growing directly from the bark of its branches and trunk. Peter Hudson, an ornithologist from Oxford University was keen to discover why the flowers should be designed in this way and who their pollinator might be.

The Young Explorers were put to work sitting quietly, concealed amongst the bushes on the ground, waiting and watching. They did not have to wait long before there was a faint buzzing noise, a brilliant flash of wings and there it was – a humming-bird reaching its long, curved bill into the perfectly formed flowers. It was *Phaethornis superciliosus*, the long-tailed hermit, and the only species we recorded visiting these flowers. The pigments in the bird's eyes enable it to see red clearly, hence the colour of the flower. Its tiny wings beat about thirty times a second allowing it to hover precisely in front of the flower and drink the potent energy supply contained within, the nectar, to fuel its super-efficient muscles. As it drinks, pollen from the long stamens is brushed onto its head and breast feathers and later carried to the next flower where the stigmas are pollinated. By producing one inflorescence only, the tree ensures that the hummingbird must visit a different tree for more nectar and so cross-pollination occurs. But it is a race against time. Before dawn has even broken moth larvae are growing within the flowers and trigonid bees soon discover the nectar supply and tear into them destroying their soft red petals. They only last one day.

Reproductive biology is one of the most exciting new areas of biological research but unravelling its complexities involves hours of painstaking work and detailed observation. Sitting in the canopy however was always an enjoyable experience. Countless animals were engaged in their daily business ranging from little brightly coloured tree frogs bathing in the trapped waters of a bromeliad to large iguanas sun-bathing in the tree crowns. From the highest observation platforms, Peter Hudson could observe flocks of foraging birds, the nest of the hawk *Leucopternis* and the howler monkeys *Alouata seniculus* picking their way along arboreal pathways in search of the fruits of the forest. The massive tree boughs of the canopy contain a gardener's paradise. One tree may hold as many as fifty to a hundred different species of epiphyte using its host as a foothold in the forest. Some trail long vines to the forest floor or draw water from a river 20 metres below while others take the water trickling along the branches on which they sit. The powerful strangler figs can take over the top of a tree entirely and on occasions our climbers, having chosen to ascend one species of tree at ground level, found themselves in another when they reached the top! A number of new plant species were collected from the walkway but it came as something of a surprise that one of them was 45 metres tall and weighed 30 tonnes. Unknowingly we had built one end of the walkway in a new species of *Couratari* tree, a member of the Brazil nut family.

A leaf-cutter ant at work.

The enormous growth potential of the forest is kept in check by many factors, such as the availability of light and nutrients and predation. The most effective plant predators are the insects. Along with many other processes they help to maintain a balance, preventing one species from dominating another or the forest from choking itself to death. Insects attack plants at all levels in the forest but some make the journey all the way from the dim forest floor into the high canopy in search of the choicest shoots of all, the young growing leaves. These small creatures are the most devastating herbivores in the Panamanian forest, capable of stripping branches of leaf material in a matter of hours and their effects are everywhere. They are the leaf-cutter ants, *Atta* sp.

Found only in the New World tropics, these creatures live in huge underground nests from which ant pathways spread out across the forest floor swept clean of débris and leading, sometimes 250 metres to a bush or tree currently in use as a food supply. Chris Willis, a Young Explorer from Jersey, and Sue McCallum from England set about mapping the trails and learning about the ant's behaviour. At dawn the workers would move out of the nests in their millions, spreading to all points of the compass, ten abreast, marching on relentlessly to begin the day's work. Woe betide anything that fell in their path, be it twig or scurrying beetle; all were cast aside or dismembered in

The meeting point of two walkways. Mike Christy and Claire Bertschinger prepare to hang two light traps for the night's catch whilst Shane Kennedy has arrived with a new rope for an observation platform 10 metres higher up.

Dr Willie Wint working in the laboratory hut. He and others at the camp were dedicated workers spending all day in the canopy and half the night recording what they had found. The YEs played an integral part in the work.

seconds. Whilst some ants fell upon bushes in the lower layers of the forest, others began the long climb into the canopy. Once there, a hundred thousand jaws sliced neat green crescents from the best leaves and these were then carried off, the ants often grasping pieces several times their own size. They travelled along well-trodden routes all the way down to the ground again and back to the nest in long winding lines of green.

On entering the nest they encountered what Sue and Chris called the 'quality control department'. Here the leaf material was examined and anything not up to the required standard was discarded. Some of the insects were clearly confused by our botanists' carefully tied specimen labels, an increasing number of which were found rejected outside the nest as the study progressed. Silver paper, plastic, in fact almost anything they could cut through, was seized by the ants only to be thrown out subsequently. Those carrying more palatable cargo disappeared into the nest where the leaf pieces were placed in storage chambers. Here a fungus is grown on the leaves and it is this that the ants feed upon. Exhausted leaf material is then gathered up by the 'refuse department' and removed to a site away from the nest where it is neatly dropped onto

Andrew Sugden and Willie Wint using the telescopic clipper pole to collect leaf samples.

an ever increasing conical pile.

Dr Willie Wint, a zoologist from the Hope Department of Entomology in Oxford, wanted to discover how much material these and other insects were removing from the trees of the canopy and what defences the leaves were employing against them. Tropical trees do not produce leaves one at a time; they do so in isolated bunches. This is known as leaf flushing. The young leaves are bright green, soft and vulnerable to insect attack but even at this stage are five times harder than a mature temperate oak leaf. It takes five days for them to reach terminal hardness after which fewer insects have jaws strong enough to damage them. To protect themselves during this period the leaves employ chemical defences in the form of phenols in their tissues which are toxic to insects. Animal predation on leaves, 'herbivory', provides a powerful selective pressure to which trees must adapt to ensure their survival and is therefore important in the understanding of their evolution.

Using a cumbersome 10 metre telescopic clipper pole the Young Explorers snipped small branches from a wide variety of trees and vines in the canopy at different heights in the forest whilst being hauled up and down in a harness. Any insects on the samples were collected in a glass bottle or 'pooter' and then all was taken to the laboratory hut by the river. The leaf-cutter ants were delighted. Someone was bringing juicy leaves down to ground for them, saving them the tiresome journey to the canopy. They invaded the laboratory in thousands but despite their efforts to ruin the samples, some surprising results emerged from the mass of leaves that were sorted, dried, pressed and finally flown back to the Botany School at Oxford. Despite a great variance in plant species and predators, the amount of leaf material destroyed in Panama and Papua New Guinea was found to be the same, around 12 per cent and this was 30 to 40 per cent higher than had previously been predicted from leaf litter samples taken at ground level. In Panama leaf-cutter ants account for 90 per cent of leaf damage whereas in Papua where these ants and leaf-eating primates do not occur, caterpillars seem to be the main destroyers of leaf material. By using the aerial walkway to obtain samples directly from the canopy we had come up with important new findings.

Not all rainforests are the same. Therefore it was important to describe accurately the kind of forest we were working in. Willie Wint and Andrew Sugden used the walkway to determine the three dimensional structure of the forest, producing maps of the position of different trees in relation to each other. Tree maps for each of the walkway sites in Panama, Papua and Sulawesi were made as well as profile diagrams of the forest. A Young Explorer on the walkway would listen and watch as Willie beat a stick on a tree trunk on the ground below to match up the tree's crown in the canopy with its trunk, something which was surprisingly difficult to do from the walkway.

At the end of an exhausting day on the walkway we would all walk back to the camp laden with safety harnesses, clipper poles and samples, our bodies itching from sweat and mosquito bites. Nothing was better than to plunge fully clothed into the cool, clear waters of the river and let the little fishes tickle and bite your skin. Having dined on Irish stew, powdered potato and squashy peas or perhaps an agouti steak if Joshua, our Guardia Nacional sergeant, had been lucky hunting the night before, Andrew Sugden would bring out his tatty guitar and sing the blues whilst Mike Christy sent the daily radio report back to base camp at Caledonia Bay, including as many long scientific names as possible to confuse the signallers. News would return of archaeological finds and drama on the Balboa trail or of impending visits by the President of Panama, but concealed amongst the forests beside the Aila River these events passed by almost un-noticed. Save for the inevitable 'tourists' from the base camp who wanted to see the walkway, life was pretty cut off and the immediate concerns were who was going to do the next *Brownea* watch or whether the river would rise and flood the laboratory again that night.

At night the rainforest comes alive and whilst one group of scientists were in the laboratory hut sorting and drying samples, others went off to catch the night time fliers. Different animals are active during the hours of darkness to those in daytime and

Caroline Ash sorts the ever growing collection of insects.

New insect traps in the rainforest

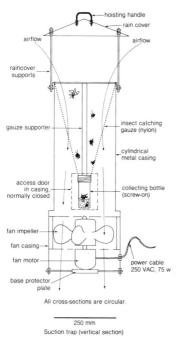

hoisting handle
rain cover
airflow
airflow
raincover supports
gauze supporter
insect catching gauze (nylon)
cylindrical metal casing
access door in casing, normally closed
collecting bottle (screw-on)
fan impeller
fan casing
fan motor
power cable 250 VAC, 75 w
base protector plate

All cross-sections are circular.

250 mm
Suction trap (vertical section)

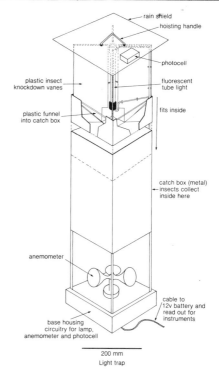

rain shield
hoisting handle
photocell
plastic insect knockdown vanes
fluorescent tube light
plastic funnel into catch box
fits inside
catch box (metal) insects collect inside here
anemometer
cable to 12v battery and read out for instruments
base housing circuitry for lamp, anemometer and photocell

200 mm
Light trap

The suction trap

The light trap

Two types of insect trap were used by the Operation Drake scientists in their study of the distribution of insects in the tropical rainforest. In the suction trap (a) a 75 watt electric fan causes a down draught of air through the trap, carrying with it most insects flying near the inlet at the top. The insects are intercepted by a nylon mesh cone positioned in the airflow above the fan. From here, they fall down, or can be brushed into a detachable collecting bottle. Four such traps were used at 30, 20, 10 and 1 metre levels above the forest floor to sample insect distribution. Light traps attract some species much more than others and can only be used at night. Suction traps can help to overcome these difficulties, but there is an upper limit of insect size which they will suck out of the air.

The light trap (b) uses a 15 watt battery driven fluorescent tube, emitting light rich in ultraviolet wavelengths, to attract insects. They fall into a collecting box below the tube when their flight is interrupted by colliding with one of the plastic vanes near the light. They cannot easily escape because the box entrance is funnel shaped. Eight of these traps were used to sample insect distribution and abundance at different levels in the rainforest canopy and below it. The traps also carried aloft an anemometer and a light intensity sensor. Information from these was fed down a cable to a display unit at ground level.

we wished to investigate where insects and bats could be found flying during the night and also how they distributed themselves in the forest. These projects were continued in Papua New Guinea and Sulawesi.

While Cathy Mackenzie set mist nets on the forest floor to catch bats, Caroline Ash, a zoologist from Leeds University, set light traps in the canopy to capture insects. (The work on bats is dealt with fully in Chapter 6 on Sulawesi.) We quickly discovered that removing an infuriated bat from a mist net is a tricky business if you are to avoid getting bitten and as bats are known rabies carriers, very special care is needed. Panama is also the home of blood-sucking vampire bats *Desmodontidae*. One had bitten John Blashford-Snell on his reconnaissance trip in 1976. Fortunately none attacked us on this occasion although anti-rabies serum had to be rushed to Cathy when she was bitten by another species.

The spatial distribution of insects is an important factor in the understanding of their ecology. At present there is practically no information on this and one of Operation Drake's major comparative walkway projects was to try to add to this meagre knowledge by trapping night-flying insects at standard heights between the forest floor and the top of the upper canopy. We supplemented this record of vertical distribution by examining the differences in catch between one tree crown and another using the walkway to provide access. This also provided further information on their horizontal distribution in the upper canopy.

Four ultraviolet light traps were hauled up into the trees each night for three hours, first to look at vertical distribution for ten days and then the horizontal distribution between the tree crowns. By keeping a meticulous record of rainfall, temperature, moonlight levels and other environmental factors, we were also able to find out which of these factors were important in determining catch size. This varied by a factor of 100, sometimes with catches ranging from ten to 1,000 mosquitos on consecutive nights. Sorting through the catch was a mammoth task. Over a ten-day trapping period hundreds of thousands of insects would be caught, many the size of a pin head or smaller. All had to be carefully counted with tweezers, transferred from petri dishes into bottles of alcohol and labelled for analysis back in England. Six years of work now lies ahead correlating the data from Panama, Papua New Guinea and Sulawesi as well as information collected from Zaire and Brunei on previous scientific expeditions.

During this two-year study pioneered by Dr Stephen Sutton, new techniques for quantifying the distribution of rainforest insects were developed. The 'Leeds Actinic' design of ultraviolet light trap, first tried out in Zaire, was used on all three rainforest projects and operated in a standard way at all three sites. This achieved a direct comparison between the insect catches in South East Asia and the New World rainforest blocs for the first time and also the African bloc using the Zaire results.

In Sulawesi two innovations were successfully tried out. The first was the incorporation of a miniature meteorological station, designed and built in the Zoology Department at Leeds University, into each of the actinic traps. In this way microclimatic conditions could be recorded wherever the light traps were situated. This data was fed down cables from the traps to a battery of analysers situated in the comfort of a hut on the ground, where information on wind speed, temperature and light levels could be instantly read off a digital console. The second innovation was the use of a suction trap developed by Dr Christopher Rees of York University which captured all insects which flew close to it including those not attracted to ultraviolet light and hence not found in the actinic traps. These suction traps, unlike the ultraviolet traps, also caught day-flying insects and so were able to provide data on the activity patterns of insects over the whole twenty-four hour period. By comparing catches in both types of trap new information about the distribution of insects within the forest began to emerge.

The results demonstrated that, in general, insects are much more abundant in the upper canopy, much as had been predicted by the early Victorian naturalists who first suggested the importance of the forest roof as a centre of activity. In a handful of cases the reverse was true, but for most groups of insects the distribution was similar to that shown below. In two groups, the Homoptera (cicadas and froghoppers) and the Agaonid fig wasps, the vast majority of specimens were confined to the upper canopy. Since virtually no extensive trapping had been done high in rainforest trees before, apart from a little in Panama, we were sampling an unknown fauna and at least nine out of ten of the species caught are likely to be new to science. The fig wasp results are particularly exciting because the great abundance we found was totally unexpected and a whole new field of rainforest research has now been opened up by this study. Each species of fig wasp is probably associated with its own species of fig, upon which it relies for the completion of its life cycle, pollinating the fig's flower in a form of evolutionary *quid pro quo*. Another exciting discovery was the Pyralid moths caught, which sometimes made up 80 per cent of all moths trapped. Surprisingly, no work has been done on the biology of these moths in the rainforest, although they were found to be the dominant insects in all three rainforest sites. Now that their significance has been demonstrated, a much greater interest is likely to be shown in this group.

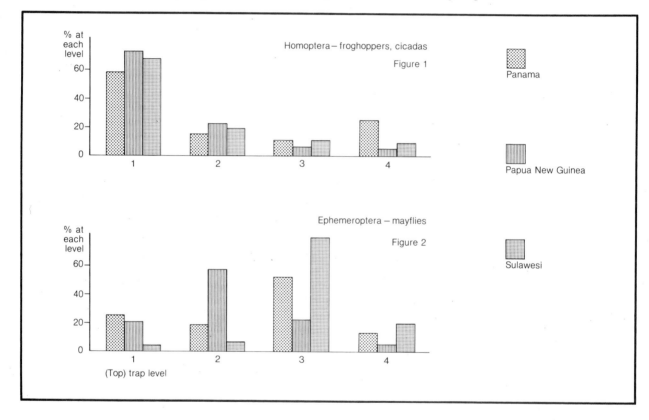

Not all groups of insects showed the same distribution from the upper canopy to the ground. The most common pattern was that shown in figure 1. Mayflies, however, seemed to concentrate in the lower layers of the forest in the area of lowest wind speed; as mayflies are weak fliers this may cause them to favour this area.

Rainfall was shown to have a marked effect, bringing out many more insects. Only in extreme downpours with up to 10 centimetres of rainfall per hour did any reduction occur. The trap catches revealed that moonlight depressed the overall numbers of insects flying and led to a higher proportion being caught near to the ground. A notable feature of the suction trap catches was that at night, mosquitos were as much as 1,000 times more abundant in the upper canopy in Sulawesi than at ground level. This accounted for the hasty retreat performed by those people who tried spending the night on the walkway platforms. By contrast, during the day the mosquitos were more common near to the ground. These first results raise all sorts of questions as to how and why these patterns have evolved and are maintained. In the case of mosquitos the

Sara Everett surrounded by members of the team that found the old gold mine at Cana.

Geoffroy's tamarin is still fairly common in the forests of Panama. A reservoir host of several human diseases, it is of particular biomedical interest. As it adapts well to secondary forest it is less threatened by the loss of primary forest than other species. However, it is widely trapped for laboratory experiments and the pet trade.

results will have important implications in our understanding of the diseases of forest animals. Many forest animals are probable reservoirs of human diseases and mosquitos, as well as other insects, are important vectors of disease between both animals and man.

Analysis of the distribution of insects from tree to tree is in progress but it is clear that in all three areas there is a tremendous variation from trap to trap and from night to night. The great diversity of insects in the forest may well be due in part, to the correspondingly great variation in plant species found over very short distances.

Detailed observations of this kind are the first step in a long process of unravelling the complex interrelationships of biological life in the tropical rainforest. By visiting three areas in different parts of the world comparisons have been made which were not previously possible. Operation Drake has shown the feasibility and value of comparative studies in the upper canopy, due largely to the use of aerial walkways. The future now lies with long-term studies in selected sites lasting three to five years which will use extensive networks of walkways. The exploration of life in the upper canopy of the rainforest has only just begun.

The mould growing on our clothes at the walkway camp and the jungle sores on our legs were becoming increasingly difficult to stop. It was now April and the rains had begun in earnest. The paradise that the Scots had dreamed of was fast becoming a quagmire and the Panama phase was at an end. The walkway was dismantled and what could be was salvaged for use in Papua New Guinea.

John Blashford-Snell had just returned from exploring the legendary gold mines of Cana in a remote valley near the Columbian border. Back in Panama City, the TAC HQ staff had worked tirelessly to support those in the field with anything from sandals to engine parts. Kim Batty had typed hundreds of letters and John's PA Sara Everett had soothed officials and dealt with endless press enquiries. Now it was their turn to go on an adventure into the jungle. John and his team including signallers, medical staff, and many Young Explorers had driven 288 kilometres down the Pan American Highway to Yaviza. The journey took just eight hours. Six years before it had taken the British Trans Americas Expedition, also led by John, ten weeks to cut a path for their two Range Rovers along the same route enabling them to drive the first vehicles ever from Alaska to Tierra del Fuego. Now, a highway cuts through the forest and on each side the devastating effects of follow-on cultivators can be seen, irrevocably peeling back the forest. The advance of the road seems inevitable.

After taking dugout canoes down the Rio Chucunaque and up to the Rio Tuira, the team began a two-day march from Boca de Cupe to the mines. In the seventeenth century they were reported to be the richest in Latin America and were mined until 1928. The tunnels were still there along with old railway lines, hundreds of porcelain beer bottles and a wooden horse-drawn gold waggon. An ancient fortress, probably of Spanish origin, was found nearby. Some of the YEs tried their hand at gold panning and were amazed to find they were successful.

At Caledonia Bay Nick Lindsay, a zoologist from the Jersey Wildlife Preservation Trust, had completed his study of the delightful Geoffroy's tamarin *Saguinus oedipus geoffroyi* and the medical team had returned from Mulatupo. It is always depressing ending an expedition, pulling down tents, packing boxes, loading boats and saying goodbye. Hundreds of plant, insect and archaeological specimens were recorded, labelled and stamped. The rain had made the airstrip unuseable so most stores were removed by sea. A Guardia Nacional landing craft beached near the 'Coral Bar' and everything was loaded. By coincidence *Eye of the Wind* left the bay on the same day that the colony had been abandoned so many years before. For the Young Explorers, support teams and scientists, their part in the expedition was over. For the crew of *Eye of the Wind*, a new adventure was beginning as she made her way through the Panama Canal to Panama City to be joined by Phase III of the YEs and to prepare for her long journey across the Pacific.

The Pacific crossing

Having crossed the hostile forests of the Darien with 190 men, nine dugout canoes and a pack of hounds, Vasco Nuñez de Balboa, in full armour, sword in hand and waving the banners of Castille and Aragon strode chest deep into the Pacific claiming all her coasts and islands for the King of Spain. It was September 29th 1513. Just over seven years later Fernão de Magalhaes, whom the French called Magellan, sailed between the terrifying snow-covered cliffs of the strait subsequently named after him to enter the Pacific via Cape Horn. When Drake entered Magellan's 'Mar Pacifico' on September 7th 1578 on his journey around the world in the *Golden Hind*, accompanied by the *Marigold* and the *Elizabeth*, the sea was anything but peaceful. Francis Fletcher, Drake's minister aboard the *Golden Hind* described the scene:

> *The storm being so outragious and furious, the bark Marigold, with 28 souls, were swallowed up with the horrible and unmerciful waves, or rather mountains of the sea, wherein myself and John Brewer, our trumpeter, being on watch, did hear their cries as the hand of God came upon them.*

Having lost the *Marigold* in the storm the *Elizabeth* turned back for England and Drake, now quite alone, headed north up the west coast of South America. His first port of call was the island of Mocha off the coast of Chile. Here two of his crew were brutally cannibalised having been mistaken for Spaniards by the local Indians who:

> *... working with knives upon their bodies, cut the flesh away by gubbets, and cast it up in the air. The which, falling down, the people catched in their dancing, and like dogs devoured in most monstrous and unnatural manner.*

Four months later, the *Golden Hind* limped into Isla de Caño 15 kilometres off Costa Rica, leaking and trailing weed. Here Drake hastily careened his vessel for, nineteen days behind him, was a force of ships commanded by His Excellency Don Luis de Toledo who had chased him all the way from Peru. On March 20th, off what is still called Drake's Bay, a small Spanish bark was attacked by a launch containing arque-

busiers, archers and shieldmen. Drake had claimed another victim. It proved to be a valuable one as on board he found two maps and a collection of charts which were later to enable him to cross the Pacific. From his raids along the American coast Drake was now in command of the richest treasure ship the world had ever seen. Within the *Golden Hind* were 1,800 bars of silver, ten medium-sized boxes holding silver 'pices of eight', nine small gilded boxes containing gold and a medium-sized chest, also containing gold. When *Eye of the Wind* arrived at Drake's Bay 400 years later, her cargo and purpose were rather less spectacular.

After leaving Panama on December 21st she had journeyed to Drake's Bay to take part in a small ceremony in which the British chargé-d'affaires, Jerry Warder, and Señor Carlos Guardia of the Department of Tourism unveiled commemorative plaques celebrating the 400th anniversary of Drake's visit, presented by the Costa Rican Government and the Lord Mayor of Plymouth. Earlier, *Eye of the Wind* hove to off San Pedro where groups of Young Explorers were put ashore through heavy surf in canoes to explore the coastline and interior of the Corcovado National Park.

Though the Costa Rican National Parks system is only nine years old it already comprises 3.5 per cent of the country's land mass, a greater proportion than that of any other Latin American country and of most other nations of the world. The Phase III YEs received their first taste of the jungle as National Park guides took them on a four-day trek into the park's interior, pointing out many of the 285 species of bird found there including brilliant red parrots, toucans and macaws. Corcovado, comprising 36,000 hectares of rich and varied rainforest on the Osa Peninsula, was created in 1973 and has eight field stations, five of which were visited by the YEs. By day they learnt to live off the many fruits in the forest often from long since abandoned plantations – pineapple, banana, lime, sweet lemon, avocado and cashew nuts. At night they slept at the homes of the park wardens or in the forest itself under leaf shelters.

Meanwhile Trish Holdway and other YEs had flown out to a small bush airstrip in the isolated south-west portion of the peninsula. Here they worked on a coastal survey for the Costa Rican Government recording shoreline animal communities, sediment deposition and the effects of coastal erosion. A full report was later submitted to the National Parks Service.

Eye of the Wind returned to Panama City where Captain Mike Kichenside took over command. His gentle but firm control of both the ship and its crew were to prove a

It is only seventy years since the days of sail finally gave way to steam. *Eye of the Wind* has a close encounter with the super tanker *British Resolution* off **Panama. BP fuelled our flagship worldwide.**

Drake was here 400 years before. John Blashford-Snell and Costa Rican officials commemorate the occasion with memorial plaques.

magnificent asset for the remainder of the voyage and on each phase the Young Explorers came to respect and admire him for his tutorship, advice and brilliant seamanship. Mike was familiar with *Eye of the Wind* having sailed her from Singapore to Britain following her original refit as had his twelve-year-old daughter, Miranda, who now also joined the ship.

Our next stop was Cocos Island 500 kilometres south-west of Panama. Superficially, Cocos is an inhospitable island with shark-infested waters, high cliffs and thick rain-forest. But it has not always been so. Geologically it is only two million years old and in some ways resembles the Galapagos further to the west. When the first explorers arrived there they found it to be covered in coconut groves, hence its name. The question is who planted them? Coconut palms do not grow naturally inland and Thor Heyerdal has suggested that early Polynesian navigators could be responsible as they used unripe coconuts as a water supply on long sea voyages, and may have cultivated the island for this purpose. Cocos is also famous for another reason. It is one of the world's real 'treasure islands'.

The successful pirate Henry Morgan is reputed to have buried his chests of gold there and the schooner *Mary Dyer*, on her way from Lima in Peru with the entire town's treasure snatched by a mutinous crew, was wrecked on the island two centuries ago. Hardly a square metre of beach has been left unturned by the many hopeful expeditions which have unsuccessfully searched the island. Now the island is inhabited by two lonely policemen and a family of hippies. The Young Explorers found neither coconut groves nor gold but the visit was interesting nonetheless. Collections were made of fauna and flora on behalf of the Costa Rican National Parks Service on a march inland to search for a World War II American fighter plane said to have crashed in the island's interior. The plane was found, much to the YEs' delight and the collection was sent on to Costa Rica.

The Galapagos Archipelago was *Eye of the Wind's* next port of call. It comprises a group of six large and several small volcanic islands on the equator, frequently called 'Los Islas Encantadas', the enchanted islands. They are governed by Ecuador although they lie nearly 1,000 kilometres off its coast. The flora and fauna of these islands proved inspirational in the formation of one of the most important theories of modern times, a treatise which influenced scientists and disrupted ecclesiasts. It was entitled *The Origin of Species by Means of Natural Selection* and written by Charles Darwin.

Darwin sailed around the world in the three-masted bark, *Beagle*, in a voyage which lasted five years from 1831 to 1836. In September and October 1835, Darwin spent five weeks in the Galapagos during which he noted the close similarities animals and plants bore to those on the Central and South American mainland. In addition he observed that, for example, the giant tortoises and finches formed morphologically distinct populations on the different islands.

Twenty-three years later Darwin and Alfred Russel Wallace published their joint views on natural selection, though Darwin took most of the credit due to his theories of human evolution which created the greater interest. The processes of natural selection and evolution are manifest in the Galapagos. The islands were originally colonised by plants and animals brought by wind, water or birds from the mainland and each settled island population adapted itself to the particular terrain. Eventually the island populations evolved into separate subspecies or species related both to each other and to the parent stock. The Young Explorers, who had been well versed in the theory on the voyage from Cocos, now had a chance to see it for themselves.

After a brief stop to clear formalities at Wreck Bay on San Cristobal Island, the administrative centre of the Galapagos, *Eye of the Wind* sailed into Academy Bay on Santa Cruz. The coast provided an aspect of inhospitable jagged lava, scattered with *Jasminocerus candelabra* cactus and the prickly pear, *Opuntia*. Marine iguanas lay on the rocks in the harbour entrance, occasionally swimming from one side to the other. The Charles Darwin Research Station (CDRS) founded in 1960 at Academy Bay has carried out an immense amount of research into the Galapagos environment and its conservation. The Young Explorers were now briefed by the Station's Director, Dr Hendrick Hoeck to help in a variety of tasks. These included censusing the wild goat population on Marchena, searching for land iguanas at Conway Bay and building a dog-proof fence there. An odd array of projects perhaps, but not when the threats now facing the wildlife of the Galapagos are considered.

Of the original fifteen races of Galapagos tortoise *Geochelona elephantopus* only eleven are known to survive. Of these, two are on the verge of extinction, one having only thirteen specimens, the other consisting of a solitary, doomed male. The populations of three others will probably survive but the remaining six are threatened with extinction by the large variety and numbers of feral mammals which have been introduced by sailors and colonists over the centuries. Tortoise population sizes had already been reduced by sailors victualling their ships before introduced and abandoned pigs, dogs, cats and black rats began attacking nests and severely affecting recruitment to the adult (breeding) population. Competition for food resources with feral populations of goats, donkeys and even cattle has largely destroyed the habitat of the giant tortoise and

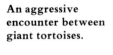

An aggressive encounter between giant tortoises.

Giant tortoises and their island shell shapes

abingdoni (one ♂ remains at CDRS)
Pinta

Marchena   ▪Genovesa

becki

microphyes

Santiago or
San Salvador

Wolf

Darwin   *darwini*

phantastica (?)
(only one ♂ found 1906)   *wallacei* (?)

Fernandina   Santa Cruz

Alcedo   *porteri*

Sierra Negra

San Cristobal

vicina   Santa Fé   *chathamensis*

Cerro Azul   *ephippium*

Isabela *güntheri*   Pinzon   extinct

vandenburghi

Eye of the Wind's route   0   50km.   *hoodensis*
(all 13 specimens
at CDRS)

Floreana or Santa Maria   ←extinct

Española

On his visit to the Galapagos Islands in 1835 Charles Darwin learned that the shell shape of tortoises could identify their island of origin. He visited only San Cristobal, Santiago, Floreana and Isabela and overlooked that even within some islands a great diversity of shell shape also occurs.

Tortoise carapaces (shells) vary from dome-shaped, such as *vandenburghi*, to the saddleback-shaped races such as *hoodensis*. (The word 'galapagos' not only means tortoise but is also the name given to the traditional prow-shaped Spanish riding saddle, thus saddleback tortoise.) On Santiago both shapes are found freely intermingling. On Isabela there are four or possibly five isolated races on each of the volcanos and each population has a different shell shape. On one of these volcanos,

Alcedo, the majority of the population lives inside the crater.

When young tortoises are taken from different islands and reared under identical conditions their shells grow into the shape characteristic of their island of origin. The shape is therefore genetically rather than environmentally determined. The raised front of the saddleback's carapace increases the tortoise's ability to stretch up for leaves and fruits and is particularly useful in the drier island habitats where food may be scarce. Also, in aggressive face-to-face encounters between these tortoises, the individual which raises its head the highest wins. In dry geological periods, such as an Ice Age, or in dry habitats, such a competitive advantage is vital.

iguana populations. Dr Ian Swingland of the Animal Ecology Research Group at the University of Oxford joined Operation Drake in the Galapagos to study this problem and compare it with the situation on Aldabra Island in the Seychelles, where he had worked for two years and where over 90 per cent of the earth's giant tortoises still survive.

Right up to the time of Darwin's visit to the archipelago, tortoises were widely distributed in the dry lowlands near the coasts even though some 200,000 were taken for ships provender from the late seventeenth century to the end of the nineteenth. By this time they were becoming so scarce that the effort of looking for them was no longer worthwhile. By the 1900s the islands of Floreana and Santa Fé had been cleared out, the Pinta and Espangnol populations had been decimated and coastal populations on other islands had all but disappeared. Human exploitation for eggs and meat was brought under control in the 1960s. It is now vital that the feral mammals should also be controlled. Their enormous populations are hard to credit but in 1971 there were estimated to be 40,000 goats on Pinta and 100,000 in James as well as 8,000 pigs. The dog packs of Cerro Azul can kill quite large tortoises up to fifteen years old. While pigs can only kill four to five-year-olds, they alone can locate and dig up the nests. Dogs are also responsible for killing large numbers of land iguanas *Conolophus subcristatus* as well as the marine species.

Two main policies are being followed to prevent the ultimate extinction of the giant tortoise and land iguana. Firstly, hunters from the National Park Service visit the islands regularly to shoot as many of the large mammals as possible and bring back tortoise eggs for hatching at the CDRS. The hatchlings are kept until they are quite large (five to six-years-old) when they are reintroduced to their island. Recently the control of dogs with a canicide has been investigated. A method that could be used with devastating effect would be the introduction of a species specific viral epidemic – swine vesicular disease for the pigs and distemper for the dogs. However, this is unacceptable as it would also affect the domestic stock farmed by the local Galapaguinos, though whilst the domestic stock remains the ever present threat of escapes and re-introductions will also.

The second precaution taken against extinction has been the removal of entire races of both land iguanas and tortoises from very small endangered populations to the research station where they are kept and bred in pens or corrals. It is unfortunate, but the only viable solution; the alternative of keeping them *in situ* and protecting them from feral mammals is simply too expensive and likely to fail. Howard Snell, principal adviser for the land iguana programme at the CDRS, showed the YEs around the captive breeding pens at Academy Bay. Normally they are not open to the public but it was important for the YEs to be able to distinguish between sexes, ages and sub-species for the work they were to do. Young iguanas, looking like miniature pre-historic monsters, scuttled under rocks and branches at their approach to hide in the darkness.

Three guides, two from the CDRS and one from the National Park Service together with an Ecuadorian Naval Officer, joined *Eye of the Wind* for the journey north to South Plaza, a small island on the eastern coast of Santa Cruz. The anchor was dropped in the narrow channel separating North and South Plaza. Stepping over disgruntled sea-lions sunbathing on the jetty the YEs went ashore to be shown round the island by Mrs Heidi Snell, who was conducting research into its land iguana population. Here was the true Galapagos much as Lord Byron had found it in 1825:

The place is like a new creation. The birds and beasts do not get out of our way, the pelicans and sea-lions look in our faces as if we had no right to intrude on their solitude, and the small birds are so tame they hop upon our feet.

People began living on the Galapagos a little over fifty years ago and even today telephoto lenses are unnecessary as the animals have little fear of man.

Land iguanas have a clever ability to appear as if they are carved from the very stone around them. By remaining perfectly still their yellow and brown coloration renders them almost invisible as they sun themselves in the early afternoon. By late afternoon they can be seen scurrying through the undergrowth between the bushes upon which they feed. Black and green marine iguanas *Amblyrhynchus cristatus* group on rocks near the shore, ready to plunge wildly into the sea assuming a fluid grace beneath the waves where they pluck seaweed from the rocks below. A third reptilian species was also present in large numbers, the lava lizard *Tropidurus albemarlensis*, often seen doing press-ups its head thrown back, displaying the bright red throat.

The sea-lion colonies provided much excitement and interest. They too were unafraid of man and appeared positively to enjoy swimming with the Young Explorers, diving down to the corals and peering at the peculiar beasts with mask and snorkel that had entered their watery domain. The YEs took great care to keep well clear of the shore. Here fat bulls with thick, powerful necks presided over their harems and territories, ready to slide down rocks polished smooth with acid urine which provided fast access into the sea for them to chase off any intruder. Adult females often suckled two pups at a time, one a year older than the other. Scarlet sally lightfoot crabs *Grapsus grapsus* intermingled with the sea-lions, picking their way rapidly amongst the rocks.

The northern cliffs of South Plaza provide a colourful roosting ground for many species of seabirds whose common and scientific names seem to vie with each other for originality: blue-footed boobies *Sula nebouxi*, masked boobies *Sula dactyla*, swallow-tailed gulls *Creagrus furcatus* and red-billed tropic birds *Pthaethon aethereus*. All soared to and fro across the cliffs in a magnificent display of flight and colour. Blue-footed boobies seemed to spend a great deal of time looking, with an air of surprise, at their brilliantly coloured blue feet. After a considerable pause they would embark upon slow, measured backward and forward steps accompanied by enthusiastic stretchings of the neck, their apparent stupidity in fact part of a complex courtship ritual.

Under the watchful gaze of prehistoric looking marine iguanas, *Eye of the Wind* **lies peacefully at anchor off Marchena Island.**

Now familiar with the animals in their habitat the crew re-embarked and *Eye of the Wind* sailed overnight to Marchena to search for goats. The island is not open to tourists or visitors and has remained virtually undisturbed since the introduction in the 1960s of a small population of goats for scientific study. Landing on the dark sands of Black Bay the YEs split into groups and moved into the hostile volcanic interior of the island. There is no water here but despite this the vegetation is thick. No goats were found though the bones of four skeletons lay amongst the rocks. Moving to James Island the hunt was more successful and one goat was shot and happily eaten for supper.

Eye of the Wind then sailed to Conway Bay on Santa Cruz where one group disappeared with Howard Snell to build the dog fence whilst another searched the iguana burrows for any remaining occupants that had not been eaten by dogs. As Gillian Rice, a twenty-one-year-old medical student from Birmingham, peered down a burrow she saw two beady eyes reflected back at her in her torch beam. After forty-five minutes of digging, an infuriated iguana bolted from the hole and into a jacket in which it was secured. The iguana, the only one we found, turned out to be a female of a rare sub-species thought to be no longer present on the island. After a comfortable night in the mate's cabin aboard *Eye of the Wind* it was presented to the CDRS and later to three frustrated males of the same iguana subspecies from which it is hoped to establish a new breeding cell.

Dr John Treherne and Dr William Foster from the Department of Zoology at Cambridge University arrived in the archipelago, as part of the Operation Drake team, in advance of the *Eye of the Wind*. Their object was to study the ocean skater of the Galapagos, *Halobates robustus*, a representative of the tiny number of insect species which have successfully colonised the surface of the open seas. Virtually nothing was known of the biology of this remarkable insect and the Cambridge scientists were able to make a number of important observations. They found that the ocean skaters fed on floating insects and were themselves attacked by fishes and birds. The insects group into large flotillas which appear to play an important role in reducing this predation. The flotillas turned out to be an ideal example from which to study the ways in which animals defend themselves against predator attack – a subject of much current biological interest. The two biologists obtained the best evidence so far available to suggest that being in a group increases the probability of detecting approaching predators. They described a novel means of signalling between individuals in the

The aptly named blue-footed booby *Sula nebouxi* is one of six tropical species. These birds nested amongst the cliffs of the Galapagos Islands and showed virtually no fear of the YEs walking amongst them.

flotillas which they named the 'Trafalgar Effect', to recall the exploits of another great English sailor.

With the work in the Galapagos complete *Eye of the Wind* sailed for Tahiti on May 29th calling in briefly at Post Office Bay on Floreana to deposit letters in the famous post barrel used by mariners for decades who collected mail there when passing through the archipelago. The Young Explorers left the islands having gained an immense respect for the work of both the National Park Service and the CDRS. Their work was also appreciated. Jose Villa, Chief of the Marine Biological Department at CDRS wrote: 'I think the best result is the experience acquired in this type of collaboration by conservation-minded young people. With this experience we can more efficiently implement future programmes.' As world interest in the Galapagos continues to grow the islands have one further threat which they must learn to live with.

Tourism, the life blood of many National Parks, can also represent the most severe threat to their existence. All conservation is directed by human needs and wishes but the enormous decrease in the cost of air travel coupled with a deterioration of habitat and hence its wildlife has put unbearable pressure on the resources and infrastructure of the few well-known conservation areas. Galapagos is one of these.

The Ecuadorian National Park Service in the Galapagos has an excellent system for coping with the massive influx of tourists from all over the world. All tourists are led by a guide, trained and licensed by the Service, who is proficient in several languages and knowledgeable about the island's flora and fauna. The tourists may not deviate from specific routes and only certain parts of the archipelago can be visited. Nothing can be taken away or left behind. A determined tourist though is as difficult to control as an escaped feral mammal. Plants are uprooted, litter dropped, trails powdered to dust, birds' eggs stolen; these are the costs of tourism which almost overwhelm the Service. The Ecuadorian Government is, however, mindful of the jewel in its care and is providing increased resources to deal with these problems. With the growing realisation in addition that what lies beneath the sea in the Galapagos may be as unique and interesting as the living laboratory on land, it is unlikely that these enchanted islands will be neglected or destroyed.

Eye of the Wind now began the longest sea voyage of her journey around the world, a crossing which confounded explorers and navigators for centuries. Progress was slow at first but after a few days the steady south-east trade winds were picked up along with the Humbolt Current to carry her across the Pacific at an average speed of just under 7 knots. The crew began to settle down to the shipboard routine of watches, chipping rust and painting, baking bread, sleeping, eating and examining life in the sea. Their next landfall was to be Tahiti, 4,000 miles and over three weeks' sailing away.

The sheer size of the Pacific Ocean preserved its relative isolation right up until the nineteenth century. The earliest explorers were amazed to discover people with fair hair, blue eyes and nordic features when they first reached the islands of the western Pacific which led the French ethnologist Jean Poirier to suggest that the Scandinavian navigators who had travelled deep into North America, may have penetrated as far as Polynesia.

The Polynesians were themselves great navigators and had covered much of Oceania before any European seafarer ventured into it. Polynesia forms a triangle centred on the Society Islands reaching to Easter Island, New Zealand and Hawaii. From here they travelled in magnificent ocean-going canoes as far west as the Celebes using navigating techniques which are only now being rediscovered. Their knowledge of prevailing winds, wave patterns between islands, ocean currents and stars enabled them to cover these long distances with ease. In addition they were excellent weather forecasters and could 'see' land over the horizon by the reflection of lagoons in the clouds or by noting the flight patterns of birds.

The detailed exploration of the Pacific by European explorers had to wait until two major improvements were made in the late eighteenth century, in navigational instruments and rationing of the crew. To fix a position in the ocean two co-ordinates are needed, latitude and longitude. To find the latter it was necessary to compute the difference between local time, established from the angle of the sun seen from the ship's present position, with the calculated time at the point from which the voyage had started. To do this accurately a reliable chronometer was essential and this did not appear until the Swiss watchmaker Ferdinand Berthoud perfected his timepiece in 1768. The tenth-century astrolabe and fourteenth-century Jacob's staff were made redundant by the arrival of the sextant in the 1750s which enabled positions to be calculated from the relative distances of the moon to the sun, planets and stars. The problem of latitude had been solved earlier from solar observations and it was now possible to position routes, islands and continents accurately. Captain Mike Kichenside prided himself in pinpointing *Eye of the Wind*'s position with the same early techniques and the Young Explorers were given good opportunity to learn the complicated art themselves, though few mastered it.

Improvements in navigation techniques provided Magellan with the knowledge he needed to cross the Pacific. Had he survived he would have become the first captain to have circumnavigated the globe.

When out of sight of land for several weeks, the sextant was the only instrument capable of giving *Eye of the Wind* an accurate position or 'fix'. Watch leader Robert Clinton explains the technique to Scott Brown, an American YE.

Food aboard *Eye of the Wind* was excellent. Leslie Reiter, a part owner and ship's purser, organised the galley watch to prepare fresh bread, delicious stews and even steaks and chickens brought up from the ship's deep freeze. Fried eggs would adorn the breakfast table and copious quantities of coffee appeared throughout the day, ending with last calls for dinner in the evening. Expert bargaining on isolated islands produced exotic fruit and squawking chickens ready for butchering on the foredeck. Careful planning meant that we were rarely short of supplies. Those who first crossed the Pacific however were less fortunate as Antonio Pigafetta, a member of Magellan's crew, wrote:

> *The bisquit we were eating no longer deserved the name of bread; it was nothing but dust, and worms which had consumed the substance; and what is more, it smelled intolerably, being impregnated with the urine of mice.*

Later these mice were hunted and sold for food amongst the crew for half a ducat apiece and the crew was forced to broil the protective leather on the mainyard to eat.

Scurvy caused their gums to swell and teeth to fall out and prevented them from chewing what little food there was. It was normal for 15 to 25 per cent of the crew to die on long sea voyages. Water was also a major problem, rapidly becoming foul in wooden barrels into which old rusty nails and stones were put as preservatives. The crew of *Eye of the Wind* had to wash in sea water making both clothes and skin unbearably itchy; fresh water was used for drinking only and carefully collected in any rainstorms through which the ship chanced to pass. It was not until the late eighteenth century that the compulsory issue of lemon juice put paid to scurvy, formerly thought to be caused by humidity, and the food on board ship improved, enabling the great leap forward in the exploration of the Pacific to begin.

During our own crossing a huge following swell made it extremely difficult to carry out any scientific work. The high average speed split the nets and rolling motions made studying neuston under the microscope a disorientating experience. The Pacific, in complete contrast to the Atlantic, was largely free of tar balls so this project was suspended but the YEs were soon put to work recording seabird species, some of which took rides aboard the ship. Different forms of anti-fouling substances were tried on sections of the ship's hull and there were always opportunities to watch dolphins playing on the ship's bow wave. Sailing on a parallel 10 degrees south of the equator, conditions were stiflingly hot below deck and most YEs chose to sleep topsides, hurridly rushing for shelter in sudden torrential rainstorms. Whales were quite often seen; one once leapt from the sea only metres off the beam, disappearing beneath the waves in a cloud of spray.

A perfect landfall was made at Tuamotu Atoll and on June 24th *Eye of the Wind* sailed into Papeete harbour on Tahiti after twenty-six days at sea. The ever present itinerary had to be kept to and after a very brief victualling stop and short visit to this fabled South Sea island she put to sea again heading for Fiji. Following a very rough storm which gave the YEs a real chance to test their skills in sailing a square-rigger we hove to off Palmerston Atoll where the local islanders came out in their canoes to exchange greetings and presents and deliver the crew's long awaited mail. Eleven days sailing, often with studdingsails set, brought us to Suva, the capital of Fiji, where the next project was to begin.

Fiji comprises some 300 islands spread over 18,334 square kilometres of the Pacific. Archaeological evidence reveals that this collection of volcanic islands and coral atolls was first inhabited by Polynesian peoples, later being taken over by the darker skinned Melanesians from the large island groups to the west. The Europeans came next and Fiji became a British dominion in 1874; now it is independent. On the island of Moala to the east of Suva, life was peaceful and happy on the evening of March 26th 1979. The next morning Hurricane Meli struck.

The cyclone ripped through the islands of the Lau group with terrifying force causing widespread destruction and forty-nine people to lose their lives. Two islands north of Moala were decimated and the survivors evacuated, 1,700 homes were destroyed, most of the buildings on Moala were demolished and the rest severely damaged. A Hurricane Relief Committee was set up to organise the provision of food for the many islanders whose crops had been destroyed, to commence reconstruction of buildings and, just as important, to restore the spirit of the people.

Rupert Grey, a solicitor from London who had previously spent a year working in Fiji, flew to Suva to prepare for *Eye of the Wind*'s arrival and offer help with the hurricane relief operation. The relief committee was initially sceptical. Of what use could well-intentioned amateurs be? However, the Prime Minister lent his personal support to the project and the approval of the committee soon followed. Moala was selected as the island on which Operation Drake could be most useful. Having selected a number of Fijian Young Explorers, said goodbye to Phase III YEs whose time with the expedition ended in Fiji and welcomed those on Phase IV who flew in, the relief team embarked upon an antiquated landing craft and enthusiastically headed in the direction of Moala. Their excitement was short lived. Not having the benefit of the

Once in the trade winds, the sails were left
set for days on end but going aloft to
perform regular maintenance also
provided much-needed exercise.

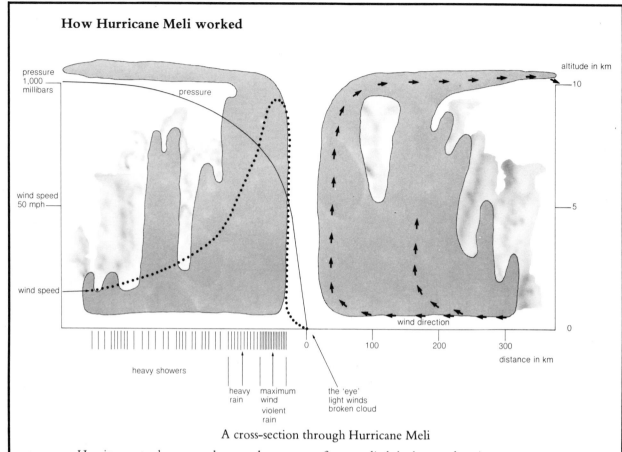

How Hurricane Meli worked

A cross-section through Hurricane Meli

Hurricanes, typhoons, cyclones and even Willy Willies as they are called in Australia, are all names given to the same kind of storm. It normally has a diameter of 650 kilometres and the winds, which are strongest around the 'eye', need to exceed 32 metres per second (73 mph) to classify the storm as a hurricane. Winds of up to 77 metres per second (172 mph) have been recorded. Surprisingly, at the very centre of the storm in the 'eye', only light winds occur.

In the case of Hurricane Meli, the vast expanse of the Pacific Ocean, with temperatures above 26 degrees Centigrade first supplied the heat and moisture to cause a build-up of large cumulonimbus clouds rising to 12,000 metres. An initial wind disturbance then organised these clouds into spiral bands and warm moist air was drawn in, spiralling towards the centre. Here it rose, causing very low pressure and flowed out laterally at the top. Winds of immense speed were drawn into the low pressure area and it was these that caused so much damage on Lou Island. The first hurricane of the year in a district is given a name beginning with the letter A. In the Western Pacific in 1979, Hurricane Meli was therefore the thirteenth.

Pacific crossing behind them, most of the new YEs were soon sprawled about the deck, wedged for support between rucksacks and cartons of provisions suffering from severe *mal de mer*. In an effort to raise spirits the ever cheerful Chris Sainsbury, ship's photographer, watch officer and raconteur concocted an infusion of sausage and potato soup which went down very well – and came up equally well.

At dawn on the following day we arrived off Moala, the first hurricane relief team to reach the island since the cyclone had struck. Disembarking at the small village of Ketira, the extent of the damage was immediately apparent. An army tent provided a classroom, while grass huts, teachers' quarters and piles of unsuitable corrugated iron roofing littered the ground. There was a feeling of hopelessness amongst the villagers and though four months had passed since the cyclone, little had been done to repair anything. Meli was not the first hurricane to strike the islands, nor was it likely to be the last.

The Chief of Ketira immediately invited everyone to take part in a Sevu Sevu tea ceremony, a traditional form of welcome. He explained how he not only had no house but also lacked a lavatory, a fact quickly put to rights amid much merriment by the Young Explorers who finely carved 'Chief's Privy' on the finished door. In the ten working days available the YEs moved 75 tonnes of soil including 5 tonne boulders to create a site for a new classroom block. Under the careful direction of Major Frank Esson, one of the ship's watchkeepers, two prefabricated houses were built as teachers' quarters. Alongside every YE there were two Fijians, the combination of their strength and the YEs' enthusiasm building a remarkable bond of friendship that grew throughout the project. Nyoli Waghorn, a nurse sponsored from New Zealand, ran a surgery twice daily for everyone – we all developed blisters.

A Fijian couple outside their home, devastated by Hurricane Meli.

Further round the coast Rupert Grey was working with another group at the beautiful village of Vonuku set amongst green glades and coconut palms bordering a wide beach of soft yellow sand. Here two teachers' quarters were built and the foundations laid for two classrooms. Another landing craft, the *Yuambula* arrived bringing 35 tonnes of materials. With much laughing and smiling the islanders and YEs unloaded the cargo into a small boat, sailed across the sparkling sea to the shore and then up to the school compound a kilometre away. There always seemed to be something to sing or laugh about with the cheerful Fijians. Chal Chute, a teacher from England, and Pam Armstrong, Capital Radio's attractive radio reporter who joined in Panama, took the odd school lesson teaching the children about Sir Francis Drake and the land from which they had come, as well as the occasional sea shanty.

Each day the work of banging, bolting, heaving and digging began at 8.00 a.m. sharp, the YEs sweating in shorts and tee-shirts, the islanders in colourful sarongs. At night they would continue by the light of hissing Tilley lamps. In the evenings Adrian Penny, a qualified YE doctor, although he did not know it at the time, tended aching limbs and cut and blistered hands until he knocked himself senseless by dropping a heavy truss-frame on his head! Local village girls cooked fresh crab, fish and river prawns supplemented with tapioca, dalo leaves and fresh bread, served on the ground in the hut the relief team had been given to live in. Some of the villagers could speak English and conversations went on well into the night mingling with soft beats from wooden drums, gently strumming guitars and Fijian love songs. The male YEs had

Studddingsails converted from parachute silk added a few extra miles to the ship's daily run.

Initial suspicions about the international YEs soon gave way and the local Fijians worked alongside them building a new school on Moala Island.

merely to lie back in the warm night under the moonlit palms and wait for the beautiful Fijian girls to ask them to dance, for theirs was the prerogative of choice which they indicated by gently touching their chosen partner's toes.

Next morning Utopia ended and the labour of reconstruction continued. The local villagers could not understand why we had come from the other end of the world to help them, to answer their prayers and all without wages! Perhaps the most significant contribution was a rekindling of the islanders' spirit to rebuild their own community in the face of disaster. For the YEs it provided an enchanting insight into a life without supermarkets, telephones, television and motor cars and a people utterly uncomprehending of pressure and the constraints of time.

It was now mid-August and the South Sea dream had to end. The work was complete and the paramount Chief and village elders gathered in the living hut along with many of the islanders. Navi the local school master, with tears in his eyes, addressed us. He expressed great sorrow that we were leaving so soon and handed over letters of thanks signed by the chiefs for onward carriage to London. The entire village of 300 people turned out to say goodbye and, with guitars playing, all danced and sang their way down to the beach and into the water, eyes full of tears. Still playing their instruments over their heads they watched the departing vessel until it was lost from sight. The small contribution to the hurricane relief work had been a success but the unique companionship developed on the island had been even a greater one and remained one of the most memorable experiences of the voyage.

Back aboard *Eye of the Wind* frantic repairs had been under way. During the Pacific crossing a major fault had developed in the propeller shaft causing so much damage that it had to be replaced. For a large company capable of purchasing the parts and flying them out this would have presented no real problem, but to an ancient brigantine stuck in the middle of the Pacific on a tightly run expedition budget it provided a real challenge. First the ship's crew scoured the Fiji dockyards for an old shaft that might fit. At the same time in London Jim Masters, head of logistics, began ringing contacts in Britain whilst others visited steel works on the east coast of America. It would be impossible to pay for such an expensive item so a sponsor and an airline willing to carry it to Fiji would have to be found. In addition, an aircraft capable of carrying such a large dead weight would have to be located. In the end we were lucky; the Fijian's fashioned a new shaft from steel on the dockside near to the ship and *Eye of the Wind* sailed on July 11th for a rendezvous with the *Golden Plover* on Turtle Island.

Here the ship was used by Columbia pictures to film the opening sequence of *The Blue Lagoon* in conjunction with *Golden Plover*, also a brigantine. Dressed in ancient clothes the crew had great fun leaping from the yards into the sea as smoke billowed from the galley and flames licked around the decks, swimming for their lives towards the shore. The money earned helped to pay for the new propeller shaft and with the YEs content with what they had earned as extras, *Eye of the Wind* sailed for the tiny island of Tikopia, half way between Fiji and the Solomon Islands.

On the second day at sea small patches of pumice stone were seen floating on the water and by the next day we were sailing through large areas of it which clogged up the neuston nets in seconds. We learned that nearby, a new volcanic island had appeared in the Tonga group emitting molten rock onto the ocean to create the pumice. Soon after, Tongan officials planted their flag upon the island to claim their new possession, only for it to disappear beneath the waves the following day as quickly as it had come.

At 13.10 on July 20th we sighted Tikopia and soon were at anchor off the north-west tip of the island. Dotted along the flat palm-strewn beaches were many small villages of huts which, despite being only a few metres or so apart, held quite separate communities. Every six months a square-rigged trading boat would call bringing rice and leaving with copra and bananas. The islanders wore attractive fishhooks made of tortoise shell which the YEs eagerly exchanged for necklaces. After a brief forty-eight hour stop *Eye of the Wind* sailed on to Honiara on Guadalcanal in the Solomon Islands.

In 1569 Alvaro Mendaño arrived in the Solomon Islands as one of the first seamen to cross the Pacific from Peru. After his return to Acapulco the islands became a legend for the appalling charts of the time meant that they were not re-discovered again until the eighteenth century. At the beginning of July 1942 the gentle peace of Guadalcanal was shattered by the invading Japanese armies which had already swallowed up much of New Guinea and the Solomon Archipelago. At the Battle of Guadalcanal later described as 'the most savage fleet action of modern times', the Americans halted the Japanese advance with a massive loss of ships and men on both sides. The Young Explorers had time to look and remember before sailing on again towards Papua New Guinea.

Shortly before arriving in Papua New Guinea, *Eye of the Wind* **called at Kwaiawata. It was remarkable to discover an island so completely without contact from the outside world.**

On the way they made a brief stop at the tiny volcanic island of Kwaiawata in the Marshall Bennett Islands. Grass-skirted islanders and topless children eagerly paddled out to meet the ship; no other had visited them for ten years. Their home consisted of a volcanic plug reaching 300 metres above the transparent sea, in places so steep that access to the top, where they lived on the only flat land, was often by rope ladder. These people were Melanesians, much darker than the peoples to the east. The island was totally unspoilt containing little evidence of the world outside; metal of any sort was almost absent and the houses were made of leaves and wooden poles. The Chief greeted the crew warmly and a long conversation ensued which neither party understood, but which seemed to provide satisfaction and consent to our visit. We persuaded the Chief to allow a number of the people aboard *Eye of the Wind* for a film show that evening. At the appointed time the decks were full of grass-skirted islanders looking into the galley and inspecting the cabins. Attractive barefooted girls with red flowers in their hair gathered in the main saloon for the show to begin. When it did they could not believe the dancing images on the silver screen and scratched its surface and looked behind it giggling with excitement. Walt Disney's *Islands of the Sea* was popular but the islanders were more fascinated by the tribal nomads of Borneo whom they watched with interest in another film.

We sadly left behind this bewitching isle the following evening and four days later the huge cloud-shrouded mountains of Papua New Guinea rose up over the port bow and many of the YEs crowded onto the foredeck anticipating what adventures lay within their mysterious forests. Approaching closer one could easily imagine the nervousness of the earliest explorers gazing at this massive relief whilst cannibals crouched in the bushes adorned with bones, teeth and lurid vegetable dyes waiting for the moment to unleash a storm of spears and arrows.

When *Eye of the Wind* tied up along the warf at Lae harbour on the north coast of Papua her reception was much more friendly. All along the quay Sing Sing dancers wearing grass skirts, bunches of colourful leaves hanging from their ears, swirled and sang. Huge necklaces of white cowrie shells jangled from their necks and men beat on drums of snake and crocodile skin as the women swayed back and forth, round and round. It was a spectacular welcome for our flagship, now almost half way around the world, and on the shore waiting to meet her was John Blashford-Snell. With him were many of the team who had already been in Papua for a month preparing for all the projects to begin amongst the humid forests of the coast, or the unexplored gorges of the interior. Here were wild tribes still fighting in the highlands, volcanos erupting lava upon the land, tree kangaroos and birds of paradise. Operation Drake had arrived in one of the world's largest, most magnificent and most unexplored islands.

The beauty of the South Sea Islanders which so captivated the early seafarers had no lesser effect on the crew of *Eye of the Wind.*

The most unexplored island in the world

The northern coast of New Guinea is exposed to the full swell of the Pacific Ocean and is rugged and harbourless. The country is all rocky and mountainous, covered everywhere with dense forest, offering in its swamps and precipices and serrated ridges an almost impassable barrier to the unknown interior; and the people are dangerous savages, in the very lowest stage of barbarism.

Thus wrote Alfred Russel Wallace, the great naturalist and explorer, in the nineteenth century. Little had changed since the first European, Jorge de Meneses, a Portuguese, landed on the north-west coast in 1511. He called it 'Ilhas dos Papuas' after the Malay word 'Papuwah' meaning frizzy haired. Thirty-seven years later the Spaniard Ortiz Retes, whilst sailing along the north coast in an attempt to reach Mexico, thought the people reminded him of those of the Guinea Coast in West Africa and so he named it 'Nova Guinea'. In 1971, following various annexations by the British, Germans and the post-war Australian administration, the National Identity Bill established the country's name as Papua New Guinea and four years later it became independent, remaining within the British Commonwealth.

Papua New Guinea is altogether a new nation, emerging rapidly from a background of tribal wars, cannibalism and almost total isolation. Today it is a land of extraordinary contrast. The major towns which, up until forty years ago, had no outside contact, now have super stores and fast-growing western consumerism, whilst the highlands and hitherto unexplored territories are still dominated by primitive and inaccessible tribes. Strong inter-tribal feuds are still a feature of the more remote areas and people will not mix or marry with neighbouring but hostile villages. A reflection of this geographical and social isolation is that in a national population of under three million people, there are 700 languages, a quarter of the world's total.

If the nation is young politically it is also young geologically. The subterranean plate upon which it sits is moving north at the rate of approximately 10 centimetres a year meeting the South Pacific plate coming the other way. This continuous collision has thrown up huge mountains rising to over 5,000 metres and a string of volcanos along the northern coast known as the 'ring of fire'. Concealed high in the mountain complex are wide fertile valleys and it was here that the majority of the island population lived, cut off from the rest of the developing world for so long.

Between 1,000 and 5,000 millimetres of rain deluges the country's rich forests annually. These hold a dazzling profusion of fascinating creatures. The largest moth in the world *Coscinoscera hercules* with a wing area of over 258 square centimetres is found here as are wallabies, phalangers, gliding possums, red bandicoots and spiny anteaters, for this is the world of the marsupials which rear young in pouches of skin close to their bodies, quite unlike the placental mammals found in the rest of the world outside the Australo-Papuan region. There are seventy species of snake, giant monitor lizards, tortoises and the largest crocodiles in the world, but the finest creatures of all are to be found amongst the 650 bird species which inhabit the island, the famed birds of paradise. Magellan was the first to bring to Europe some of these glorious birds of unimaginable colours and feathered plumes almost a metre long, as gifts for Emperor

Charles V. They were believed to originate from some celestial paradise as their legs and feet were removed by early collectors leading to the misconception that they:

> *. . . keepe themselves continually in the ayre, without lighting on the earth, for they have neither feet nor wings, but only head and body, and for the most part tayle.*

Their brilliantly coloured plumes of feathers are designed to attract during courtship displays which are some of the most spectacular in the animal kingdom.

The plants too are equally diverse; 12,000 species of flowering plant have so far been recorded in the region and further research is likely to add several thousand more. Vandopsis, with blooms over 2 metres long, is just one of the 2,500 types of orchid that fill almost every niche. The people use the plants and animals of the forest to decorate themselves for ceremonies and battles. Bird of paradise feathers, vegetable dyes of scarlet and yellow, leaves as earrings, possum fur and cowrie shells, all combine to create a headdress and costume characteristic of the tribe or clan.

Operation Drake had its headquarters, or TAC HQ, in a collection of wooden houses that formed the Lae Lodge Hotel. Tents and radio masts were scattered about in the hotel grounds around which men in jungle green uniforms scurried back and forth carrying stores, mending engines, planning movements, shouting orders and making occasional detours to the swimming pool. On a typical day the Operations room resembled the Stock Exchange attempting to cope with a collapse of the western financial system. Eleven different people try to use two telephones to discover why ten YEs have not arrived on the flight that morning, where to obtain paint for the ship's hull, spare parts for a vehicle stranded in the mountains, alcohol for botanical specimens and a boat to transport three scientists and a journalist to one of the camps as the local village captain, who had promised his, was now in prison on charges of drunkenness. On the other end ten YEs try to explain why they missed the flight, three newspapers want to know if any romances blossomed on the ship's Pacific crossing or if we have discovered the longest lizard in the world yet, and a company director offers to sponsor a local Papuan. No one can get through because the lines are permanently engaged. Around the walls impressive flow charts show who is supposed to be where and what they are responsible for, intermingled with press cuttings and photographs depicting the expedition's progress. The Operations Officer, in this case Captain Mike Knox of the Royal Highland Fusiliers, is visibly going grey as he attempts to match the ever growing requirements of the expedition's projects in the most inaccessible

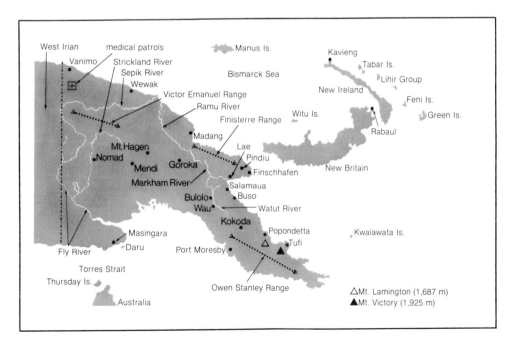

A map of Papua New Guinea showing the main project areas.

The making of a tribal headdress

The people of Papua New Guinea wear some of the most magnificent headdresses in the world. This man from the Central Highlands has feathers from many birds captured in the forest including at least seven complete plumes from *Paradisea raggiana*, one of the most beautiful of the birds of paradise. Around his neck are cowrie shells gathered from coral reefs on the coast and traded inland. Brightly coloured vegetable dyes are used for facial paint and the tail of a tree kangaroo *Dendrolagus*, decorates the chest. Bangles made from vines adorn arms and leaves provide earrings. A ballpoint pen is often favoured through the nose nowadays and bright green beetles make superb jewels. Fibres from beaten tree bark give excellent material for a loin cloth. The forest provides a spectacular wardrobe.

The Highlanders of Papua New Guinea
were the most spectacular people we
worked with on the whole of the
expedition.

country in the world with the limited availability of light aircraft, aged Land Rovers and the occasional landing craft. Sara Spicer-Few, the Public Relations Officer, encourages sponsors to donate food, office space, medical supplies and motor cars whilst the Quartermaster, Warrant Officer Len Chandler, refuses to let anything out of his store unless it is prayed for and Signals Sergeant Pete Lavers relays copious messages to the other side of the world on his remarkable Clansman radio. Sitting in the middle of all this like some amiable chieftain is John Blashford-Snell, cracking jokes and issuing orders with equal dexterity and working harder than anyone else planning new projects, meeting ministers and coping with everyone's problems.

The wreckage of the P-47 fighter found by the YEs deep in the forested mountains near Lae. From the name on the fuselage it was possible to trace the aircraft to its pilot, Colonel J W Harris.

It came as something of a surprise to discover that Colonel Harris was still alive as he had not been piloting the plane when it had crashed. He sent us this photograph of his aircraft shortly before its last flight.

Out of this seeming chaos a remarkable array of projects began to take place covering the whole of the country. Forty Papua New Guinean Young Explorers had been selected and sponsored to join the expedition, each for a month, and with those from other countries they were sent off on initial jungle acquaintance courses amongst the forests and rivers to the west of Lae where the TAC HQ was based. Experts from the Papua New Guinea Defence Force (PNGDF) Igam barracks taught them how to cope with snake bites and the rudiments of medical care in the jungle. A three-day march across raging rivers and sticky swamps accustomed them to conditions and working together as a team.

Following this the YEs were deployed amongst the various projects in progress. Some continued their jungle course by searching for wartime aircraft that had crashed in the mountains of the Finisterre Range. Papua New Guinea saw some of the fiercest fighting of the Pacific War. In January 1942 the Japanese occupied New Ireland and set up a garrison of 200,000 men and ships in Rabaul. Later they occupied Lae and much of the north coast finally advancing on Port Moresby, the capital, across the Owen Stanley mountains along the Kokoda trail. Here the Australians held them aided by their knowledge of the country and the appalling terrain through which the Japanese were attempting to advance. In September 1943 General MacArthur evicted them from Lae and Salamaua where the underground hospitals and gun batteries visited by the YEs now lie overgrown with creepers and vines. Amongst other aircraft whose positions were known, including a US DC-3 troop carrier still containing bones and weapons, the YEs discovered a United States Army Air Corps P-47 fighter with the painting of a voluptuous lady intact upon its fuselage. It had been missing since April 1944 when a bomber pilot flew it out from Lae to test its guns and disappeared without trace.

At the request of the government, the diving team led by Royal Engineer Captain Tony Molony, surveyed the coastline at Salamaua, Madang, Finschhafen and Rabaul to locate and report on the position and safety of wartime wrecks. Diving conditions were superlative and over forty wrecks were investigated. Whilst exploring the forests near Pindiu to the north-east of Lae another patrol led by Robbie Roethenmund discovered a seam of low grade coal in an eroded river gorge. It was the first significant coal find in Papua and was estimated to contain 40 to 50 million tons. Accompanied by government vulcanologists, still other groups scaled Mount Victory (1,925 metres) and Mount Lamington (1,687 metres) to monitor temperature and take magnetometer readings, both of which change prior to eruption. Community projects included helping to erect a library and establishing a market garden as part of the Mirigeda Youth Project to help the country's unemployed but often educated youth. Most of these were short but taxing projects designed to show people other parts of the country or to give the YEs an opportunity to operate in smaller groups prior to joining one of the expedition's major projects.

One of these took place at the attractive coastal site of Buso to the south of Lae. Steep forest-clad mountains reached in to the crystal sea, beneath which lay coral reefs, brightly coloured fish and, if you were lucky, the occasional dugong *Dugong dugon* feeding on the beds of sea grass. Concealed amongst the palms and *Callophyllum* bushes of the shore were several long, low huts on stilts which housed the twenty to thirty scientists, Young Explorers and support groups assisting in our study of the forest. Opposite was a string of steep green islands and beyond the vastness of the Pacific. It was the most idyllic camp site on the whole expedition.

The walkway, first used in Panama, was again erected here amid sweat and swearing by the indomitable Sergeant Louis Gallagher and his team of Royal Engineers and PNGDF soldiers led by Sergeant Robert Aki, who could scale a tree in minutes with the aid of a stout vine alone. Dr Mike Swaine, a botanist from the University of Aberdeen, put his rock climbing skills to work and advised on its construction in between plant collecting and Dr Willie Wint, assisted by Estelle van der Watt from Oxford, continued the work on insect herbivory in the canopy that he had begun in Panama. Dr Angela

Wilkins from Leeds University raised and lowered the light traps recording insect spatial distribution in the forest whilst Dr Roger Stobbart from the Zoology Department at Newcastle arrived to study mimicry in butterflies. Finding few examples, he engaged himself instead in investigating the osmotic relationships of freshwater shrimps. Dr Laurence Cook could be found scrambling amongst the mangroves searching for snails specially adapted for living there, later to study his results in his Manchester laboratory. Jon Martin collected Homoptera (sap-sucking bugs), for the British Museum (Natural History) whilst Ben Gaskell balanced precariously on the walkway spreading mist nets in the canopy to discover, for the first time, which bats might be found there.

Thanks to the remarkable generosity of the Royal Australian Air Force, two teams

The tranquility and seclusion of Buso scientific camp was enchanting.

of scientists joined us from Queenland by C130 Hercules transport. Dr David Lamb, Dr David Yates and Steve Goosem were botanists interested in the way in which nitrogen fixation took place at different levels in the forest and they soon converted part of the palm roofed laboratory into a complex system of glass vials, tubes, gas bottles and incubation chambers with which to make their measurements. After a forest farmer has burnt and cleared a site he is only able to grow his crops for one or two seasons before the soil fertility is reduced, forcing him to abandon it and move to a new site. After about twenty years he may return during which time the forest will have taken over the site again and restored soil fertility to its previous level. The question is, how does this recovery of soil fertility occur?

The key process is nitrogen fixation, the conversion of atmospheric nitrogen into a form that the plant can use as a nutrient. Tropical plants often employ nitrogen fixing *Rhizobium* bacteria in root nodules to do this for them in a symbiotic relationship but now there is evidence that fixation also occurs in bacteria or blue green algae growing on the leaf surface of some rainforest plants. This micro-habitat at the leaf surface is known as the phyllosphere and it contains free living bacteria, blue green algae, as well as lichens. It seems that nitrogen fixers of the phyllosphere could have an important role in restoring and maintaining soil fertility but at present little is known about this process. Understanding the micro-environment of the leaf is an important part of understanding the workings of the forest as a whole. By using the walkway the botanists were able to take measurements from leaves at different levels and examine the radiation and temperature fluctuations that occurred at the leaf surface. These helped to show how leaf metabolism could not only cope with but also exploit the enormous differences between the shaded forest floor and the harsh sun of cleared areas.

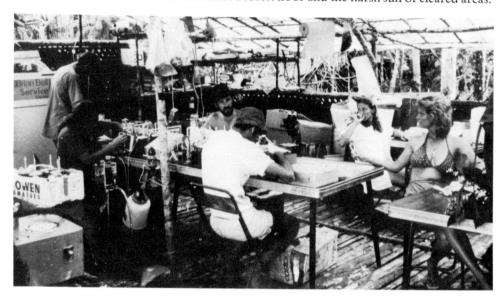

Scientists at work in the laboratory hut at Buso.

Dr Ian Fanning and Dr Bob Domrow from the Queensland Institute of Medical Research, with the willing assistance of Joppa Johns and Boniface Bolotti, two local YEs, worked hard capturing small mammals from the forest. They were keen to discover whether they acted as reservoirs of disease which could be transmitted to man through the insect vectors which feed upon them, such as ticks, mites and mosquitos, in a process known as *zoonoses*. Despite using willing YEs as bait few mosquitos seemed to be around, perhaps due to the time of year, though as soon as Dr Fanning left to return to Australia, they appeared in abundance.

Papua New Guinea has a rich heritage of traditional medicines distilled from years of detailed knowledge of forest plants and their properties. In many areas witchdoctors or 'glass men' as they are sometimes known, supply the only medical attention the population receives. Now, with the advance of modern medicine, this knowledge is rapidly being lost. Dr David Holdsworth, a biochemist from the University of Papua New Guinea, had organised a survey of traditional medicinal plants in the outer islands of the Bismarck Archipelago using *Eye of the Wind* as his means of transport.

Eye of the Wind left Lae harbour on September 15th on a three-week voyage visiting Lou Island and later Plitty aid post on the south coast of Manus Island. All the patients at the aid post are treated entirely with traditional plant medicines collected from the surrounding forest. Powdered bark is boiled with water, filtered through muslin and stored in bottles for use in the treatment of malaria, diarrhoea, hookworm, asthma, backache, tropical ulcers, pneumonia, bruises and even mental illness. On arrival we were given an energetic display of Manus dancing and one YE on remarking that it was very good of the hospital staff to do so was told: 'They're not the staff, they're the patients!' The remedies evidently work. The ship sailed on, visiting Taskul on New Hanover and Kavieng and Konos on New Ireland during which time David Holdsworth and his team collected eighty-five different medicinal plants, recording each ailment for which they were used and testing them for the presence of alkaloids, nitrogen compounds indicative of medicinal properties. The World Health Organisation is now showing increasing interest in the use of plant derived drugs for combating malaria and in contraceptives.

One of the most rewarding projects undertaken on the PNG phase was also in the field of medicine. Due to the impossible terrain most of Papua New Guinea is without roads, movement being either on foot through the forest or by light aircraft between isolated airstrips. Medical aid is often non-existent. Our medical work was a continuation of that started in Panama amongst the Cuna Indians but, at the request of the Institute of Medical Research at Goroka, it was extended to obtain information on health conditions in some of the remote areas which we were to visit. This would enable the PNG Health Service to plan future health facilities in areas which had never been surveyed before.

The medical team led by Dr Hugh Savill consisted of one or two doctors, a nurse, three PNGDF medics and usually three Young Explorers. For the first phase the team travelled by inflatable boats to villages near Buso covering up to 50 kilometres per day. Later, in West Sepik Province, most of the work was done inland travelling on foot from village to village and carrying all the equipment, assisted by porters. The villagers always lent us a hut to live in and showed us great kindness bringing coconuts, pawpaws, pineapples or fish and cooked sweet potatoes. There was never any hostility, largely due to our excellent medics from the PNGDF who acted as interpreters, negotiators and helpers, constantly smiling and cheerful. Only once when porters, hired in one area, accompanied us to a traditionally rival village, did we narrowly escape an ugly incident. We had no maps and sometimes no guides and much was left to common sense and initiative. Outside help was usually too far away to be of any practical use.

The main purpose of the work was not to treat the sick or set up clinics. This is a naive and potentially dangerous plan for a short-term expedition as the amount of good done by treating people for a few weeks or months is minimal and can even have a negative effect if they are then left without any follow up medical care. In addition, the most important and effective work often lies not in treating the individual, but in improving nutrition and water supplies and preventing illness by long-term pest control and vaccination programmes. Obviously if we could help by treating simple illnesses or injuries we did, but this was not our main objective.

Operation Drake's comparative medical survey carried out in Panama, Papua New Guinea and Sulawesi was planned by Freddy Rodger, consultant in opthalmology at Swindon Hospital in England and Geoffrey Haslewood, Emeritus Professor of Biochemistry at Guy's Hospital, London. There were eight projects. The first two looked at diet by compiling a 'mention index' of the foods the people had eaten over the previous twenty-four hours and in particular identifying the source of vitamin A which is particularly rich in dark green leafed vegetables and orange red root crops. These enquiries were carried out by the YEs around the village huts and in forest gardens; meanwhile villagers were brought in to take part in the other tests studying disease and malnutrition.

The day would start for the medical team with a meagre breakfast of tea and army compo biscuits during which time the day's patients would arrive in a gaggle of half naked women, shy children and men with the odd bow and arrow. Numbers varied from none to twenty-five depending on the co-operation of the village head man and the trust they had in us. The allocated number was first drawn onto the patient's forearm to prevent confusion as the tests were done and to enable the results to be married up later. For project 3 everyone was given a sugar drink. This formed the basis of a new technique to examine the patient's ability to absorb nutrients from food

A new way of looking at malnutrition

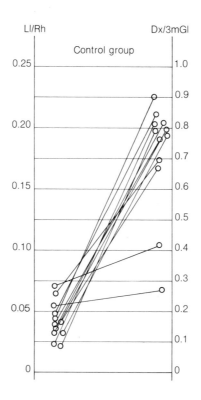

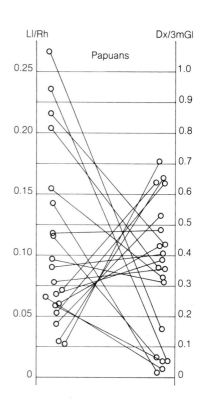

Ingested sugars

Lactulose = Ll
L-Rhamnose = Rh
D-xylose = Dx
3-Methyl-glucose = 3mGl

These sugars were swallowed in the form of a pleasant drink but being unwanted by man, they simply pass through the intestines into the blood and are then eliminated by the kidneys. The percentage of each ingested sugar excreted in the urine is estimated and expressed as two ratios: lactulose to rhamnose indicating intestinal permeability and D-xylose to 3-methyl glucose indicating absorptive efficiency. Results on the left are responses from members of the expedition and Young Explorers (the control group), and those on the right, responses from villagers in Papua New Guinea. That there is a difference is obvious. The test suggests that the Papuans have suffered some form of intestinal damage which alters intestinal permeability and absorption. This is the first group of many to be examined by Dr Ian Menzies at St Thomas's Hospital, London.

into his body. Several diseases and intestinal parasites can interfere with this so that only a small proportion of nutrients are absorbed. For those already on only a barely adequate diet, malnutrition will result. The test consisted of drinking a solution of four different sugars all of which are absorbed in slightly different ways. All urine passed over the next five hours was collected, the volume measured, and a sample sent back to St Thomas's Hospital, London for the relative concentrations to be measured. Some tribal people were frightened as they believed that giving away a part of their body or something it produced gave others the chance to practice some evil sorcery upon them. On the other side of the world Dr Ian Menzies at St Thomas's Hospital Chemical Pathology Department was able to show that the absorption spectrum of people in tribal communities in Panama and New Guinea was quite different from that found amongst apparently 'normal' people he has tested in Britain and work is now continuing to try to discover why. For the test to be a success it was necessary for the patients to have eaten nothing the previous night, but the problems of getting them to arrive with an empty stomach and then collect all their urine were enormous. One little boy was so ashamed of his contribution that he got all his friends to top his bottle up!

Once they had drunk the solution the YEs divided the patients into three groups. The first would be started on project 4 which involved YEs asking them about their family and their past and present illnesses, often through interpreters so that on some occasions this session bore more resemblance to a game of Chinese whispers than a medical experiment. They were then examined for evidence of disease and their height and weight were recorded. Terrible conditions rarely encountered in our clinicised western world were common in some areas, particularly in the poorly developed West Sepik Province; leprosy, elephantiasis, fungal skin disease, yaws, scabies and tuberculosis were only a few. Evidence of malnutrition and repeated malarial infection or injury was also detected at this stage.

Local villagers always took a great interest in anything that we were doing. Dr Hugh Savill explains the medical project to the people of Kui.

The second group then started on project 5, a simple test of eyesight, and project 6, which aimed to assess vitamin A deficiency. As vitamin A reforms one of the light-sensitive compounds in the retina, rhodopsin, which is responsible for vision in very low light intensities, it is especially important in sight. It is thought that as many as 100,000 children worldwide may go blind each year as a result of vitamin A deficiency and malnutrition. By darkening the patients' eyes with a mask for forty minutes we converted the rhodopsin into its active or light-sensitive form. With the mask still on, we then used a new instrument, a mini field dark adaptometer, to measure the minimum light intensity needed to see a tiny radio-active light source. By using filters, the intensity could gradually be increased until it was visible to the patient. If he could see normally in everyday life, the measurement on the adaptometer would provide a good correlation with his vitamin A status.

Blood samples were taken from the third group which were either made into microscope slides to determine the parasites in the blood, especially malaria, or put onto filter paper squares. These were sent to the University of Lyon for fluoroscein antibody analysis. When viruses or bacteria infect the body, antibodies are specifically produced by our defence systems to combat them and these can be present in the blood even after recovery from the illness. By detecting them through fluoroscein analysis we could get an idea of the diseases the person might have at the time and also what he had suffered from in the past. The three groups rotated so that by the end of the five-hour period all had completed the tests and, with apparent pride, urine samples could be handed in. These were tested for kidney and bladder disease and spun in a centrifuge to separate out any parasites which were then sent to the Liverpool School of Tropical Medicine in England for identification.

In the tropical heat, the work was exhausting. Entire families would turn up but only one member take part, leaving the remainder to be amused with drawing, singing songs and generally kept out of the way. But there were usually a few hours free in the afternoon to explore the surrounding jungle with its beautiful flowers and fascinating birds. In the evenings through conversations with villagers in broken 'pidgin' we learnt much about their history and way of life as well as answering questions about our own countries. To them, simply coming from the other side of Papua New Guinea was the same as coming from the other side of the world. In one village we were lucky enough to be there during the preparations for a local 'sing sing' or festival. The evenings were spent watching and joining in as the people danced, festooned with feather headdresses, grass skirts and ritual spears accompanied by drums, conch shells and chanting.

All the projects were specially designed so that the doctor had only to examine the patient and the rest could be done by Young Explorers. The survey would have been impossible without them and many became expert at taking medical histories, eye tests and blood samples and preparing slides. They were an integral part of the work and they demonstrated well how valuable previously untrained people could be. In return most got great satisfaction out of being able to make such a worthwhile contribution to the medical research.

After working for seven weeks in coastal villages near Buso the team moved into the remote region of West Sepik Province. This is the north-west corner of Papua New Guinea, bordering West Irian on the west and the Bismarck Sea to the north. The main town, Vanimo, is on the coast 32 kilometres from the border. The province has fewer facilities than most others. In an area of 19,500 square kilometres there are 112,000 people but only 720 kilometres of roads, the bulk of which are isolated systems not linking with any others. All vehicles have to be brought in by sea or air but most of the province can be reached only by small planes flying in to primitive airstrips and then on foot. Terrain is variable; in the north, swampy valleys are separated by steep mountains all of which are thickly covered with tropical rainforest, in the south there is the upper valley of the huge Sepik River and beyond this the mountains of the Victor Emmanuel range. The border is an artificially drawn straight line, separating families and tribes and although no roads cross it, movement across is officially restricted. It is impossible to patrol effectively. There is a steady trickle of people entering the country from Indonesian controlled West Irian and we examined some of them in a quarantine centre at Yako.

Dr Subhas and his wife were two of the three doctors in the province. They have no surgical facilities so that all operative cases have to be flown 272 kilometres away to East Sepik Province. There are several missions and government clinics, but as most can only be reached by air, the transport is very expensive and 40 per cent of the provincial health budget goes on air travel. Aid posts run by orderlies who have had between one and three years' training are being introduced in many villages and, in view of the prevalence of tuberculosis and leprosy, an on-the-spot centre, capable of supervising long-term treatment is essential. The emphasis has to be on preventive medicine and in villages readily accessible by road this is advancing but it caters for a very small proportion of the population. The majority live in isolated areas only reached by long and hard journeys on foot and in these remote villages epidemics can occur, with many deaths, and be over before word gets out and help can be organised.

A child suffering from severe malnutrition in West Sepik Province.

Dr Subhas gave us immense help in enabling the team to reach some of these remote villages.

Two factors contribute to make the coastal people very much more fortunate and healthy than those of West Sepik. Firstly, they have relatively easy communication and access by sea, with other people and the coastal towns and, secondly, they have the sea and the wealth of protein it provides. This means the children grow up with a reasonable diet and are then able to travel to towns and earn money, most of which is sent back to the villages acting as a kind of insurance system for the care of the old and sick. Much of what is owned is communal or at least, shared amongst whole clans or families. The setting of these villages resembles a South Pacific paradise with long, empty sandy beaches, lined on one side with coconut palms and on the other with coral reefs and tiny wooded islands. The huts are built just beyond the reach of the tide and, in general, are made entirely of local materials with hardwood frames, plaited sago palm roofs, interlocking sago stem walls and slatted bamboo floors. They are built on stilts providing ventilation and easy cleaning and only in the highlands did we encounter huts using the ground as the floor for warmth. The many rivers provide a plentiful and easy source of clean water.

A pig feast at Konos on New Ireland in the Bismarck Archipelago.

The inland villages in the low lying hills of West Sepik, are outwardly similar, but the lack of protein from the sea causes malnutrition and the difficulty of overland travel, greater isolation and poverty. In addition, they are not always set by clean rivers, and in some we visited, the only source of water was the local swamp. Paths linking the villages are frequently no more than rough overgrown tracks with fallen trees used as bridges over small rivers; the larger ones either have to be waded, up to the shoulders in places, or crossed by canoe. Here the major source of food is the sago palm, the interior of which is used to form a sticky carbohydrate mush which is eaten with relish but provides inadequate all round nourishment. In most of Papua New Guinea the pig is the all important source of protein, wealth and trade. Young pigs can even be given preferential treatment over children whose mothers will suckle them to ensure that they quickly become healthy and strong. In the areas we visited, however, food was so scarce that even pigs could not be reared easily. Because of this overall dependency on pigs, authorities are particularly concerned about a disease known as cysticercosis which at present does not occur in Papua New Guinea but which is creeping steadily eastward across West Irian and will soon reach the border.

It is caused by the larval stage of the pork tape-worm *Taenia solium* which on being eaten migrates around the body before forming cysts, sometimes on the brain causing epilepsy and death. Reports by local villagers that devils were attacking them and throwing them into the fire led to the disease being recognised in West Irian. Cysts on the brain of unsuspecting victims sleeping beside fires at night in the cold highlands caused fits and if they fell into the fire terrible burns, resulting in the so called 'fire burn' epidemic. Dr David Bowdler's team travelled between small villages concealed amongst the forests of the border country near Kamberatorro collecting information on disease in the region which had never been surveyed before. Fortunately no evidence of cysticercosis was found. However, hookworm, a major cause of anaemia, and roundworm were common. Tuberculosis, leprosy and filariasis – the disease that leads to elephantiasis – were all found. The erratic distribution of the latter amongst the villages was probably a result of tribal isolation and the custom of only marrying into friendly villages. Thus inborn susceptibilities and resistance tend to remain confined to certain village groups.

The two communities, coastal and inland, suffered from a similar spectrum of diseases but malnutrition was higher in West Sepik and resistance to other diseases was consequently lowered. This is part of the reason why minor illnesses such as measles

An inhabitant of the forest near Buso, the little coroneted fruit dove *Ptilonopus naina.*

and 'flu frequently kill in these communities. The young are particularly susceptible for, when illnesses are encountered for the first time, the body's defences are at their lowest. They have not had the chance to build up any immunity of their own and possess only what they inherited from their parents. Infant mortality is as high as 50 per cent in some areas and probably around 30 per cent in the villages we visited.

We found that malnutrition had an interesting age distribution first becoming apparent at about six months when supplements should have been added to breast feeding. This is rarely done early enough as the local people do not believe in adding food until teeth appear which may not be until the children are nine to twelve months old. The situation is further exacerbated by local 'tambus' (prohibitions), which for instance, prevent pregnant women from eating eggs or those breast feeding from eating pigeon. In some areas families prefer equal numbers of boys and girls as marriages between friendly villages involve an exchange, the girl taken away being replaced by a sister of the groom. Unwanted children of a particular sex are sometimes badly neglected as a result, especially if they are one of twins.

One helpful piece of information in assessing the adequacy of a community's diet is obtained by taking the height and weight of children and comparing this with standard charts for their age. However, there is no national register of births in Papua New Guinea – it would be impossible to implement – and the people do not celebrate their birthdays. In Christian areas the only way of getting an estimate was to ask how many Christmases they had had but the answer was usually vague. We found that severe malnutrition, as judged by physique and abdominal distension, continued to be common through infancy and early childhood but decreased markedly as the age of ten or twelve was reached. Some of the reasons appear to be social. Firstly, food is distributed in the family in order of seniority so the youngest get the remains and secondly, children start foraging and hunting for themselves once they are old enough. Apart from a few exceptions we saw no severe malnutrition in people over the age of twelve.

Malaria was the commonest disease we encountered and it is known to contribute as much as 25 per cent to infant mortality figures in some areas. Papua New Guinea is an endemic area; the disease is present all the time and people are constantly exposed to it so developing an immunity. Its danger therefore lies in the first few attacks, in other words to children, while to adults it usually manifests itself as a fever from which they recover in a few days. In the remote western part of the country a rare form of the disease has emerged which is resistant to the most effective and commonly used drug, Chloroquine. Despite taking tablets to protect ourselves, some forty members of the expedition contracted malaria and some have had recurrences many months after returning to temperate climates.

One preventable but common problem which affected us as well as the local people, was that any tiny cut, graze or insect bite would rapidly get infected and fester in such hot and humid conditions where cleanliness was difficult. If not looked after carefully, these could develop into large tropical ulcers and damage both the skin and underlying muscle. If left untended these usually healed but in some instances might take years and cause severe and deforming scars in the process. Another common skin problem was superficial fungal infection. This did not itch or hurt, but could cover large areas of the body and be very unsightly and, especially in children, cause shyness and shame. One kind produced whorls of parallel scales all over the arms, legs, face and trunk.

Most of the conditions mentioned, malnutrition, malaria, tuberculosis, leprosy, filariasis and fungal skin infections cannot be cured by a short course of drugs, but require months or even years of treatment combined with health education and public health projects. Collecting information, such as we did, is the first stage in the long medical and political campaign to help these people. In many parts of the world where this is more advanced than in Papua New Guinea, the process has involved far more than simply health. Although lifestyles have to change if progress is to be made, whole communities and customs have been destroyed to be replaced by western values and materialism where they never previously existed.

To some extent this is inevitable but, unless done very carefully, the resultant upheaval can cause bewilderment, misery and even worse poverty by the loss of old ways and the forced adoption of a new life and even a new place to live. The answer is not to deny people progress and better health but to recognise that change must be gradual and based on education and consent rather than on well-intentioned but often insensitive sweeping decisions by a distant bureaucracy. So far, much of the progress in Papua New Guinea has been accomplished very successfully with the minimum of disruption to their traditional and happy way of life. The people seem, to a large extent, to have been able to accept the progress they need without being tempted by the trappings which would radically alter their social structure. This may partly be due to the fact that it has all happened comparatively recently so that those outsiders who have been involved have learnt from the mistakes made in other countries in the past, practical help replacing ideological change.

To the east of the medical team lay the huge Sepik River. It rises in the huge Victor Emanuel range and meanders north to the Bismarck Sea. The Strickland flows south from the same range joining with the mighty Fly River emerging in a vast estuarine swampland. Together they form the largest river system in the country. Recent exploration has played a major part in opening up the wild corners of Papua New Guinea but some areas remain unknown, existing only as blank spaces on the map. One of these is the Strickland River Gorge.

In 1876 the Italian naturalist d'Albertis travelled 928 kilometres up the Fly in his steam launch *Neva* and discovered the entrance to the Strickland River which was later explored by Captain Everill of the Royal Scottish Geographical Society. Since then patrols have visited the upper Fly and Sepik but, perhaps due to the rugged terrain, there are no reports of any of them having examined the upper section of the Strickland in the region known as the 'Devil's Race'. On maps the area is recorded as being obscured by cloud and only one patrol in 1954 travelled some distance along the

Roger Chapman, leader of the Strickland Exploration Group and Bob Woods (left) with porters and members of the Pogaia tribe at Tigaro.

river below its junction with the Bulago River. Quite simply nobody knew what was there.

Roger Chapman, a soft spoken ex-army Major, was chosen to investigate the region for the first time at the request of the Papua New Guinea Government. Roger was no novice having taken part in many expeditions including the navigation of the treacherous white water cataracts of the Blue Nile in Ethiopia and the Zaire River in West Africa on previous Scientific Exploration Society expeditions. An air reconnaissance of the Strickland revealed many terrifying rapids and reports showed that the water level could rise from 3 to 6 metres in hours; also, very strong winds would make resupply by parachute difficult. A group of porters had once been blown off a bridge, to be swallowed up in the boiling waters below. Roger proposed to shoot the upper rapids with two 'Avon Professional' inflatable boats equipped with rowing frames. He would later meet up with a larger scientific team at the village of Nomad to make a collection of animals and plants and take a census of the crocodile population from the lower Strickland and Fly Rivers.

Roger, two PNGDF soldiers, and three other members of the expedition, including Bill Neumeister a Canadian, who made his living by parachuting into forest fires as a 'smoke jumper' to prevent them spreading any further, walked into the Strickland valley from the small village of Kopiago to make a riverside reconnaissance prior to attempting it by boat. After only a few days the weight of their 22 kilogram packs laden with seven days' rations and the steep mountain crags began to take their toll. The two PNGDF soldiers had to be sent back following knee injuries. After some delay the party moved on, the local porters preferring to travel barefoot through the tall Kunai grass growing between the sharp, limestone rocks carrying the boots they had been given around their necks. The river bank was frequently impassable owing to rapid water level changes forcing an agonising 500 metre climb out of the gorge to search for a new route. It was almost impossible to chart the river accurately.

After fifteen days' forced marching they reached a point in the Strickland Gorge where they had to climb 1,000 metres up the steep slopes onto a plateau above. Whilst looking for a spot to take a parachuted re-supply, they stumbled across a collection of low thatched huts and cultivated forest clearings. No settlements were thought to exist there. The rectangular huts were built close to the ground with thick upright wooden poles insulated with mud and leaves. Smoke spread out through the roof. A 2 metre-high stout wooden fence, lashed together with vines, surrounded the garden. Timidly at first some men appeared, all hunters, gazing at the strange intruders. Small, well-built and bearded, they wore wide belts of tree bark from which hung a woven twine loin cloth in front and large bunches of 'tanket' leaves behind. Most wore thin arm-bands, also of bark. One man, later known as Kemba, the chief, wore a necklace of large cowrie shells and a half moon shaped 'Kina' shell on his dark chest. They had discovered Tigaro, home of the Pogaia.

Through several interpreters translating from English, to Pidgin, to Duna, to Pogaia it was revealed that 'white' people had never visited the village before and few of the inhabitants had ever ventured outside their valley. Two highly prized metal axe heads had been traded in from the Bulago Valley down river; possibly they were those brought into the area by an earlier patrol led by an Australian 'Kiap' officer named Hunter in 1968. Apart from that all their other possessions were made from natural materials. Barbed or notched arrows of razor sharp split bamboo were used with 1.5 metre-long hardwood bows for the daily cuscus or wallaby hunt. Some arrows had three or four prongs, presumably for catching birds or fish. The women appeared in the evening carrying taro and sweet potatoes or 'Kau Kau' in 'bilums', net baskets hung from their heads. The following day the villagers helped clear a landing zone for their own 'close encounter of the third kind'. On September 21st a giant twin-rotored Chinook helicopter from the Royal Australian Air Force roared out of the sky and descended upon the amazed tribesmen who clutched their pigs towards them as their world was buffeted by the massive down draft. The patrol, which had previously

**The power of white water is unimaginable.
Yogi Thami and other members of the team
underwent extensive training before
challenging the rapids of the Strickland.**

radioed in its position for the pick up, quickly bundled themselves into the helicopter and suddenly they were gone leaving the men of this nomadic group of the Pogaia tribe at Tigaro to wonder at what they had seen.

The helicopter dropped the team down in the gorge to continue their foot reconnaissance after which they returned to Lae. Three weeks later the newly formed white water team began the descent of the river in the rubber boats which had been parachuted in near the headwaters of the Strickland. Yogi Thami, a Nepalese YE, experienced in river running, had joined them. Even with rowing frames the powerful rapids sucked and swirled the boats around the rocks threatening to capsize them at any moment. Then, two-thirds of the way down the upper reaches of the river, disaster struck. Whilst manoeuvering an unmanned boat through a particularly dangerous rapid the 2.3 tonne breaking-strain line holding it snapped like a bow string and the boat with all its equipment was snatched away and vanished into the rapid. It was now impossible to continue further as there were too many people for one boat. The other was later recovered upside down on a sandbank, 40 kilometres downstream. The gorge remains unconquered.

The team was again evacuated by helicopter through the kind assistance of the RAAF who found the hazardous flying in the gorge excellent training. It joined up with the scientific group at Nomad. Nineteen members of the group then travelled down one of the Strickland's tributaries from Nomad, in a 12 metre canoe and four Avon inflatable boats. The next three weeks were spent drifting or motoring down the Strickland to the Fly River, stopping at a series of camps for detailed collections to be made. Jim Croft and Osia Gideon collected plants for the National Herbarium at Lae. Several YEs helped Rupert Grey to conduct a Rural Life Development Survey of all the villages on the river banks for the PNG Government. Others assisted zoologist Ian Redmond in collecting lizards and frogs and anything else that looked interesting. One poor frog committed suicide by jumping into Roger Chapman's cup of tea but his untimely end was not without value as he turned out to be a species new to science.

Once night had fallen Jerome Montague, an American zoologist with the United Nations Development Programme crocodile project, went out with the YEs in search of his favourite reptiles. There are two species of crocodile in New Guinea, the freshwater crocodile *Crocodylus novaguinea* and the larger and more dangerous saltwater or estuarine crocodile *C. porosus*. The latter are the largest reptiles on earth growing in excess of 7 metres and weighing 1,000 kilograms; they have been known to attack canoes far out at sea. The uncontrolled shooting of crocodiles in New Guinea in the 1950s and 1960s, greatly reduced the adult population of the saltwater species and, with their decline, hunting pressure on the freshwater species rose sharply. The Department of Primary Industry now encourages the local people to farm crocodiles for the sale and export of their skin, 95 per cent of which, at present, comes from the freshwater crocodile. It was to assess population levels in an area which had not been shot out or

White water river running: what went wrong on the Strickland

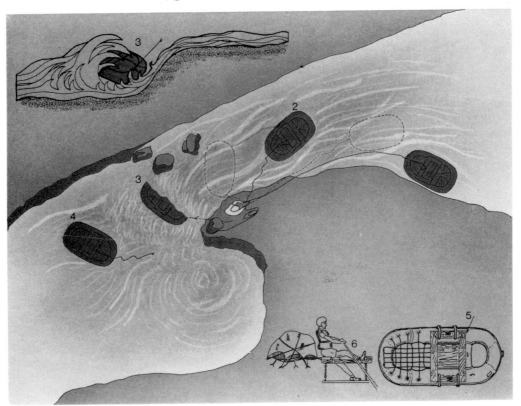

The boat was ready to be 'lined' through a very dangerous rapid and was gradually floated down river (1). It was swept suddenly into the rapid (2) but became trapped in a 'stopper wave' at its base and the force of water broke the line (3). The boat was snatched away and disappeared downstream (4).

Operation Drake used adapted Avon Professional inflatable boats (5) rigged with a specially designed aluminium rowing platform. Lightweight marine plywood can also be used. Only one oarsman is required assisted by others with paddles. The oars must be of strong hardwood such as maple or ash with a slight give, yet strong enough to withstand the ferocious power of white water. The oarsman, facing forwards, guides the boat bow first into negotiable rapids. His feet are supported on a plywood platform slung from the rowing frame on chains (6). This avoids poor grip on the flexible and moving boat floor. All kit has to be tied into the boat in case of a capsize.

The world's giant lizards

Caroline Buxton from Jersey measures up against a small specimen of 'attrelia' *Varanus salvadorii*, brought in by local villagers.

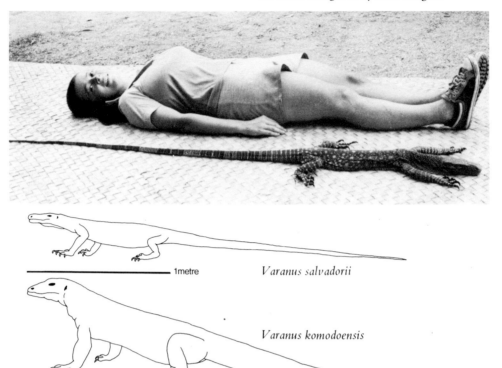

1metre

Varanus salvadorii

Varanus komodoensis

The family Varanidae, or monitor lizards, includes both the largest and longest, living lizards. More than thirty species of monitors are found throughout the warmer regions of the Old World in habitats ranging from desert to tropical rainforest. All are powerful carnivores except for one species which feeds on fruit.

The world's largest lizard is the famous Komodo dragon, *Varanus komodoensis*, found only on certain of the Lesser Sunda Islands of Indonesia. With its thickset, stocky body and a tail about half the total length, a 3 metre specimen weighs over 160 kilograms. A large Komodo dragon can successfully kill a fully grown half tonne water buffalo.

The longest measured specimen was 3.25 metres long. The Papuan 'tree climbing crocodile' known in Pidgin as 'puk-puk bilong tri', *Varanus salvadorii*, may grow to more than 3.6 metres in length, though such a specimen has yet to be accurately measured. Salvador's monitor has a slender, more lightweight build than *V. komodoensis* and a remarkably long tail, twice as long as its body. This makes it the longest lizard alive today. The largest and longest lizard ever, *Megalania prisca*, was also a monitor. It lived in Australia during the Pleistocene period and grew to twice the length and 8 times the mass of a modern *V. komodoensis*.

farmed that Jerome Montague conducted his survey. The technique was simple. A powerful searchlight scanned the river bank and water surface as the boat drifted quietly downstream. Crocodile eyes reflect like burning red coals and, whilst dazzled, their owners can be approached closely for identification before they are seized with panic and disappear beneath the surface in a flurry of spray. In all, over 850 crocodiles were recorded on the descent of the Strickland, providing much needed information for the UNDP project.

**The long journeys between camps on the
Fly River provided time for Ian Redmond
(right) to catch up on cataloguing his
amphibian and reptile collections.**

The expedition's time in Papua New Guinea was almost over. As *Eye of the Wind* sailed into the mouth of the Fly River to collect the survey team on December 8th, John Blashford-Snell prepared for one last project – the 'Giant Lizard Hunt'. Local reports of 6 metre-long tree-living dragons capable of dropping onto a man and killing him were too much to miss. After an eventful sea journey in a government launch, he and his search party, including Ian Redmond, landed at Masingara, split into four groups and marched inland. Days of searching the bush with local helpers could not reveal the savage monster but then a hunter brought in a prized specimen of 'attrelia'; it was 2 metres long. Not quite the giant John was hoping for. Ian pronounced it to be *Varanus salvadorii*, Salvador's monitor lizard which was known to grow to over 3 metres and possibly more. Its extremely long tail which helps it to balance in trees – they are good climbers – enables it to exceed in length even the mighty Komodo dragon *Varanus komodoensis* of Indonesia. Several other large monitors were caught, not *Salvadorii*. Ian stayed on and saw one specimen possibly over 4 metres but was unfortunately unable to capture it as proof.

The amazing range of projects carried out in Papua New Guinea had to end at last. It is impossible to cover all in detail but by December almost everyone had gone; Young Explorers to Fiji, the United States, or New Zealand and TAC HQ staff to London to plan the next phase. In Papua forty local YEs who had taken part talked of their experiences enthusiastically and of setting up their own Drake Fellowship. A seed had been sown which, by the end of the expedition, was to blossom into a new movement within the country.

Sulawesi: a nature reserve is born

Indonesia is a remarkable archipelago. Counted amongst its 13,677 islands are five of the largest in the world, yet only 922 are permanently settled. The country is wider than the United States though its sea area is four times larger than its land area. It is a land of extraordinary beauty and diverse cultural influences ranging from Malay, Hindu and Islamic to Portuguese, British and Dutch, reflecting the successive waves of migrating people and colonial administrations. Indonesia straddles the equator and has an equatorial climate with only two seasons, the hot being slightly hotter and only slightly less wet than the wet. Within its islands and forests are orang-utans, rhinoceros, tigers and even elephants but surprisingly none of these are found in Sulawesi, one of its larger islands despite the fact that it is in the very centre of the archipelago. It is this that makes it truly fascinating.

During his travels through Indonesia and the Malay Archipelago, Alfred Russel Wallace described Sulawesi, formerly Celebes, as:

> . . . closely hemmed in on every side by islands teeming with varied forms of life . . . it is yet wonderfully rich in peculiar forms, many of which are singular or beautiful and in some cases absolutely unique upon the globe.

Sulawesi has examples of animals and plants from both South East Asia and the Australian region but the marsupials such as kangaroos and wallabies range no further to the west and the larger placentals, excepting man himself, no further to the east.

The island has remained geologically isolated from those of the Sunda shelf to the west and the Australo-Papuan region to the east for thousands of years and consequently has developed a Pandora's box of animals and plants which are found nowhere else in the world. Excluding bats, over 90 per cent of Sulawesi's mammals are endemic. They include such unusual species as a dwarf buffalo, just 100 centimetres high, a grotesque hairless pig, a black monkey once thought to be an ape, a giant or brown palm civet and its own species of tarsier. Sulawesi also has the longest snakes in the world. A giant python measuring 10 metres was collected from the Togian islands off its eastern coast in 1912 and won a place in the *Guinness Book of Records*. In 1978 the body of a small Chinese man was extracted from an extremely bloated 6 metre python just to the north of the area which Operation Drake's team was now to survey.

The Indonesian Government places high priority on the protection and conservation of its valuable forests, and under its present five-year development plan, it intends to make 5 per cent of its total land area into reserves. Every ten days however, forest areas the size of London are felled for agriculture, timber and cheap energy. The loss is irreversible. But what can be done about it? Countries like Indonesia need the foreign exchange for timber and the local people need farming land.

Until recently the only major conservation area in Sulawesi was the Lore Lindu National Park gazetted in 1980. In 1978 an area which included steep, thickly forested mountains rising to 2,800 metres and a huge flat alluvial plain ending in Tomori Bay, was identified as being a possible site for a reserve. Two forested islands, Nanaka and Tokobae, stood in the bay surrounded by coral reefs; 'Morowali' had been discovered. Its plain was the largest area of relatively undisturbed primary lowland forest still

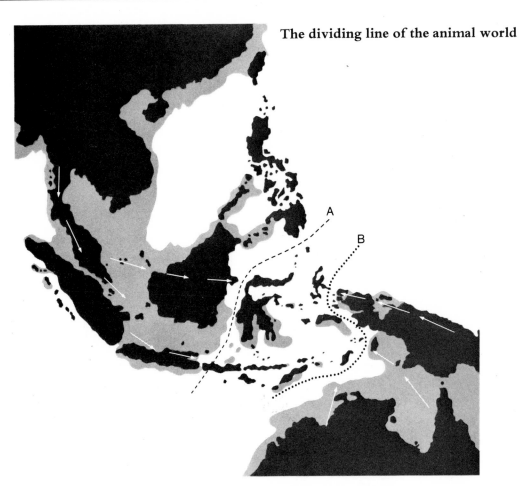

The dividing line of the animal world

As recently as 18,000 years ago it was possible to walk from the Malayan peninsula to Borneo across dry land. Many species migrated along this land route and spread amongst the Sunda Islands of Borneo, Java and Sumatra and are thus common to all of them. A similar situation prevails in Australia and New Guinea which were also once connected by land and today share many species. But along line A and line B deep water trenches existed which were never crossed by land bridges, leaving Sulawesi and its surrounding islands isolated in between. The larger mammals of the Indo-Malayan region to the west of Sulawesi never managed to reach the Australo-Papuan region to the east enabling the marsupials there to continue to exist in splendid isolation. Alfred Russel Wallace was the first to notice this division when he made his collections in the region and so the line dividing Borneo from Sulawesi was named after him.

remaining in Sulawesi and it seemed the perfect choice. Not everyone wanted it for conservation however. Man was moving in fast and Morowali was due to die.

Beneath the alluvial plains, 150 million tonnes of chromite from which chromium is derived lay waiting for extraction and Morowali's tall trees were due for the mills. Its flat, forested plains were destined for agricultural development by families imported from overcrowded Java and Sumatra under the Indonesian 'transmigration' programme. Prior to any exploitation, Operation Drake, with generous support from the Indonesian Government and the World Wildlife Fund, was asked to conduct a full survey of the area and to produce a management plan for its possible future development as a nature reserve.

The task was formidable; 2,000 square kilometres of mountain ridges, thick forest, jungle tracks, coastal islands and coral reefs – and no map. In fact, a map did exist, but it consisted largely of blank spaces and proved so inaccurate as to be useless. The proposed reserve boundary, it was later found, ran along a 3,000 metre ridge which was not there, mountains were in the wrong place and rivers flowed in the wrong direction. Here was true exploration as well as scientific discovery.

The logistics of setting up the Sulawesi phase of Operation Drake were a nightmare. Once the 60 tonnes of equipment and supplies had arrived by steamship at Surabaya in Java from England, it was still another 2,000 kilometres away to the

An aerial view of the base camp beside the Ranu River. Two more accommodation huts were added later.

The Ranu River was tidal at this point which made bringing stores into the base camp all the more difficult as it seemed impossible to predict when it would be high or low.

planned base camp beside the Ranu River on the east coast of central Sulawesi. On arrival at Kendari, the nearest town of any size to the proposed reserve, all the stores had to be transferred by hand to coastal launches or 'Bugis' sailing schooners for transshipment to Morowali. On January 10th 1980 an RAF Hercules flew in to Kendari bringing 8,618 kilograms of stores from Papua and the advance party sailed in an unstable coastal launch on a two-day journey to the mouth of the Ranu River. Here, boats were inflated, the stores heaved on to them and moved up the small river flanked by mangroves to the site chosen for the base camp the year before by Wandy Swales, the deputy leader of the Sulawesi phase. Through a small gap in the trees was a clearing in the forest containing a large hut on stilts which Mr Dandy, the local tribal owner, had kindly agreed to lend to the expedition. Bob Powell, the chief engineer, hired a group of local 'buru' craftsmen and set about constructing the camp from materials in the forest around him. A village of sleeping huts, a cookhouse, medical centre, survey centre, operations and signals huts and a laboratory 20 metres long had to be built to house the 141 people on the survey. Meanwhile thousands of kilometres away, in America, Australia, England and many other countries, scientists, support teams and Young Explorers flew out and headed for Morowali. In Indonesia local scientists and students funded with money raised in Jakarta by the Indonesian Committee under the Chairmanship of Dr Didin Sastrapradja, head of the Indonesian Institute of Sciences, also made their way to Morowali. Away to the east, *Eye of the Wind*, having left Papua New Guinea, was sailing through the Spice Islands and on to her arrival in Tomori Bay on January 22nd with the Phase VI Young Explorers.

Anthony Bedford-Russell equipped to capture butterflies.

Soon the base camp was a hive of activity with the YEs helping the geologists, biologists and doctors unpack insect traps, mist nets, bat traps, plastic bottles, generators, microscopes and all the other paraphernalia of scientific research. Within days of the camp being completed, local guides were leading patrols, armed with theodolites and compasses, deep into the jungle to begin making accurate maps of the region. Botanists snipped and clipped in the forest gradually building-up a picture of its complex flora. Entomologist Anthony Bedford-Russell lunged through the clearings collecting butterflies whilst Bill Timmis, an ornithologist and curator of Harewood Bird Garden in Yorkshire, patiently searched the trees for Sulawesi's magnificent hornbills and imperial pigeon, one of the fourteen endemic pigeon species on the island. In the evening the sound of crickets, scraping cicadas and the clinking of mess tins mixed with Martin Brendell's buzzing generator as he laboured under a cloud of moths, beetles and other insects attracted to his flickering ultraviolet light. It is not difficult to find new species in a country like Sulawesi where so little work has been done before. The problem is finding someone who knows anything about them.

Four months was a very short time to produce a plan for conservation. Our aim was to collect as much information as possible about the animals, plants, people and places of Morowali. At the end we would piece it all together so that Dr Andrew Laurie, a consultant zoologist financed by the World Wildlife Fund, and other key members of

After heavy rain the number of insects attracted to Martin Brendell's light trap was exasperating. None had ever been collected before from the area. He is holding a pooter to suck up small specimens and a glass jar for the larger ones.

the expedition, could draw up the management plan. This would advise on the borders the reserve should have, detail the kinds of vegetation and animals it contained and specify the reasons for maintaining it as a reserve. It would also suggest what the local people would do if traditional practices such as hunting and farming were curtailed and recommend the way in which development should proceed so as to preserve the natural environment. All these questions needed answering and, in contrast to the other phases, all the resources of the expedition were channelled, by its leader, Derek Jackson, into this one enormous task. Within it there was a multitude of separate projects which provided scope for everyone's aspirations. There were mountains to be climbed and valleys to be explored, tribal groups to encounter, mammals to trap, rare plants to collect, coral reefs to dive upon and the Indonesian way of life to experience.

We had very few directing staff on this phase and the YEs were given a high level of responsibility to which they responded eagerly, from running the camp to leading their own patrols and gathering information to be incorporated into the management plan. Many of them were students, qualified geologists or doctors, surveyors or outward bound instructors and so were able to make a positive and informed contribution.

As few had been in a jungle before, the YEs first spent a week near the mouth of the Ranu River. Here, survival expert Eddie McGee taught them the art of making fish traps, how to produce soap from animal fat, which plants could be safely eaten in the forest and how to make strong ropes from grass and waterproof shelters from leaves. At the end of their week each YE had the chance to make a dream come true – to live

Phil Maye leads Mike Prior and Sandy Evans through a grass clearing and up the side of Mount Tambusisi.

as a castaway on a desert island. With a litre of water, a packet of biscuits and a tin of sardines, they were abandoned each on a different part of one of the islands in Tomori Bay. Here they had to stay and survive for three days.

The first day was easy. Those who remembered their training built shelters and began searching for food; others, less mindful of the hardships ahead, ate most of their rations and soon ran low on water in the intense heat. By the end of the second day, they began to realise the true meaning of hunger and thirst. One YE, so tantalised by a coconut far out of reach, ended up cutting down the whole palm to get it! Others took to cooking small lizards or gathered fruits from the forest. All of them found the jungle frightening and oppressive at times. Jan Morton, walking into a huge spider's web, shrieked as the huge yellow and red-legged occupant, larger than her hand, scuttled over her face and down her back. By the third day some felt so weak that they could only sit and wait for the boat to come and collect them. Being a castaway was evidently not so idyllic after all.

One of the first tasks was that of producing a reliable map of the area on which to plot our findings. Phil Maye, a Royal Engineer surveyor sent patrols to explore the interior taking bearings of rivers, junctions and other features whilst he led a party to climb Mount Tambusisi. This 2,400 metre mountain had only been ascended once before by a Dutch surveyor in the 1930s and Phil wished to revisit the triangulation point they had built on the summit to take sightings of the other peaks in the reserve. After an arduous climb his party, including Claire Bertschinger, the first woman ever to climb the mountain, reached the summit. Using a theodolite they surveyed in the main features of the proposed reserve. They quickly realised that the huge ridge running north of the mountain along which the boundary had originally been drawn was a figment of the cartographer's imagination and in fact comprised a series of transverse valleys. Further to the north stood the mighty 2,835 metre peak of Katopasa and to the east the limestone shoulders of Tokala at 2,600 metres. In between was a huge rectangular looking ridge of limestone rising like Conan Doyle's 'lost world' out of the centre of the proposed reserve. Thick forest grew on its flat summit and waterfalls cascaded from its cliffs into the Morowali River below. 'Table Top mountain', as we called it, was not marked on any maps and it blocked off the head waters of the Solato River 50 kilometres short of its previously estimated length, whilst the Morowali River stretched many kilometres up valleys unknown to exist before. It was clear that to cover the whole of this area would be an enormous task. Meanwhile, somewhere far below the surveyors on the mountain, others were gradually finding out what the forests contained.

Preserved in alcohol, an ever increasing pile of plants collected by botanist Geoff Grimes waited in the laboratory for shipment to the Royal Botanical Gardens at Kew for identification. Bottles of beetles and boxes of butterflies were also accumulating and sightings of some of Sulawesi's unique animals were at last coming in.

KK Gurung, a Young Explorer from Nepal, saw a dwarf buffalo *Anoa depressicornis* on the lower slopes of Tambusisi and others found droppings near the summit. These shy, dark brown buffaloes normally roam the forest singly or in pairs and if startled can be aggressive using their short, sharp horns to good effect. Along river banks close to the base camp or on forested ridges, a small black monkey appeared. Feeding on leaves and fruit in the forest canopy it moved in family groups of ten to fifteen but these were known to band together to raid village crops. They were the Celebes black macaques, once thought to be apes because of their very short tails. Four species are thought to inhabit Sulawesi, the one at Morowali being *Macaca tonkeana*. Like the anoa, they are endemic to Sulawesi and its nearby islands.

There are only two marsupials found in Sulawesi; both are phalangers and one is endemic. The bear phalanger *Phalanger ursinus* is hunted for its fur which the local Wana people use for ceremonial hats. One of these marsupials was brought into the camp in a cage. The rusa deer *Cervus timorensis* was introduced to Sulawesi many years ago from other parts of Indonesia and since then it has flourished throughout the island. Despite being an officially protected animal, it too was hunted for meat in the grasslands of Morowali's plain, so important in a land where protein is scarce. Some of the deer, however, suffer an unusual fate.

If cut with a blade, the male flowers of the *Arenga* sugar palm produce large quantities of sap which can be drunk as it is or fermented to make a beer. If distilled, this mixture becomes a very alcoholic, gin-clear liquid. In one small village a large glass jar of this liquid contained the perfectly preserved embryo of a rusa deer. The mixture, called *sopi anak rusa*, is only made in this part of Sulawesi where it is described as having strength-giving properties, a kind of elixir of life. It is served as a refreshment in the hut near the airstrip at the village of Beteleme. It is perhaps no stranger than the belief that the scrumpy in the west country of Britain brewed with the odd rat in it is the only kind with true flavour.

Sopi anak rusa

One mammal remained disappointingly elusive, though members of the team could often hear it tantalisingly close. Its shrill bird-like calls punctuated the pre-dawn period but careful searching within the tangle of palms and creepers of the forest failed to reveal the animal. Then, one night, high on one of Tambusisi's mountain ridges, a group of scientists were collecting insects with the aid of a powerful lamp set in a clearing amongst the trees. Suddenly, they could hear the shrill calls again, this time very close. The next instant, a tiny monkey-like creature leapt into the area lit up by the lamp, calling furiously, its huge round eyes staring out as it clung to the branches. It was a tarsier.

Tarsiers are widely considered to be one of the most primitive of the world's

For the biologists the ladder up to the walkway was a stairway to heaven. It had a disturbing habit of flipping over when a climber was half way up, leaving him suspended beneath in a somewhat alarming way.

primates with a curious mixture of both primitive and highly advanced characters. Their diet consists largely of insects and they have flattened faces with enormous round, dark eyes which they use to hunt their prey at night. Their small furry bodies, only 15 centimetres long, are difficult to see on the tree trunks and even more difficult to follow as they leapfrog from tree to tree, gripping the bark with tactile pads on their fingertips.

The Sulawesi tarsier *Tarsier spectrum* was once thought to be extremely rare, even on the verge of extinction. Then, once their characteristic calls had been recognised it was realised that far from being rare, they were perhaps one of the most common mammals of the forest; they were even heard in town gardens and parks.

Bill Timmis was occasionally able to find Sulawesi's extraordinary maleo bird *Megacephalon maleo* hidden near a river bank digging a deep hole in the sand with its feet. Once the single egg had been laid the adult vanished into the forest and paid it no further attention. Heated by the sun's rays, the egg incubates in the sand until the fully developed chick, already capable of flight, hatches and burrows to the surface from which it instantly bursts like a missile into the forest to avoid detection.

Bill was, however, less successful with the imperial pigeon. One day, whilst on his way to the summit of Tambusisi, he was delighted to discover a nest with eggs in a perfect position for study. As almost nothing is known about these enchanting birds, he vowed to return to it later. On his way down he was dismayed to discover the nest destroyed and feathers all over the ground. On returning to the mountain camp he found Harim, one of our local carriers, eagerly stirring the contents of a large pot over the fire. He too had noted the nest, but unaware of the unique opportunity it presented to the ornithological world, was about to consign the bird to his stomach!

Another interesting endemic species is the giant or brown palm civet *Macrogalidia musschenbroeki*, seen only twice since 1930 and photographed in the wild for the first time in 1979. This creature we never saw nor did we see Sulawesi's most extraordinary animal, the babirusa or pig deer *Babirousa babirussa*. Not really belonging to either pig or deer it is a single species genus having no close relatives in the world. Its face is adorned with barbaric tusks, two of which, in the male, grow straight up through the roof of its snout curving menacingly in towards the eyes. Local knowledge suggested it was present but it did not grace us with an appearance.

Forty minutes walk away from the base camp through the forest, beside a small stream, a small sub-camp lay almost hidden in the trees. The work here was all happening 30 metres up in the forest canopy. Two Sapper engineers, John Rimmer and Mike Prior, had built the aerial walkway for the third and last time and the insect traps were suspended from it and from nearby trees as they had previously been in Papua New Guinea and Panama. High above the ground, small bags and neatly written labels adorned the trees as Andrew Lack, a botanist from Swansea University continued the pollination studies. On the ground, Stephen Sutton and Christopher Rees prepared for the next trapping run while Jan Morton laboriously sorted through the previous night's catch.

Ben Gaskell, who had joined the expedition in New Guinea to study and collect bats for the British Museum, climbed gingerly into the canopy each night to check the mist nets he had set there to trap bats. Once after a violent storm, he sent Barbara Harris, a YE ballet dancer from the United States, into the canopy ahead of him where she discovered a creature quite unlike any other she had seen before – a harlequin fruit bat. These enchanting bats, *Styloctenium wallacei*, are one of the very few species to possess white eyebrows which are used for signalling to each other. Only five specimens had ever been caught before.

The use of the walkway has opened up a new perspective on the bats to be found in tropical forests. The only effective way of catching bats without harming them is with mist nets, and even these will not catch insectivorous bats which, with their highly developed echolocation system, can easily detect and avoid the fine mesh; most trapping takes place just above ground level in the forest. For the first time anywhere

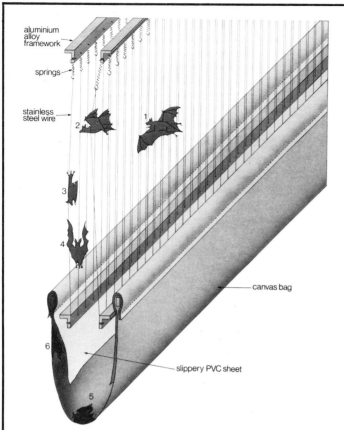

aluminium alloy framework

springs

stainless steel wire

canvas bag

slippery PVC sheet

Emptying the bat trap on the walkway.

An automatic bat trap

The idea of using a double curtain of wires to capture bats was perfected by Tuttle in 1974. It does not harm the bats it catches nor does it need to be attended. The trap is sited in a suspected flight path. Approaching bats (1) fail to see the fine steel wires and collide with the first curtain (2). As the wires are on springs, they give way and the momentum of the bat carries it through the first curtain but not the second (3). Trapped between the two the bat slides down (4) into a canvas bag at the bottom (5). Escape is impossible because the bag is lined with slippery plastic and there is not enough room to fly. Bats crawl under the plastic (6) and settle down, protected from the elements. Later they can be collected.

Siting is all important. In Papua New Guinea no good sites were found but in Sulawesi one site proved so interesting that the trap was left there for three months. Though only thirty-one bats were caught these comprised eleven different species. Despite 400 bats being caught in the mist nets there were only seven species. Most of the eleven species caught with the automatic trap were rare, several had never been found before in Sulawesi and one, a *Hesperoptenus*, was an undescribed species. This great diversity of bats found flying in just one 2 × 2 metre trap site is the highest recorded anywhere in the world.

in the tropics, Ben was able to set mist nets, up to 12 metres long, right inside and above the forest canopy from poles attached to the aerial walkways. This technique proved extraordinarily successful. On one night, Ben and two YEs took six hours to extract and record the catch from just three nets. Many species, previously thought to be very rare, were apparently common high up in the canopy while control nets on the ground frequently caught no bats at all. Ben estimated the density of fruit bats in the canopy to be ten times greater than at ground level; perhaps they seek the abundant fruit there. There was one marked exception however – the adult males of the small blossom bat *Syconycteris crassa*. These, in particular males with swollen testicles, appeared to

This harlequin fruit bat *Styloctenium wallacei* was only the fifth specimen ever to be recorded.

stake-out territories on the ground, luring down females with high-pitched cries and attractive odours from special armpit glands.

Bats can often produce the unexpected. Morowali's forest floor is covered with ebony seedlings *Diospyros* sp. Why the mature forest was not full of ebony trees puzzled Dr Peter Kevan from the University of Colorado. With a team of Young Explorers he set about trying to find out why. In the process he made an intriguing and unforseen discovery. Sixty per cent of the hard ebony seeds found on the ground had small round puncture marks in them which could not be attributed to any known ground-living ebony seed-eater. Then at night and 30 metres up, a bat flew into one of Ben's mist nets with an ebony seed, almost a third of its weight, firmly clasped in its jaws. By matching the puncture marks in the seeds with the jaws of various bats, it was shown that one bat species *Rousettus celebensis* was responsible for most of the puncture marks and was probably an important dispersal agent of the seeds and so vital to the success of the ebony trees. The answer to the original question, however, still remains a mystery.

These studies however, covered only a tiny part of the forest. What of the rest stretching for hundreds of kilometres into the north and to the east? To study these, the Operation Drake team reached into outer space, where, orbiting 920 kilometres above the globe is the Earth Resources Technology Satellite, Landsat.

Landsat is one of the many 'spy-in-the-sky' devices now orbiting the earth, though its purpose is entirely peaceful. Landsat 1 was launched in 1972 and it orbits the earth about fourteen times a day, enabling its multi-spectral scanners to cover the entire globe every eighteen days. These perceive reflected light from the earth's surface in four spectral bands from the visible to near infra-red. Different vegetation and soil types and, for example, housing, all produce distinct reflection patterns to which false colours can be attributed, so producing a map from outer space. The sensors transmit these electronic signals to receiving stations around the world and they are then converted into photographic images at NASA's Goddard Space Flight Centre in Greenbelt, Maryland. Reproducible copies of what the satellite sees can then be obtained from the Earth Resources Observation System (EROS) Data Centre in Sioux Falls, Dakota.

For greatest accuracy, however, a computer compatible tape (CCT) is needed containing much more detailed information but in a digitised form. It was this that Robert Warwick-Smith, a geographer from the School of Oriental and African Studies in London obtained from EROS and fed into the interactive data processing computer at RAE Farnborough. This produced a colour image of Morowali's forests as seen from space. The next step was to go to Sulawesi and compare what the satellite had seen with what was actually on the ground.

Obtaining 'ground truth' can be a hot and sticky business. Assisted by Dedy Darnaedi, an Indonesian botanist, and Richard Tarlov, a Young Explorer geologist from the USA, Robert squelched his way through Morowali's humid forests trying to match up the blue, red and green patterns on the satellite image with the types of vegetation on the ground. Once a good correlation can be established between a particular colour and a specific vegetation type, say red with mangrove or blue with alluvial forest, all areas on the image in that colour can be attributed to the corresponding vegetation type without visiting them. Robert studied many cultivated areas, coastal plains and mountain ridges, gradually building a picture of the distribution of Morowali's forests. Now that the map is complete, it will be a simple task to monitor any changes that occur in these forests as a result of timber exploitation or shifting agriculture, and all from the comfort of a computer terminal.

The management of all reserves relies on many factors: social, political and environmental. None can be considered in isolation, so whilst it is important to study the birds, mammals, plants and insects, the people and their dependence on the area must also be taken into account and here the Young Explorers really came into their own.

When Noel English, a diamond sorter from the East End of London, first heard that he had been selected to join Operation Drake's Sulawesi phase, he was very excited, telling everyone about it. Nobody seemed to know where it was, and he then realised that he didn't either! Now he found himself with other groups of Young Explorers disappearing into the forest with local guides for anything up to three weeks contacting villages and isolated settlements largely occupied by the Wana tribe. We needed to know where they lived, whether they hunted in the proposed reserve and what they traded outside it but initial attempts to contact the Wana were extremely difficult. It seemed that there were two groups, the 'friendly' Wana and the 'wild' Wana or Kayu Merangka. The former, the Young Explorers were told, had regular contact with village people belonging to the Bugis or Mori tribe from the coast. Through them they

Rube, one of the elders of the Wana group from Kaipoli, discusses the finer points of making palm beer with Derek Jackson, leader of the Sulawesi phase.

The Wana people always received us with great kindness. The forest belongs to them and hopefully the reserve will perpetuate rather than restrict their way of life in the future.

had contact with the outside world of coca-cola cans, tape-recorders and tee-shirts. It was these people whom we first met at the tiny settlement of Kai Poli on the Morowali River, though even they ran into the forest in fear at the team's initial approach. They later became firm friends and often visited the camp at Ranu. Here, Eky Setiawan, one of the Indonesian Young Explorers, came across one of Sulawesi's giant pythons. It was the skin of a 7 metre-long specimen which had been shot through the eye with a blow-pipe dart while it was trying to kill a Wana hunting dog.

Of the Kayu Merangka, however, the story was very different. They were a savage hunting tribe living amongst the forests of the interior, often in caves above waterfalls from which they could observe their unsuspecting enemies approaching along the river valleys below. Displaying genuine concern, the coastal chiefs informed us that the 'wild' Wana had telepathic powers and occasionally raided villages. Should Operation Drake's personnel venture into their territory, they would certainly be killed by poisoned darts shot from the tribe's long blowpipes. The Young Explorers would never see them coming. No one was prepared to guide us into the Kayu Merangka country.

Such an interesting group of people living in the reserve could not be ignored. Fortunately a local Wana tribesman who had relatives amongst those inland agreed to guide a patrol to the village of Uwewaju on the edge of Kayu Merangka country. Bob Powell managed to take a break from his constructional tasks and, after a boat journey around the coast, led the group to the village of Taronggo on the Solato River. Here the local guru, Tuan Lamananko, warned them to be careful as the Kayu Merangka already knew they were coming. With this rather disconcerting news they marched on up the Solato valley, passing through the deserted village of Sangkioe, a relic of an earlier attempt by the government to 'villagise' the Wana and gain administrative control over them. Two more days of walking took them over the huge limestone ridge which divides the southern part of Morowali from the north. From here they could see a magnificent waterfall where the Solato river plunges over the edge of another ridge below; a further unsuspected asset for the reserve. On the north side of the ridge they looked out over a huge basin enclosed by mountains and valleys. Most of the forest had been replaced with bright green *Ischaemum* grassland and in the valley bottom a river we later knew to be the Sobuku flowed rapidly. It was evident from the grassland and cultivated areas that large numbers of people were living here but of them, there was not a sign. Another hour's walking through the coarse waist-high grass brought the team in sight of some huts. The guide, Tuan Tea, motioned them to stop saying that he would go forward first. An hour later he returned with an old woman. He said that the rest of the villagers were hiding in the forest but soon two attractive younger women and some children appeared and tension gave way to friendship. Later, Wana men walked in wearing only loin cloths and carrying long, thin blowpipes of hollowed cane. At their hips were bamboo canisters of poisoned darts. In the evening a feast of Wana rice and sweet corn mixed with dehydrated army rations was prepared. Our first contact with the Kayu Merangka had passed without incident.

Over the following months a number of different patrols visited the Wana communities in various parts of the reserve and, from the Young Explorers' reports, we were able to build up a complete picture of the settlement pattern and way of life of this shy and gentle tribe. In total contrast to the coastal people's belief, the Wana were never hostile and always showed great friendship and hospitality. They said they distrusted government officials and particularly 'men in green', a reference perhaps to the Dutch patrols of many years before. In time past they had been headhunters, worn clothes of tree bark and raided villages which perhaps explained the outsider's fear of them. They preferred to retain their old way of life as shifting agriculturalists and so retreated into the mountains to avoid contact with the world they did not understand outside.

The Wana lived in extended family groups rather than villages, in two or three huts scattered over the valley. A family would clear about a hectare of forest of all its trees and when the wood had dried, burn the wood-growing crops amongst the fertile ashes. Hence the term 'slash and burn' agriculture. Much ceremony is associated with the time of burning, after which dry rice or maize, sugar cane, sweet potatoes, pumpkins or cassava are planted. At harvest time the women gather the rice into large bark and split bamboo baskets on their backs and later pound it to remove the husks. It has a very delicate flavour when cooked.

They did not appear to have any religion and had little contact with missionaries. They were keen hunters; some claimed to have killed 200 anoa in their lifetime although the numbers they take in total are small for the whole area of the reserve. Shooting the occasional monkey, bird or phalanger with the fast-acting poison on their blowpipe darts does not pose a major threat at present to the status of most animals in Morowali.

Dan Etter, a YE from the USA and Ram Pi Tantu from Indonesia were leading a YE patrol up the Samara and Ula river systems surveying local villages when they were given the chance of visiting the Wana's sacred *Impoc* tree, from which they gather their poison. With David Hudson and Sue Richardson, they marched for three days to a place called Bintana. There, almost 30 metres high and surrounded with bamboo scaffolding, was the *Impoc*. An old Wana man with a straggly beard and wearing a loin cloth showed them how the white sap could be milked from a machete

A Wana 'kebun' or farm cleared by hand from Morowali's lowland forest. The crop of rice has been harvested and is drying on a stand in the centre. The small family huts are dwarfed by the massive trees at the edge of the clearing.

cut in the soft spongy bark. When dried and used on their darts it can kill a man in five minutes.

The cutting of rotan vines in fact climbing palms, *Calamus* sp. from which cane furniture is made, and to a lesser extent the collection of damar gum, has caused extensive damage. The rotan is rafted down river and shipped from coastal ports by Chinese traders. Damar is the hardened resin of the *Agathis* tree and is obtained by milking it from a deep slash in the bark. The Wana will carry up to 50 kilos in rucksacks made of tree bark through kilometres of forest to sell the gum to the middlemen on the coast. In 1979 1,500 tonnes of rotan was exported from Kolonodale and 211 tonnes of damar. This was less than in previous years but high prices could maintain an unsustainable demand on the forest; this must be carefully monitored in the future.

Operation Drake's comparative medical research project was also operating in Sulawesi. The team, under Dr Ian Gauntlet's direction, was joined for a time by Dr Ferdy Limengka of the Indonesian Health Service and travelled by boat, visiting coastal villages and also moving inland on foot to reach some of the Wana villages. Mary Garner, a nurse with the New Zealand Red Cross, worked tirelessly, talking to local villagers, tending cuts and grazes and helping them to enjoy taking part in the tests, as they journeyed through the Solato, Siambok and Sumara valleys on the project.

They found that the Wana suffered from many diseases that were not so common on the coast, including tuberculosis. Goitre, due possibly to the lack of iodine in the area, was common inland and the coastal people were generally healthier. It is not unusual for a Wana family of ten to lose four of their children before they reach maturity. Results from the tests that Operation Drake carried out in Panama and Papua New Guinea as well as Sulawesi are now being examined in laboratories in Britain and France.

To return to the base camp at Ranu after a long and sometimes exhausting patrol was always an enjoyable experience. Fiona Muat, one of our three nurses, would tend the septic scratches and festering ulcers that many suffered on their legs with liberal

Tony Short leads two fellow Australian YEs up the Ranu River carrying supplies to the walkway camp. Though small, the river was the easiest way of transporting heavy goods through the forest. Coming downstream was much easier.

splashings of orange mecurichrome. Patients limped around the camp covered in orange dabs as if they were in the throes of some hideous smallpox attack. Fiona not only attended our ills but also those of Daisy, the camp cow. By some extraordinary coincidence, Mr Dandy, who owned one of the huts in which we were living, also possessed an inquisitive, brown-eyed Jersey cow that wandered aimlessly around the camp clearing, soon becoming a firm favourite with everyone. Everyone that is except David Smith, the cook. David, who normally ran a pub in Newcastle, managed to transform effortlessly our tinned and somewhat unappetising rations into *haute cuisine* seemingly with equal ease whether it was ten for dinner or 120. Unfortunately, Daisy would occasionally discover an unattended blueberry pie or the dough rising for the day's bread. Having gleefully consumed everything in sight, she would later be seen scampering into the forest pursued by an animated cook wielding a large frying pan.

At the end of a hot, sticky day we could bathe in the warm waters of the Ranu River observed by friendly monitor lizards which inhabited the opposite bank. They were powerful swimmers, often plunging themselves into the water, thrashing the surface with their tails. In the evenings at the camp, the sound of radio reports coming in from patrols mingled with croaking frogs and the chatter of evening conversation. The Indonesian YEs would sometimes sing beautiful traditional songs in harmony followed by equally memorable versions of 'Old Macdonald's Farm' led by John Cornish, the quartermaster, and Ben 'the boat' Cartwright. Having quenched our thirst with luke-warm Bintang beer, we would flop into our hammocks and listen to the spatter of tropical rain on the palm leaf roof, dreaming of the adventures that the following day would bring.

Morowali is dominated by two huge mountains, Tokala and Tambusisi. The former, despite the efforts of Ray Lloyd-Jones, our signals officer and a determined group of YEs, remains unclimbed. Each has a different geological history, Tokala's limestone crags being raised from the ocean floor whilst Tambusisi has its origins deep within the earth's crust forced out as ultra basic volcanic rock. The tops of high mountains in the tropics are exciting both for the scientist and the explorer. From them one can look over that green sweeping world under which one is living and in a country like Sulawesi most of the endemic species are to be found there. In addition, from lowland to summit, there is an interesting transition from humid, alluvial forests to dry, tall hill forests, finally ending in the most peculiar forest of all – the moss forest.

To reach the moss forest 2,000 metres up on Tambusisi took three days. It began with a journey down the Ranu River in the huge Avon inflatable boat *David Gestetner* and across the waters of Tomori Bay to the village of Tambajoli, set amongst the mangrove swamps at the north-west end of the bay. Having negotiated with porters and guides it was a full day's walk through alang-alang grass and over the first hills to reach the small settlement of Kabalo on a river of the same name. From there a steep day's climb takes you to the last point where water can be obtained on the route. This is Tambusisi Damar. The climb is exhausting and clothes soaked with sweat become cold and clammy as cooler altitudes are reached.

Several scientific sorties were made to Tambusisi Damar just below the moss forest. Dr Chris Watts from the Veterinary Research Institute in Adelaide found it to be one of the richest trapping sites for small mammals he had ever visited, in complete contrast to the surprisingly impoverished lowlands. Blood and tissue taken from these animals are now being examined for relationships with the small mammals of Australia. Of the rats he caught on one of the highest ridges, two were later discovered to be previously unknown species. Few insects had been collected in Sulawesi above 1,300 metres. The British Museum should feel eternally grateful to David Smith and Christopher Rees who laboured up Tambusisi carrying a 30 kilogram generator and stores to power an ultraviolet lamp for capturing night flying insects. It was worth it. Twelve species of hawk moth were caught in this way, one of which was new to science as well as an Atlas moth with a 30 centimetre wingspan along with a myriad of other insects.

Just prior to packing up the camp a particularly large high-flying Danaid butterfly which had eluded all efforts to catch it throughout the expedition, fluttered through the clearing, for once at chest height. Everyone grabbed what nets they could find and advanced towards it. As it approached, the expedition's Scientific Co-ordinator made an unskilled entomological swipe and completely missed. However, the butterfly was unprepared for the turbulence which followed and promptly nose-dived into the ground where it was instantly pounced upon by Anthony Bedford-Russell. With a wingspan of over 15 centimetres it was not only the largest new species of butterfly to be caught for years but it was also the first to be captured in its genus *Idea* for ninety-seven years, and is now named *Idea tambusisiane* after the mountain where it was caught.

From the small clearing on Tambusisi Damar a narrow track led up to a steep ridge lined with thin trees. This was the way to the moss forest and the summit of Tambusisi. The team carried water in hollowed out bamboos. At about 1,900 metres the forest changes abruptly. The canopy is only 10 metres high, roots are twisted over one another and everything becomes enveloped in moss. Proceeding higher the moss becomes thicker and in sheltered gullies may be as much as 20 centimetres deep around tree trunks. Long green strands hang from branches giving the forest an elfin-like quality. Members of the group had to force their way through a tangle of branches as blocks of sponge-like moss flopped into their faces sending trickles of icy water down the spine.

No streams are found here but there is water in abundance. The moss itself provides moisture in plenty and when squeezed can be used to fill a water bottle with its bitter brown liquid. Add a teabag or oxo cube and it is quite palatable. But nature has provided an even better source of water. The moss forests of Tambusisi abound with insectivorous pitcher plants *Nepenthes* sp. At least eight different species were found, some shaped like wine glasses, others resembling egg cups and half pint mugs. Within these vessels, hanging from stunted trees or growing on the ground, is a bountiful supply of water. Into their personal reservoir, pitcher plants secrete a powerful digestive enzyme which also acts as an insecticide. Insects attracted to the sugary coating on the underside of the pitcher's 'lid' fall from its slippery sides into the deadly bath below. Within fifteen seconds most are dead and provide a source of nitrogen which the plant cannot obtain from the nutrient poor environment on the mountain

K K Gurung squeezes water from moss on the way to the summit of Tambusisi.

top. However, despite its digestive qualities, pitcher fluid is exploited by the larvae of mosquito species resistant to it which filter-feed on the protozoan broth within the water. Frogs lay their eggs in pitchers and use them as a home and predatory ants capture insects strong enough to climb out of the fluid but too weak to withstand attack. A handkerchief can filter off this extraordinary ecosystem leaving clean water for the parched climber to drink on his way to the summit.

Petra Regent, the expedition's diarist, was not used to climbing mountains but she became the second woman to reach the summit and the first to sleep there, along with

Eye of the Wind **lying at anchor in Tomori Bay.**

the rest of the group, huddled in their sleeping bags against the damp and chilling cold. In the morning the view was magnificent; mountains, thick with forest all around below and, to the south, the coast with Tokobae and Nanaka island standing out in Tomori Bay, slowly discernible in the purple dawn.

Standing on the mountain top one had time to reflect both on the future of Morowali and on what one would remember most, now that the survey was almost over. Would it be the extraordinary rhinoceros beetles or praying mantids, or perhaps the challenge of scrambling through the vine-clinging forest, the beauty of the butterflies, the fun of

**One of the pitcher plants found near the
summit of Tambusisi. It belongs to an as
yet unidentified species.**

an evening at the base camp, the smile on a Wana child's face, or the chill of dawn on
the mountain itself?

Over the four months of the survey Martin Brendell collected 20,000 insects for the
British Museum (Natural History) and the Zoological Museum at Bogor in Java. Bill
Timmis recorded over 200 species of birds. Many new records of bats were made; the
last one, on the final night was an undescribed species. Arie Budiman had studied the
mangroves for the Indonesian Institute of Biology, and the expedition's diving team
had surveyed the coral reefs around Morowali's shores, teaching many Young
Explorers to dive in the process. Now the 1:100,000 scale topographic map is complete
and eighty-five field reports have been filed by the YEs alone; many more are in
preparation by scientists in various parts of the world. The World Wildlife Fund
Management Plan was published in 1980. The chromite-bearing sands proved
uneconomic for extraction and soil surveys showed the plains to be infertile and
unsuitable for agriculture. Finally, the Japanese timber firm hoping to log Morowali's
forests was persuaded to look elsewhere for its revenue. In the spring of 1980, Morowali
was given the official sanction of the government becoming Indonesia's newest nature
reserve, a true reward for all the efforts of the Operation Drake team.

From the Spice Islands to East Africa

Sailing across the Pacific, Sir Francis Drake had been sixty-eight days without sight of land and, passing south of the Ladrone Islands, he put into Ternate in the Spice Islands, now known as the Moluccas. Drake received the Sultan of Ternate on board the *Golden Hind* and concluded a valuable treaty with him promising support against the Portuguese. Four hundred years later, *Eye of the Wind* also passed through the Moluccas on her way to Sulawesi from New Guinea. Here, she nearly suffered a disaster. In a savage squall the 13 metre-long main boom snapped in half, sending sail and ropes flapping viciously about the deck. Five days later she limped into Ambon where the crew trimmed a suitable tree to size and lashed it to the deck to await the ship's arrival at Morowali. On a beach near the Ranu River, Spider Anderson carefully shaped it to perfection and it was now fitted to the mainmast again.

Eye of the Wind had left Tomori Bay whilst the survey was still in progress at Morowali. Now she was at anchor and Mandy Roberts, an Australian YE on board, could gaze out along the line of the bowsprit and see a small forested island surrounded by golden sands. Being down wind, the warm air carried a strange, musty tropical smell which would have informed the early navigators that they would soon be approaching land. In between *Eye of the Wind* and the shore a small Avon rubber boat was bringing back a party from exploring the island. This, they thought, might be 'Crab Island'. A number of historians believe that, whilst beached on the shore of this small island for nearly a month, Drake had careened the *Golden Hind* to remove weed and goose barnacles from her hull and make the necessary repairs prior to her journey home across the Indian Ocean to England.

No evidence was found of Drake's presence on the island (now known as Pulau Potil Kecil and part of the Banggai Islands off Sulawesi's east coast), although it did fit his description. However, some of the Operation Drake biologists who had travelled with the ship, made good use of their time collecting specimens from the island and from others surrounding it. These were of particular interest as the Banggai group exhibits many species which demonstrate the transition of flora and fauna found between Sulawesi and New Guinea.

Having completed his repairs and given his men a good rest, Drake left 'Crab Island' on December 12th 1579. Bad weather forced him to sail south of the Banggai Islands and on the evening of January 9th his great voyage nearly came to an unexpected end. Under full sail and without warning the *Golden Hind* ran up onto a submerged coral reef with a resounding crash. Initial panic gave way to calm as the crew realised that she was not in immediate danger of sinking; she could not however be moved. Over the bow the water was shallow but over the stern no anchor ground could be found with which to pull her off and all 'now turned into awaiting for a lingering death'. The padre Francis Fletcher, blamed Drake believing it to be Divine judgment for his past evils, including the execution of Thomas Doughty in South America for suspected treachery.

Brushing this aside, Drake ordered six pieces of ordnance, three tons of cloves and some provisions to be thrown overboard and soon after low water on the following day, the ship, now unsupported by the sea, miraculously heeled over and slid from the reef. Drake then shackled Fletcher to a hatch in the forecastle and promptly excommunicated him in front of the crew placing a band on his arm which read: 'Francis fletcher, Ye falsest knave that ever liveth'.

North-east of Tomori Bay lies Vesuvius reef and it was here that Drake was believed to have been so nearly wrecked. *Eye of the Wind*, with the diving team aboard, anchored off the kidney shaped reef to study it and to initiate a search for Drake's cannons. The reef still remains a maritime hazard; even as we arrived a local vessel, grounded in a squall, was having to jettison part of her cargo of metal reinforcing rods in order to get off, in an extraordinary repetition of Drake's mishap. Neither a proton magnetometer survey of the reef by a Royal Australian Air Force Orion aircraft nor a careful surface search produced anything other than the reinforcing rods and it was therefore decided to concentrate on a much more exciting discovery – the reef was one of the richest coral gardens in the world.

Coral reefs are the tropical forests of the sea. The diversity of the life forms inhabiting them is unimaginable and they form the largest living structures on earth. Surprisingly, however, the components from which they are built-up are minute. The tiny soft bodied animals or polyps which form them resemble miniature sea anemones, with one end resting on a firm substrate and the other containing a mouth surrounded by a ring of tentacles which captures planktonic animals from the sea around it. These scleractiniad, or reef-building corals, are confined to warm and shallow tropical seas

Robin Bacon (left) supervises the YEs as they dive on Vesuvius reef.

for two reasons. Firstly, they have a tiny unicellular protozoan lodger or symbiont, living inside them which provides oxygen for the polyp by means of photosynthesis. This requires light so the polyp must live in the euphotic zone, near to the surface. Secondly, the polyp protects itself by producing a calcareous skeleton, which is formed best in warm temperatures. The polyps live in colonies which produce beautiful skeletal designs, characteristic of each species. The remains of these, over thousands of years, form the reef. Although corals cover most of the reef surface, it can be dominated by different phyla such as sponges, tunicates and algae or other soft corals, anemones and hydroids. A multitude of different fish inhabit the reefs and graze upon the corals.

Vesuvius reef is enormous. Wearing aqualungs, the YEs flipped over the side of the rubber boats and down into the silent coral gardens below, stretching for kilometres in each direction. Under Trish Holdway's direction, they began a detailed investigation of the reef structure and the creatures which had formed it. They had been trained a few weeks before during an earlier study of the corals off the Banggai Islands in conjunction with the Indonesian Oceanological Institute's research vessel, *Samudera*. The visibility was excellent and both the Young Explorers and the experienced divers were overawed by the massive sponges, some of which were big enough to hold a human inside their apical opening, and by the fragile table corals, some as large as 4 metres in diameter. The reef has added significance as it provides a home for one of Indonesia's most threatened mammals, the dugong *Dugong dugon*. These rather unattractive creatures may surprisingly have given rise to the seafarers' tales of mermaids: they have prominent breasts from which they suckle their young in an upright position in the sea whilst holding them upright in their flippers. Sadly, they have almost been exterminated from Indonesian waters as their tusks are much prized as cigarette holders, they are easily hunted for their meat and the grass beds on which they feed have been destroyed. Coral reefs are themselves extremely susceptible to human changes in the environment. Rivers whose drainage basins have been deforested carry eroded soil far out to sea, increasing the turbidity of water many kilometres away, clogging the polyps with silt and blocking off the light upon which their algal lodgers depend. Dredging can have the same effect. Eager tourists remove specific creatures of beauty, so creating an imbalance in the delicate reef ecosystem. In Indonesia vast areas of coral reef have been dynamited out of existence to supply the building industry with lime.

Fortunately, the reefs and lagoons of Vesuvius have been subjected to none of this yet. A few local fishermen sail to the reefs from the Banggai Islands to collect fish and giant clams but merely to supplement their own meagre food supplies rather than for commercial profit. The diving team spotted dugongs on three occasions around the reefs and Indonesia is now considering Vesuvius as its first dugong reserve.

Animal life in a coral outcrop

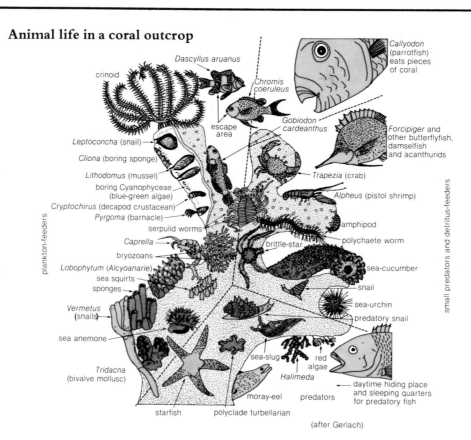

(after Gerlach)

Coral reefs are sometimes described as the largest living structures on earth but they are, in fact, comprised of millions of individuals. The calcified remains of the tiny polyps which create the reef structure provide numerous nooks and crannies for fish, clams, crabs, worms and snails to live in. Together they make up the reef community which is as diverse and productive as any life system known.

The animals fall into a number of different groups: the radially symmetrical sea urchins and starfish, segmented animals such as beautiful fan worms and coloured shrimps, shelled creatures like cowries which glide across the reef and, of course, the soft-bodied beasts which include the corals themselves and jellyfish. Finally,

more advanced than any of these, are the backboned fishes. These lend character and colour to the reef darting amongst great outcrops of coral in flashes of brilliant yellow and green or peering with purple eyes from a dark recess within. It is at night, however, that the reef can be seen at its best, for it is then that the coral builders themselves make their appearance, emerging from their tiny cells to carpet the reef in a translucent film of tiny tentacles as they filter food from the sea. There are many other creatures that filter-feed including crinoids and serpulid worms. The method by which they gather their food is another way of dividing up the reef community into predators, detritus feeders and those that sieve plankton.

Robbie Williamson giving diving lessons in Tomori Bay in preparation for the marine survey work and the search for Drake's cannons.

Dr Patricia Holdway and YEs conducting a survey of Vesuvius reef as *Eye of the Wind* lies at anchor in the distance.

The survey complete, *Eye of the Wind* sailed back to Morowali and on March 9th she left the Ranu River with a crew of Indonesian and international YEs for the sixteen-day sail to Jakarta. Some YEs had elected to make their own way there overland, studying ancient megaliths in the Lore Lindu reserve on the way and all arrived safely for the final receptions and farewells. The ship was honoured with a visit by the Vice-President of Indonesia, Adam Malik, and a scientific seminar to review the results of the Morowali survey was held, chaired by the Director of Nature Conservation. *Eye of the Wind* then sailed out with the Phase VIII YEs who had flown in for the journey across the Indian Ocean.

Dodging the wooden Macassar schooners which failed to show up on the radar, the inexperienced struggled with the wheel and the motion of the ship, quickly learning that the only thing to stop them dropping from the t'gallant in the squalls

'One hand for the ship and one for yourself',
a maxim not always easily adhered to; but
adhesion is the most important considera-
tion when aloft.

was their own fear of falling. Dawn on the following day found them opposite one of nature's most impressive demonstrations of power: the volcanic island of Krakatoa. One hundred and three years before, much of the 46 kilometre square island had been lifted over 50 kilometres into the air in a gigantic explosion, producing a tidal wave which destroyed 163 villages and killed 36,000 people. In 1980 it was active again, sending a column of dust and ashes thousands of metres into the atmosphere as flames licked around its base lending a red glow to the dawn.

Sailing into the Indian Ocean the crew on *Eye of the Wind* encountered enormous swells moving to India from the Antarctic. Sails flapped limply upon the yards and smoke from cigarettes hung in the air; the heat was sweltering. The ship was in the doldrums. It was easy to imagine the frustration of earlier voyagers who lacked engines to motor them out of the doldrum calms. These are formed by rising hot air at the equator which creates low pressure and variable winds. The hot air moves north and south, later cooling, falling earthwards and creating high pressure which then flows back towards the equator. Then, deflected to the east and west by the rotation of the earth, it creates the trade winds. A few days later *Eye of the Wind* thankfully picked up the south-east trades which would blow her all the way across the Indian Ocean with an almost constant force 6 to 7 wind, accompanied by clear blue skies dotted with cumulus clouds.

After 878 nautical miles *Eye of the Wind* put into Port Refuge in the Cocos Keeling Islands amidst a violent squall and equally violent oaths from the ship's engineer as the propeller was not functioning properly. This tiny collection of atolls was first controlled by the Scottish Clunies-Ross family who developed them into copra plantations with local Malay labour. Having begun as a family 'kingdom' with its own currency and stamps, the islands became a British protectorate and have recently been sold to the Australian Government. The Clunies-Ross family still live on Home Island with some 700 Malay workers. Here the YEs were to carry out a number of community tasks to benefit the islanders. There was a cyclone shelter and a council meeting hall to be built, a copra drying shed to be pulled down, and stamps to be franked – one of the more tedious activities on the expedition. A set of commemorative covers was produced for each phase; it was always amusing to arrive at some tiny out of the way post office and ask an amazed postmaster for 5,000 small denomination stamps and whether he could possibly frank all these covers as one had so many relatives to write to. Groups of YEs were sent to assist in the task which took at least a day, or longer if they ran out of stamps. After five days of hard labour during which John Poskus from Cornwall prided himself with tiling the floor of the men's lavatory in the council house, Dee Macleod, a female farm manager from the United States, pulled down the entire copra drying shed with a very ancient tractor and others shifted a mountain of coconuts from the jetty, the crew gathered aboard the ship and set sail for the Seychelles. No one was sadder then Greg de Francis, an American YE, who was taken ill with suspected appendicitis six hours before sailing and had to be left in the care of the local hospital before flying to Australia. Fortunately he was able to rejoin the ship in the Seychelles.

Building the council meeting house on Cocos Keeling Island epitomises the ideals of Operation Drake by bringing together YEs from England, the USA and Iceland in the service of others.

The Seychelles is an archipelago of forty breathtakingly beautiful granitic islands and over fifty coral islands and atolls. The granitic islands are relatively close-knit; all lie within a 56 kilometre radius of Mahé, the main island and they account for over 80 per cent of the land area. Rugged and mountainous they are dotted with fine silver beaches and clear lagoons, and contain varying amounts of lush tropical vegetation. There are no rivers but instead many short streams which flow directly into the sea. The coral islands, flat and generally only a few metres above sea level, extend 90 to 1,000 kilometres distant from Mahé. Most of them are uninhabited.

Although used as a stopover for mediaeval Arab and Malay traders *en route* to and from Africa, the Seychelles were first settled by the French and their African slaves as late as the 1770s. Like other Indian Ocean islands, they became pawns in the Anglo-French rivalry for the control of India and France ceded them to Britain under the 1814

The prince of palms

FINIS·CORONAT·OPVS

For centuries the propagator of the largest seed in the world remained unknown. On many coasts and shores around the Indian Ocean a huge nut, shaped like a female pelvis, was on rare occasions washed ashore. Its suggestive shape ensured that its contents became a celebrated aphrodisiac. Sixteenth-century navigators brought news of the nut to Europe where it also became prized. Eastern scholars concluded that its parent grew on the sea-bottom and that the ripened nuts floated to the surface, later to drift ashore, hence its name coco-de-mer.

It was not until 1768, when Chevalier Marion arrived off Praslin in the Seychelles, that the mystery was solved. One of his party discovered the island to be thickly covered with the largest palms in the world and the ground littered with their huge nuts. The coco-de-mer palm reaches heights of 30 metres and an age of 800 years. It has the largest leaves in the vegetable kingdom and supports anything up to 180 kilograms of fruit at a time. The nuts, which average 10 to 12 kilograms each, take seven years to mature. The only places in the world where you can see these magnificent trees are on Praslin and Curieuse in the Seychelles and they are depicted on the islands' coat of arms.

Treaty of Paris. Despite the fact that they are only a few degrees south of the equator the islands enjoy a pleasant climate thanks to the sea breezes which help to modify extremes of heat and humidity. The abundant vegetation bears witness to the ample rainfall, most of which falls in short, sharp showers after which the skies soon clear; there is a daily average of seven hours sunshine.

Few archipelagos have such an exciting diversity of animals and plants as the Seychelles. It has been said that exploring the islands is like visiting a museum of natural history, so rich and varied are the botanical and zoological specimens. Some of the flora is unique, like the fabulous coco-de-mer tree *Lodociea maldivica*, which grows only on the islands of Praslin and its neighbour Curieuse and nowhere else in the world as well as the greatest number of giant land tortoises. At the same time the

The Red Ensign is lowered at sunset as *Eye of the Wind* **rides at anchor off the Seychelles.**

islands provide a home for some of the rarest land birds in existence; at least three species are down to their last few dozen pairs.

During the month they spent in the Seychelles, the Young Explorers visited North Island, Praslin, Curieuse, St Anne and other islands in the marine National Park off Mahé, as well as Frigate and the African Banks, Darros and St Joseph in the Amirantes. They conducted a variety of short-term projects directed by Dr Ian Swingland and local government scientists.

One of these involved *Toxocarpus schimperianus,* one of the rarest plants in the world. This small, rather insignificant vine is thought to have valuable pharmacological properties but is known only from thirteen specimens on Curieuse and Mahé. Equipped with compasses, maps and plant identification photographs, groups of YEs fanned out to search the valleys and hillsides. Looking for a small green vine amongst a mass of green vegetation was not easy but success was theirs. They managed to double the known numbers of the plant, and whilst fighting through the 2 metre-high bracken on Mount Sebert on Mahé, discovered one more specimen of the jellyfish tree *Medusagyne oppositifolia,* increasing the world population by 20 per cent. It was so named after its flowers which resemble an upside-down jellyfish. Curieuse was also the home of *Geochelone gigantea,* the giant tortoise. These were once common all over the Seychelles but are now only found in any numbers on Aldabra, many kilometres to the south. Thirteen years ago a number were released on Frigate Island and more recently on Curieuse to see if new breeding populations could be established. A careful census of the introduced population was carried out by the YEs. Unfortunately the superior-tasting female tortoises on Frigate are poached for meat leaving a preponderance of lonely males. However as giant tortoises are believed to live for anything up to two centuries, they have time to wait until new introductions are made or they happen to find a mate!

It is perhaps the birds of the Seychelles, however, that are most spectacular. Amongst the coconut fronds of Frigate Island, the YEs searched for the Seychelles magpie robin *Copsychus seychellarum,* a handsome bird with gleaming black plumage. Only about seventy were recorded. Ornithologists blame the introduction of cats to Frigate Island for the virtual elimination of the magpie robin, for in the morning and evening the bird leaves the safety of the trees and hops around buildings where it is vulnerable to

Dr Ian Swingland instructs Tom Hood from England and other YEs on how to measure and sex tortoises on Frigate Island.

Counting terns on the African Banks.

152

attack. On Praslin they were fortunate to see the endemic black parrot *Coracopsis nigra barklyi* now confined to coco-de-mer palms of the Vallee de Mai. Only about thirty pairs remain in the world.

Having provided a base from which the various groups could explore the islands, each one of which proved a new paradise, *Eye of the Wind* sailed 200 kilometres west to the African Banks. The two islets comprising the banks are famous for their seabird eggs which are harvested by the crateful in the cool season from the end of May to late July. Schooners ship the spotted eggs to the market in Mahé; they make a welcome change to the islanders' diet and are especially tasty as omelettes or scrambled.

The sooty tern *Sterna fuscata* is the most numerous of the eight species of tern which breed in the Seychelles and it provides the bulk of the seabird eggs sent to Mahé. When the breeding season is over the birds fly away to an unknown destination to return again the following May. To export the eggs from the islands requires a licence but needless to say, many are poached and it was therefore important to establish just how many birds were there. One sandbank was only a few hundred metres long and had three palm trees on it but the ground was literally covered in nesting seabirds. How on earth would it be possible to count them? The technique is surprisingly simple. Whilst *Eye of the Wind* was anchored a short distance offshore, some YEs positioned themselves on either side of the island in dinghies while the remaining YEs grouped at each end of the island. When a signal flag was hoisted on one of the boats, the YEs on the island ran shouting, screaming and gesticulating down to the other end and back again. The terns did not approve at all and took to the air whilst the YEs on the boats quickly photographed the mass of screeching, flapping birds. Later when the film was analysed by computer to assess numbers it was found that there were over 25,000 birds present. It appears that, whilst the egg trade has not significantly reduced the bird numbers, the new practice of killing adult birds for food may pose a far more serious threat in the future.

Ian Swingland flew back to Mahé and on to his new post at Kent University. Trish Holdway completed a comprehensive marine biological survey of the bays and reefs of St Anne's Marine Park and the African Banks before *Eye of the Wind* set sail on the last leg of her journey across the Indian Ocean to Mombasa. On the way a stubborn blue-footed booby perched on the shoulder of a Young Explorer appropriately named Bill Bird in the middle of the night whilst he was trying to furl the t'gallant sail. It refused to let go, so much to the amusement of the other YE helping Bill, that he nearly fell off the mast. Whilst *Eye of the Wind* had been in the Seychelles, the Operation Drake logistical machine had been working hard to set up a new series of projects for the YEs in Kenya. Originally, it was planned to visit the Sudan but two months before the projects were due to start they had to be cancelled for a variety of political reasons. All arrangements had to be drastically and quickly re-thought.

At the kind invitation of President Daniel Arap Moi it was agreed that Operation Drake should go to Kenya and various government departments were asked to suggest projects that the facilities of the expedition could help with and to which the Young Explorers could make a positive contribution. John Sutton, a highly respected conservationist, found himself, at short notice, chairing the local Steering Committee. Richard Leakey, Director of the National Museums of Kenya and a member of the committee, came up with a demanding and exciting idea that was to provide the perfect link with the Spice Islands of Indonesia on the other side of the Indian Ocean: the survey and excavation of the mediaeval town of Shanga.

The story of the spice trade is one of the most remarkable in trans-oceanic navigation. The demand for South East Asian spices was enormous. Apicus, author of a famous first century AD cookery book incorporated many of our most commonly used spices such as cinnamon, cloves, ginger, nutmeg, sandalwood and tumeric into his 478 recipes. Their value and the fact that they were brought over such vast distances across the Indian Ocean, resulted in an extremely lucrative trade, built-up to serve the Roman world and Christendom. By using the south-east trade winds, human ingenuity

American YE, Greg de Francis trying to identify a feathered hitchhiker. Birds, exhausted when blown off course by strong winds, often rested for several days on the ship.

Arab towns as they must have looked in Drake's time. This Braun and Hagenberg lithograph dates from 1588 and shows Aden at the top and Mombasa, Kilwa and Sofala below.

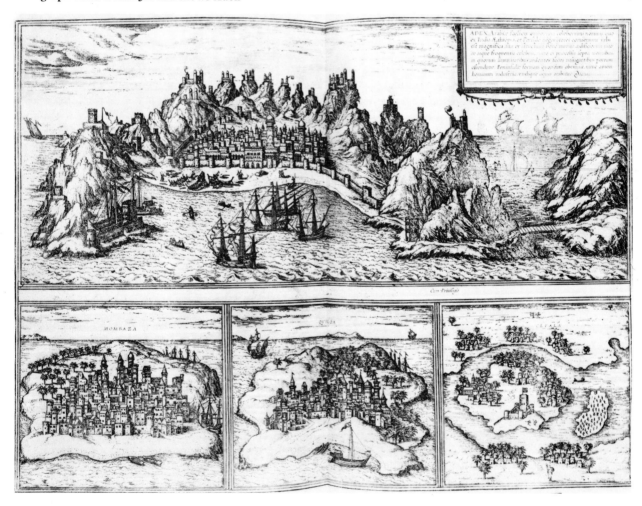

ensured that these precious products could travel thousands of miles, long before the Age of Discovery in the sixteenth and seventeenth centuries. Pliny wrote that the traders came to Rhapta, to the south of Mombasa, carrying goods:

> . . . *over vast distances in Rafts, which have no rudders to steer them, nor oars to pull them, or sails or other aids to navigation.*

From East Africa the spices may have been taken to Somalia and from there via the Red Sea to Egypt. In addition to these cargoes, Africa had its own riches to offer; ivory, precious stones, wood and a wide range of aromatic spices such as frankincense and myrrh. *Eye of the Wind* had sailed across the Indian Ocean from the Moluccas, the former Spice Islands, using the same south-east trade winds. Later in the year, the same winds would blow in the opposite direction, carrying the traders back to India and the Moluccas from the east coast of Africa, so completing the trading triangle.

As the demands of the mediaeval world increased, the cargoes grew larger. Elephant ivory became immensely popular in the tenth century AD as a medium for carving and the trade which is largely responsible for the wholesale destruction of elephant populations in Africa today was born. The growth of Islam encouraged these trade networks which became extremely well organised and diverse. Sophisticated dhows were built that could sail close to the wind and regularly plied between the Persian Gulf, India and Africa. Others set out from Egypt and Yemen, down the Red Sea to Arabia and India. From the tales brought from these voyages, legends such as those of Sinbad the Sailor originated. Few historical documents have survived from this period and it has therefore been difficult to appreciate the complexity of the trade. Recent archaeological excavations at some of these trading sites on the Kenyan coast have thrown fascinating new light on these early traders and with the work now planned at Shanga there was a real opportunity that further discoveries could be made.

From Mogadishu in the north to Cape Delgado in the south, is the coastal area now known as the Swahili. This narrow belt of homogeneous language, culture and the Islamic religion claims its origins back in the eighth century AD from the establishment of a dynasty of exiled rulers from Persia and the Arabian Peninsular. Today in Kenya the traditional culture is best preserved in the Lamu Archipelago on its northern coast, often considered the centre of the Swahili coast. Here, a series of flat islands of sandstone and coral, all forming part of a drowned river delta, create protected waters and magnificent harbours. It provided an ideal area for the traders from the African interior to meet the ships from the east. Although there is no running water on the islands there are wells and today the islands are fairly densely populated by the descendants of these early traders and settlers. The largest island is Pate and on its most seaward side lies the site of complex ruins known as Shanga.

Neville Chittick, Director of the British Institute in East Africa, examined the ruins initially in the 1960s. It was clear that they were of great significance. Some of them were in a precarious state and the full extent of the town was not known. Mark Horton, who had directed the excavations in Panama, joined Operation Drake again in Kenya with a team of archaeologists from Cambridge University and Athman Lali, curator of Lamu Museum, as co-director. Together they set about carrying out the National Museum's request to clear the bush and make an accurate and detailed survey of the 20 acres of ruins. Every wall was to be recorded and stratigraphic excavation undertaken to date and interpret the site. Funds provided by the National Museum enabled us to employ forty local workmen to help clear the site together with fourteen Young Explorers, including locally sponsored Kenyans.

Following *Eye of the Wind*'s arrival in Mombasa in mid-June the team travelled down in a convoy of trucks loaned by the Kenyan Army, the Young Explorers squeezing in besides stores, boats and surveying equipment. Everything had to be unloaded and repacked onto the traditional small dhows that have plied the coast for the last 800 years and are still the only method of reaching the island. Shanga, which means sand dunes, is located on a small peninsular of low-lying ground with a silted-up mangrove creek on one side and the Indian Ocean on the other. Everyone waded ashore onto the muddy beach and gazed with apprehension at the mangrove swamps and tangle of bush covering the ruins. In Panama, snakes and falling coconuts had been the only dangers but here there were ominous signs of black mambas and baboons and on another mainland site, elephant and buffalo. The large, tented camp was set up amongst the sand dunes near to Shanga and donkeys were purchased to bring the daily water supply from a well a kilometre away. At 2 degrees south of the equator, the south-east monsoons kept the temperature at a pleasant 32 to 38 degrees Centigrade.

To begin with Penny Ward and Liz Marquis surveyed the vegetation amongst the ruins in 10 metre square quadrats, the species collected later being sent to Kew Gardens in London. Here they were identified to see whether there was any correlation between past human occupation and the present vegetation pattern. Then clearance began and as the bush receded, houses with virtually all their walls still standing became visible, complete with large courtyards and elaborate rooms. Nearly half a kilometre of a surrounding town wall emerged, complete with five gates, all of them narrow enough to allow human and animal passage only. Facing the Indian Ocean was a sea wall with parallel walls running down to the beach, perhaps forming a breakwater or harbour installation. The town was composed of a maze of narrow zigzagging streets, some of which led out through the gates whilst others ran between the houses.

All the 140 houses discovered were built of coral blocks and lime, the traditional building materials used on the coast; in many cases the complete plan and walls have survived up to roof level. All had toilets and store rooms and large courtyards dominated the front of each house. All but one of the houses had a single storey only, and in many cases, traces of the roofs, with the imprint of their supporting mangrove poles, were still intact. The vegetation was so dense that the YEs had to use compasses to find their way around the maze of streets covered in bush. Once cleared, a half-hour scramble through a tangle of branches, never quite knowing what you would put

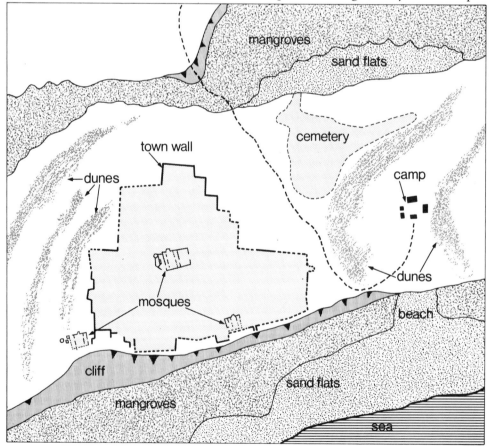

A plan of Shanga with its surrounding sand dunes and mangrove swamps.

After two months of intensive clearance, Shanga is revealed.

Mark Horton down a test pit at Shanga. The layer of sand reveals a period of abandonment when the surrounding dunes enveloped the settlement.

your foot on next, was reduced to an easy five-minute walk along the streets of what once was Shanga.

As clearance progressed three mosques were found, each with a decorated *mihrab* facing towards Mecca. The gnarled and dried bushes were extremely tough and thorns tore flesh and clothes but each day was exciting as the team never knew what building might be discovered next. Outside the town walls was an enormous cemetery containing almost 300 tombs, one of the largest so far discovered in East Africa. Each tomb was aligned east-west and made of coral and lime occasionally decorated with inscriptions.

Mike Carter then began a comprehensive wall by wall survey of the town's buildings. Using a theodolite, he established a network of seventy accurately fixed points incorporating a traverse of the site 2.5 kilometres long. From these points he plotted in the positions of 3,000 separate walls creating a 1:200 plan of the town, 4.7 × 3.4 metres in size. The YEs soon became adept at the technique and also set about photographing and describing every building and scale drawing elevations of intricate plaster work and decorated coral. It was soon apparent that the size of the town far exceeded earlier expectations; it had clearly been a major settlement.

Many of the walls were crumbling and all were in a dangerous condition. Mangrove scaffolding which could have been used would not provide a permanent solution. Nearby, a quarry was discovered and it was decided to reconstruct a lime kiln, not only to provide mortar for the restoration but also to record the materials that were used to make a traditional lime kiln in the form of an ethno-archaeological study. A local 'fundi' or craftsman was employed to build it in the best traditional Swahili fashion whilst Julia Barnley, a YE from Kenya, recorded the exact quantities of coral and timber that were needed and the cost of labour. Coral was mined from the original quarry and a line of singing and stamping men carried it to the kiln where it was heaved into a conical pile above the timber. Finally, after days of exhausting work, a replica of the project leader's house was built for good luck, and a goat ceremoniously sacrificed before the fires were lit and the huge pile of coral began to burn. The lime it produced was then used in restoration work around the site and in preventing certain buildings from collapsing.

There were many times during the survey when the YEs, just as Prince Charles had said they would, wondered why on earth they had joined Operation Drake. Three metres down a pit scrabbling amongst the earth for fragments of bone and unexciting sherds of pottery is not everyone's idea of an 'adventure of a lifetime' and there were

inevitable moments of frustration. Remarkably, Mark in his tatty gym shoes and mud-stained shorts, in permanent danger of a rapid descent to his knees, managed to keep everyone working incredibly hard.

The local villagers were sometimes confused by our work. One man walked all the way across the island from another village with a harrowing tale. He had heard that we were hunting for gold and jewels in pits amongst the graves of Shanga and had a dream that there was gold beneath his house. So he dug a deep pit straight down through his living room floor but alas found nothing. He had walked to our camp to see how we did it and to borrow a pair of binoculars which, he had heard, was how we could 'see' into the ground and locate where to dig. No amount of persuading could convince him that they were for any other purpose!

Transport between the islands was entertaining. It took an hour to walk across Pate through pleasant coconut groves to reach the village of Siu. Here we would take a small, extremely unstable and leaking canoe down the mangrove creek to its entrance into the sea and wait for the daily dhow to Lamu. After several hours it would appear and sail past without stopping, the occupants completely failing to understand our wild gesticulations and shouts which they returned with correspondingly enthusiastic waves. As the canoe rocked alarmingly, in imminent danger of sinking, it was neccessary to pole our way all the way back up the creek to Siu and return defeated across the island to the camp.

Our 9 metre inflatable boat, the *David Gestetner II,* driven by two large and thirsty outboards, was controlled by the equally large and thirsty Peter Durey, who grinningly occupied a great proportion of the rear of the craft. Battling with his temperamental engines, Peter roared across the water at great speed carrying stores, Young Explorers and excited local villagers between Pate and Dondo, a possible Swahili/Portuguese site we were also studying on the mainland. Breakdowns and remarkably sticky mud banks often made the journey longer than expected. Bringing supplies in from TAC HQ in Nairobi was just as complicated. First transport had to be arranged and driven to Mombasa. The second day involved driving up the coast towards Lamu and crossing a river by raft before discovering that the Tana River was in flood, the road under water and an intricate detour inevitable. On arrival at the roadhead opposite Lamu Island, the tide, which had a mind of its own and followed no known predictions, was usually out or only in at 2.00 a.m. in the morning when fuel drums and stores would have to be loaded onto boats for the long journey to Pate. There was an airstrip at Pate but this too was suspect after a light aircraft bringing in Captain Mark Mans, the Operations officer for a flying visit sank into a bog and could not be removed for a week.

The camp itself, apart from being a pleasant place to live in, provided moments of light relief and occasionally not so gentle rivalry. On one occasion certain members of the archaeology team were accused of not doing their fair share of the cooking and so they produced an especially hot Vindaloo curry for their accusers and a mild Madras for everyone else. Unfortunately they got the labels mixed up and their accusers said they had not tasted better whilst the remainder of the camp gasped for water and could not speak for several hours. After that the archaeologists were left in peace to sieve sand and stone rather than flour and spices.

The most interesting building on the Shanga site was the Friday Mosque, named after the Moslem Holy Day when everyone would have gone there to worship. Located in the centre of the town, it survived as a large chamber with open courtyards to the east and west. On the mosque there was a striking facade of pillars that rose above the roof which had originally been supported by circular columns, with an elaborate stone *mihrab* at the north end. The *mihrab* had fallen face down to the ground but a stone by stone analysis revealed it to be one of the most interesting on the coast, complete with fine Koranic inscriptions in *Nashki* script surrounding the edge. The archaeological evidence suggests that this belonged to the thirteenth century which would make it one of the earliest decorated *mihrabs* surviving on the East African coast. The western courtyard of the same mosque was investigated in great detail and excavated down to the first floor level. Soon a complex washing area emerged showing two tanks with conduits and drains where the worshippers had washed their feet before going into the mosque to pray. Serrated lumps of brain coral had been plastered onto the floor for them to rub their feet clean on.

Surveying Shanga's ruins.

The major question now remaining for a site of this size and complexity was to establish when it had been founded and when it had become important. Shanga has escaped the notice of all the early travellers and geographers; only the oral traditional histories mention it. Who then, founded it? To answer these questions it is neccessary to dig down into the ground excavating each successive layer of occupation as signified by subtle changes in soil colour, texture and the range of 'finds' one comes across in the process until the soil surface on which the settlement was first built is reached. In a sense one is going back in time.

Three metres of earth or 'fill' had been deposited by successive generations of rubbish and rubble from buildings and it was into these compacted layers of soil that a series of test pits were dug around the site in order to establish the depth and nature of the deposit stratigraphy. In some places it was found to be quite shallow; but surprisingly, in the north-east corner, well over 3 metres of complex layers were found. Around one of these, a larger area was opened up and carefully excavated by Kate Clark from Cambridge and Ann Marie Gibson, a Young Explorer archaeologist from Scotland together with other YEs. All the deposits were removed with trowels and brushes and sieved. It was a laborious task in the dusty heat which tested the most resolute of the Young Explorers.

A total of 350 separated layers of deposit were lifted off producing over 500 kilograms of pottery and a large collection of animal and fish bones. Five major periods of structure were identified, of which the first four were mud and timber buildings, the earliest having been built directly onto a sand dune. Right at the bottom of the pit was a series of mud houses built with post holes with lime floors and containing handmade pottery bowls. From nearby rubbish and fire pits we collected Iron Age pottery,

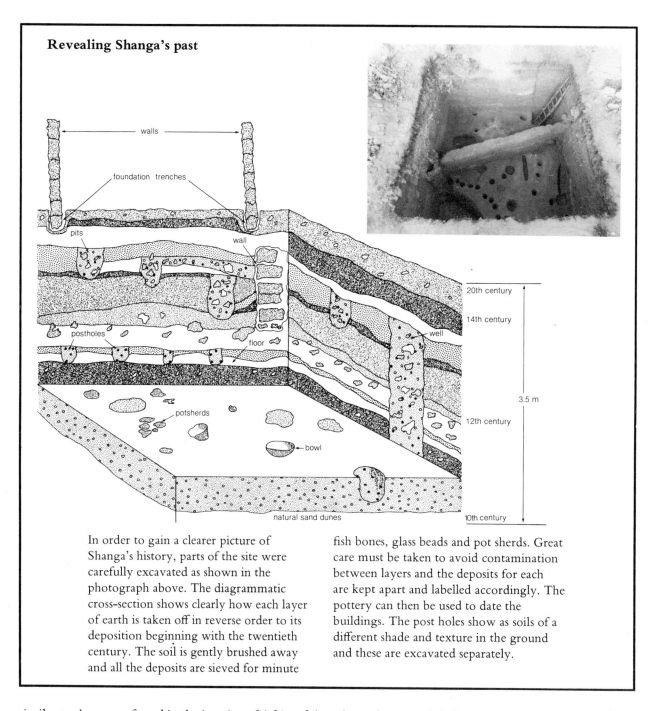

Revealing Shanga's past

walls

foundation trenches

pits

wall

postholes

floor

well

potsherds

bowl

20th century

14th century

12th century

10th century

3.5 m

natural sand dunes

In order to gain a clearer picture of Shanga's history, parts of the site were carefully excavated as shown in the photograph above. The diagrammatic cross-section shows clearly how each layer of earth is taken off in reverse order to its deposition beginning with the twentieth century. The soil is gently brushed away and all the deposits are sieved for minute fish bones, glass beads and pot sherds. Great care must be taken to avoid contamination between layers and the deposits for each are kept apart and labelled accordingly. The pottery can then be used to date the buildings. The post holes show as soils of a different shade and texture in the ground and these are excavated separately.

similar to the wares found in the interior of Africa, fish and goat bones and shells. Not only were there shell beads but also carved stone grinders for their manufacture, a fine polished stone axe, a piece of decorated gold, perhaps a bead mount, a gaming counter and dice made of coral. These were all meticulously logged and recorded by Maria Mabee the American archaeologist who had worked with Operation Drake before in Panama. Most significant of all, however, were the minute quantities of Sassanian Islamic blue pottery discovered, all of which belonged to types well known in the ninth and tenth century AD from Persia. Fourteenth-century Chinese celadon ware was also found in other layers. It was particularly valued in China during that period because of the erroneous belief that it would reveal the presence of poison in food by cracking. As most high-ranking orientals expected to be poisoned at some stage in their life by a wife or son, it was prudent and reassuring to eat off celadon. Being a luxury it was a valued trading product and so brought to Shanga. It seems therefore, that the origins of Shanga were much earlier than we had expected. Having started at the surface in the present day, the pits had reached back into the tenth century AD. In addition, the large range of imported wares showed that Shanga had maintained trading links all over the Indian Ocean as far as China.

It is premature to attempt a full reconstruction of the town's history but perhaps it was something like this. The earliest deposits – the daub soils lying directly on white sand dunes – date to the early tenth century AD. From then on the centre of the site was intensively occupied by buildings successively constructed on top of their predecessors, until the town was rebuilt in stone in the latter part of the thirteenth century. During the thirteenth and fourteenth centuries the town displayed its greatest prosperity, with its population rising to well over 1,000. The mosques were rebuilt and the dead commemorated in fine tombs.

The end came suddenly. The complete absence of any fifteenth-century pottery on the site bears witness to the sudden decline of Shanga, but its cause is a mystery. It may have been due to the harbour silting up or the water supply becoming salty. Elizabeth Wangari, a Kenyan YE, did some research of her own amongst the local people living near Shanga and was told this interesting story by a seventy-year-old man from Siu. His name was Mmaka Mohamed and he said the story was about 700 years old:

> *The Sultan of Shanga was Mfalme Kimangemange. The people of Shanga came from Shangai in China. This is actually where the name Shanga came from. They were traders and also fished. After they had settled in Shanga they wanted to have a bigger kingdom and so fought with the people of Siu and defeated them. After that, the people of Pate joined together with the people of Siu and defeated those from Shanga. The Shanga people ran away to their own country. A few ran to Faza (a nearby town); you can still see people with eyes like those of the Shanga in Faza today.*

The Pate Chronicle, compiled from oral traditions still existing on the island in the early 1900s provides another clue concerning a Sultan called Muhammed bin Ahmad who:

> *. . . fought with the people of Shanga, a country near Pate on the side of the rising sun. This country he conquered in war, plundering it and killing the males. The youths and maidens they made prisoners.*

A strange miracle appears to have happened during the battle:

> *There was a young maiden sitting on the ground grinding Frankincense and a soldier entered and seized her. This maiden said to the earth, 'Open, that I may enter', and the earth opened and swallowed her up, leaving only the border of her upper robe above ground.*

The Sultan on hearing the tale made a shrine above the spot which was tended for many years.

Muhammed was king of Pate, a town situated on the north side of the island. If this account is true, his destruction of the town and subsequent enslavement of its inhabitants may have been the reason for the demise of Shanga in the late fourteenth century. In any event, no one came back to break the silence of the decaying ruins and the walls were left as fossils for archaeologists to discover in the twentieth century. Now that the archaeology team has gone, goats are once again the only occupants of the town of Shanga.

Kenya's savage paradise

The dusty Land Rover bumps and rattles along an ever dustier track, jarring every bone from coccyx to cranium. Grass, waist-high, swirls among the dust devils speeding towards distant hills. Behind them, they would be coming in their thousands and hundreds of thousands, but now the grasslands are quiet and, concealed among green and golden blades, dik dik, gazelle and impala pick their way carefully, lions, lean after months of hunger, watch and hyaenas sniff the air. It is August in the Mara and the arrival of the most spectacular animal migration in the world is just about to begin.

Another hour of driving brings us to the top of a hill. Stretching ahead lies the Serengeti plain of Tanzania, behind, the Mara plain of Kenya and in between, the green strip of forest that is the Mara River. Scattered as far as the eye can see and moving towards us are columns of wildebeest and zebra. Ecologists are trained to convert animals into energy budgets and kilograms of animal biomass per hectare but here is the ultimate African experience: plains seething with wildlife as they must once have been before man began his destruction. In these days of gloom and despondency about the future of wildlife, it is refreshing to come across an area where the animals, far from declining, are steadily on the increase.

The Mara Reserve forms the northern extension of the Serengeti ecosystem. Together they cover an area of some 40,450 square kilometres spanning the Kenya/Tanzania border. Millions of animals including the elephant *Loxodonta africana,* zebra *Equus burchelli,* wildebeest *Connochaetes taurinus,* giraffe *Giraffa camelopardilis,* many species of antelope and their predators inhabit these productive grasslands. The Serengeti Research Institute began monitoring wildlife movements in 1963 and, more recently, similar work has been carried out by the Kenya Rangeland Ecological Monitoring Unit (KREMU). Sixty-one Young Explorers took part in Operation Drake's Kenya-based projects, one of which was to help KREMU in a series of game surveys designed to coincide with the annual migration of wildebeest and zebra into the Mara reserve.

All projects undertaken during the Kenya phase were controlled from Nairobi, its capital. Here, as in Papua New Guinea, TAC HQ had managed to persuade the owners of a very comfortable hotel, the Norfolk, to lend them offices not 20 metres away from its inviting swimming pool. Visitors were greeted with a list of things to do or ingratiating smiles depending on whether they were expedition members or sponsors. Both came away with the feeling that the TAC HQ staff survived on cold cups of coffee and endless sandwiches as they once again tackled the impossible task of keeping everything going on resources stretched to the limit. Somehow Carolyn Longhurst and 'Margot' Barker kept their smiles, spending most of their 'adventure of a lifetime' behind typewriters and answering the telephone, their role as vital as any on the expedition. John Blashford-Snell was once again Director of Operations in the field running the complete Kenya phase from the main TAC HQ office at Kahawa Barracks.

The majority of the expedition, when not working on projects, lived just outside Nairobi at Kahawa enjoying the kind hospitality of the small British Army force there, sitting within the much larger Kenyan Army compound. Here a team of mechanics from the Royal Engineers and REME laboured day and night to keep our fleet of ten ageing Land Rovers on the road, as they came in from the outlying projects with broken axles, shattered windscreens and problems with the inevitable big end. Kahawa was the first taste the incoming YEs of Phase VIIIA had of Kenya. This extra phase was brought in to cope with the enormous demand for places on the expedition from all over the world and its composition proved interesting, not least because of the YEs who came from the newly formed Zimbabwe.

Rhodesia had passed into history only one month before the YEs, eight black and eight white, arrived in Kenya from Zimbabwe. Some, still only teenagers, had spent their adolescence fighting and killing their fellow countrymen and tensions clearly still ran high. The racial harmony of Kenya appeared to make some of them, mainly the whites, uneasy. The expedition environment, where young people of many creeds and colours worked together on an equal footing, was alien to them and initially some had difficulty in accepting it. After years of hatred and guerilla war, the chance to get involved in a totally different experience in a friendly black African atmosphere had a remarkable effect and helped them approach each other's views with new understanding.

The projects were split into four groups, Northern, Central, Southern and Coastal. Each was self-contained with its own camp and vehicles, needing, in theory at least, only occasional resupply of YEs, spares and petrol. The Northern Group's tasks were twofold: to mark the boundary of the Sibiloi National Park on the eastern shore of Lake Turkana and to survey the flora and fauna of the lake shore zone using an ancient fisheries research vessel, the *Halcyon,* now ungraciously used for transporting wages from one side of the lake to the other. Alec MacKay, a herpetologist and 'Chum' Van Someren, an ornithologist from the National Museum in Nairobi were to direct the work. The enormous size of the lake made the project a major undertaking. Another group, led by Captain Charles Weston-Baker of the Queen's Royal Irish Hussars, was to cross the Koroli desert by camel to retrace the route taken by Count Telki von Szek

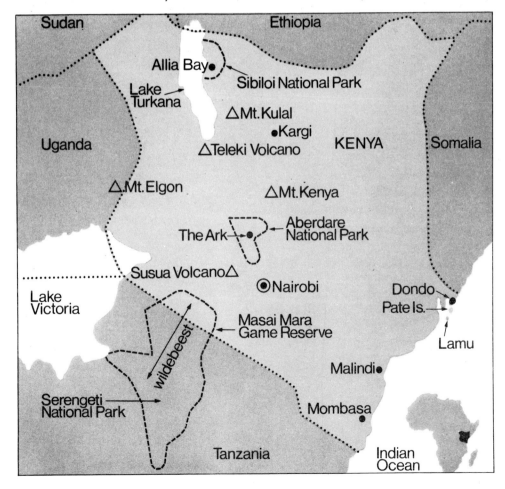

Operation Drake's Kenya based projects.

in 1888 which led him to the discovery of Lake Turkana.

Central Group, under the direction of Lieutenant Nick Ray and the amiable, rotund figure of Charlie Bailey, supervised the reconstruction of the entrance walkway to the Ark lodge in Aberdare National Park. The earlier structure, much to the surprise and unfortunate injury of some of the tourists using it, had collapsed due to a design fault in January 1980. The YEs cleared the site and lifted in 8 tonne prefabricated spans which they had made at the campsite, an enormous task as it all had to be hoisted by hand.

The Coastal Group not only contained the archaeology team working on the excavations at Shanga but also the diving team studying the marine national park at Malindi. Marine biologist James Dumont, aided by Royal Marine divers, under the direction of Sergeant Ian MacDonald, taught the YEs how to dive and recognise the components of a coral reef. They were then put to work on a transect survey of the intertidal zone to analyse the distribution of tiger cowries *Cypraea tigris* now threatened by that most persistent of predators, the tourist. The YEs also plotted direct disturbance to the reefs by tourists in the areas most used by them. All the findings were finally sent to the Kenyan Wildlife Planning Unit which had requested them to assist in the formulation of a management plan for the park.

Lastly there was the Southern Group, camped a day's journey south-west of Nairobi beside the Masai Mara Game Reserve. The route to the Mara leads down into the huge African Rift Valley, once teeming with wildlife, now dotted with only the occasional herd of impala *Aepyceros melampus,* giraffe or gazelle *Gazella thomsoni*. The road along the valley floor passes the hills of Susua Crater to the left and the perfect volcanic peak of Mount Longonot to the right. In between stands a huge white radar reflector, looking strangely out of place as it searches the sky for some unseen satellite. At the small town of Narok, the tarmac ends giving way to fine white powder almost 10 centimetres deep. Three hours later you arrive at the Masai Mara Research Station, exhausted and looking like an advertisement for a brand of flour.

Situated in a valley nearby was the Southern Group Camp. For the YEs, this was the perfect image of a safari camp; a semicircle of brown tents set amongst golden grass with only a few trees and bushes breaking the view of hills and rolling plains. Impala strolled a few hundred metres away and elephants regularly fed in the bushes behind the camp at night, cracking branches like pistol shots and making flatulent noises. A particularly mischievous group of vervet monkeys *Cercopithecus aethiops* spent their day sitting in trees under which the tents had been placed for shade. As soon as backs were turned they would scamper down to the ground and creep inside, later dashing out and up the tree clutching anything from a packet of peanuts to a pair of socks.

In August the herds of wildebeest that we had come to study were approaching the Mara River in thousands. The surveys comprised a repeated series of counts of large herbivores. These were undertaken from Land Rovers along predetermined transects, each of 50 kilometres, either along tracks or through the bush itself and equated to a 25 square kilometre sample of the entire reserve. All herbivores within 250 metres of the Land Rover, as measured by a rangefinder, were given a species code and entered onto specially prepared charts. The YEs noted the number of males, females and juveniles in each herd, the vegetation category they were in, their behavioural activity and the other species which were most closely associated with them. The work was kindly organised by Dr John Stelfox, Senior Resident Ecologist at KREMU and was directed in the field by Mworia Mugambe and his assistant Jemjo. From this data KREMU hoped to obtain information on age-structure and recruitment to the adult population of the various ungulate species using the reserve to assist in estimations of potential rate at which the animals could be cropped. Information was also needed on the habitat preferences of wild herbivores to see how they would compete with domestic livestock outside the reserve. Data obtained from these ground counts could then be compared with the results of aerial surveys. The particular habitat types occupied by different species during the day affects their visibility from the air and

**Zebra and wildebeest eye the Land Rover
with suspicion on a game count in the Mara.
Tall grasses almost hid the smaller animals
as well as lions for which we kept a careful
lookout.**

John Stelfox took the YEs up in the KREMU twin-engined aircraft to demonstrate the technique of aerial counts. This is a particularly difficult task to do accurately as bias according to species visibility and an observer's search image easily occurs. The work all forms a valuable part of a complex programme to study the population dynamics of this magnificent ecosystem in an effort to understand how it functions and therefore how best to utilise it in a sustainable way in the future.

The intention was to complete the first survey before the migration arrived. One group covered the eastern sector of the reserve, another the south. After two days of training, the YEs began their first day collecting real data. The high altitude of the plains (over 1,560 metres) make it surprisingly cold at dawn and, as the Land Rovers sped to their starting points, the first rays of sun would light the tips of 'red oat' grass, *Themeda triandra,* turning the plains into a sea of gold. This is the time to start, when the hunters are finishing the night's catch or looking for just one more kill, when the vultures circle and swoop to tear and rip flesh still warm from life and black-backed jackals pace to and fro picking at titbits. It is a savage paradise.

The migration caught us by surprise. Only a few days into the first survey thousands of wildebeest and zebra began to cross the Mara River into Kenya. They pay a heavy price. In places the Mara River runs deep and swiftly and many wildebeest are swept away and drowned. Their bodies, bloated in the sun, clog bridges and shallow streams along the river providing a macabre banquet for hundreds of vultures and snapping crocodiles. Nature is never wasteful.

Having crossed the river, the advance continues. The animals rush away from the thick riparian bush into the open grassland. Their characteristic grunting, bleating and snorting can be heard all day and all night. Male wildebeest fight to establish a hierarchy and to maintain a territory and a harem in a loose social organisation that is always on the move. The fights ensure that only the fittest will pass on their genes and, though often violent, they are rarely fatal. Gentlemanly behaviour is adaptive, murder is not. As the herds move the grass gets shorter until it resembles a dry, old football

pitch. It has been turned, amongst other things, into young wildebeest. In just four weeks the luxuriant grassland has been transformed into short-cropped plains. Over 800,000 wildebeest have entered the Mara.

There is, however, a careful order in this milling mass of wildlife. Why do they migrate? The grasslands are prolific in converting the sun's energy into available food, producing as much as 944 tonnes of grass per square kilometre. In May, with reducing rainfall, the Serengeti plains become progressively drier and when the primary productivity falls below 670 kilograms per hectare it cannot support a high density of wildebeest. They are forced to migrate northwards to the wetter and still productive Mara plains. Here lies a huge source of untapped food but, by about November, this too is used up and the wildebeest must migrate back to the Serengeti where the short rains have replenished the grass in time for their arrival.

The grasslands of the Serengeti Mara ecosystem support a live weight of animals equivalent to all the people in Greater London. How can it do this without destroying itself? Each species using the grassland is carefully adapted to use a particular part of the habitat. In this way competition between species is reduced and the grazing is actually enhanced, allowing a very high density of animals to be sustained on the same piece of grassland. The secret is the process of grazing succession.

Di and Howie, two YEs from Canada, were soon able to notice that zebra were often associated with herds of wildebeest and topi. Zebra were also the first to enter the

The migration has arrived. A seemingly endless stream of wildebeest has crossed the Mara River in the background and moves into the reserve. Beyond the river, more are coming.

reserve, their numbers peaking a few weeks before the wildebeest. Like most horses, zebra are adapted to eat coarse grass with a low nutritive value. This is insufficient to support wildebeest. First zebra eat the coarse outer stems, followed by topi *Damaliscus korrigum* which, with their pointed muzzles, reach the lower stems. Next, wildebeest with horizontal muzzles pick the now accessible and more nutritious horizontal leaves. Later the small Thomson's gazelles move in to clip the soft, young shoots which sprout after a few days, and finally the harvester ants and locusts get their share. Thus a complete succession of grazers contribute to each other's life support systems. Other species such as impala prefer a mixed diet of grasses and leaves from woody vegetation. The giraffe's agile tongue is adapted for plucking leaves from thorny trees and shrubs such as *Acacia* and *Balanites* and elephants, when not too numerous, avoid undue pressure on any one plant species by feeding on a wide range.

These competitor-avoidance systems are complex but vital in maintaining the carrying capacity of the grassland. The most destructive herbivores belong to man. Cattle, sheep and goats or 'shoat' as they are known, provide the main source of wealth for the Masai tribespeople near the Mara. They are excluded from the reserve but one of our transects extended well outside the reserve boundary in order to assess the changes that occur in the wild herbivores' distribution when domestic livestock are in competition with them. The effect was dramatic. As our Land Rover crossed the reserve boundary, the grass height dropped from almost a metre to a few centimetres. Moving groups of cattle sent clouds of dust into the air as their proud, tall keepers herded them towards a water hole. The number of wild animals was lower too and only giraffe and gazelle appeared regularly.

Improvements in combating disease result in ever-increasing numbers of cattle and shoat. As grazers, goats are disastrous, eating every last morsel they can find and leaving little for the wild herbivores. Poisonous or spiny plants take over with reduced competition from any others. It was perhaps ironic that another of Operation Drake's projects was to build two cattle dips for the Masai in the area to combat East Coast fever carried by ticks which cling to the cattle's skin. However, the hope is to improve the quality of the cattle, not just their numbers. In contrast to the generally poor-looking cattle, the wild herbivores remain beautifully sleek by selectively utilising the full range of plants available. They are unaffected by many of the diseases to which man's introduced cattle have failed to build up a resistance in the 4,000 years of their existence in Africa.

It is not by chance that wildebeest and zebra are often seen together in the Mara.

For the predators, August is a time of plenty. The herds of wildebeest offer a huge store of food for the lions, hunting dogs, spotted hyaenas, vultures and jackals. The life of a wildebeest is one of constant vigilance. On a particular morning transect count the sight of circling vultures was too much to resist. A short detour brought us close to the triumph and tragedy of the night's hunt. Lions, bloated with their meal, moved sluggishly in the grass while salivating hyaenas giggled and crunched bones with jaws specially designed for the task.

On a different occasion one of the Land Rovers stopped close to a pair of courting lions enjoying the shade beneath an *Acacia* tree. As Bill Bird, a Young Explorer from Maidstone, Kent, peered through his camera viewfinder from the tenuous safety of the uncovered Land Rover, he saw the male rise, yawn and then leap towards him. An adult lion could cover the 9 metres which separated Bill and the *Acacia* tree in about 2.7 seconds. This ability enables it to overtake prey from a concealed position with a sudden burst of great speed. Land Rovers are not designed to do this and, despite Mugambe engaging first gear with remarkable dexterity, our departure was less spectacular. Concern for expensive cameras, tape-recorders and lunch packs was instantly lost and replaced with an eager desire to scramble into the front seat as far away from the rapidly approaching lion as possible. Fortunately, the lion was content merely to display the power which maintains him in the position of top predator on the plains for, having seen off the bothersome intruders, he returned to a more enticing occupation with his mate.

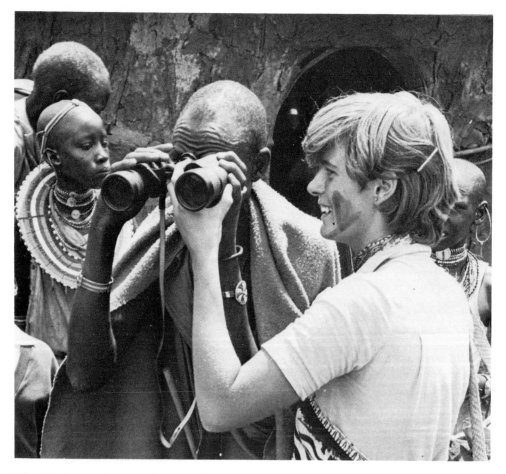

The Masai were always welcome at the Mara camp and invited us to their manyattas also. Clare Darrah, a YE nurse from London, introduces an elder to binoculars at Kilgoris.

Andrew Maara

Just when it seemed that nothing could alter this perfect life the one thing that we prayed would never take place on Operation Drake occurred. Whilst returning from posting some letters at nearby Keekorock Lodge, one of the Land Rovers containing three Kenyan YEs spun off the road and turned over twice. Andrew Maara, a seventeen-year-old YE from Starehe Boys School in Nairobi was critically injured. Minutes later, the other Land Rover, fortunately with Clare Darrah the YE nurse aboard, arrived. Helped by the other YEs, Clare put all her nursing skills to work and, despite his injuries, managed to keep Andrew alive for four hours but he died just before the Flying Doctor's aircraft arrived at Keekorock. Insuperable problems with radio communications had delayed them but it was unlikely that he would have survived, even if they had arrived sooner. Andrew was the youngest boy on the expedition and had been a particularly popular and amusing member of the Mara camp. His death cast a gloom over everyone there but work went on and spirits eventually rose. Then, incredibly, only a few weeks later, Richard Hopkins a twenty-year-old YE from Yorkshire died instantly in another Land Rover accident in the Aberdares. Set against all Operation Drake's previous projects, some carried out in extremely dangerous conditions, it seemed cruel and ironic that both these fine people should have died in this tragic way.

Despite these sad events work continued on all the projects in Kenya. With one vehicle written off, the Mara survey had to be curtailed and we concentrated instead on finishing the cattle dips. The data that the YEs did obtain has now been processed by the KREMU computer to convert the gazelle, topi, wildebeest and zebra into kilograms of animal flesh per unit area or biomass density per hectare. This can now be compared with statistics from other areas and taken at other times of the year, in relation to the primary productivity of the habitat. Animals in the language of a computer print out are less romantic but much easier to deal with. Information on changing animal densities is vitally important in the management of the reserve. Since 1963 the wildebeest population has been increasing at the rate of 10 per cent a year. The intriguing question is, when will it stop? When will it crash?

The camels are loaded
and wait in the first
light of morning for
the day's trek to begin.

In some species the crash has already occurred and often man was responsible. During the 1970s roughly half of the world's commercially sold rhino horn appears to have come from Kenya with the result that there are now only about 1,500 black rhino *Diceros bicornis* left in the country, a reduction of 90 per cent in under a decade. Contrary to popular belief, the horn, which is not ivory but tightly compacted hair, is not widely used as an aphrodisiac but as an ingredient in medical potions for the treatment of fevers, headache, toothache and other ills. Only in certain parts of India is it still sold as an aphrodisiac. Elephants too have suffered at the hands of the poacher

What price a rhino's horn?

There is little doubt that the world's rhinos are being hunted into extinction for their horn. Black market prices can reach $18,000 per kilogram. In the whole of Africa rhinos are now estimated to number between 18,000 and 20,000, yet just ten years ago, Kenya alone had as many. Now Kenya's population numbers less than 1,500. Between 1970 and 1976 Kenya, Tanzania and Uganda officially exported 24 tonnes of rhino horn – the product of over 8,000 animals. The only large populations left occur in Zambia, Tanzania, Zimbabwe and South Africa. The black rhino is probably already extinct in Zaire and numbers under 50 in Botswana, Chad, Ethiopia, Malawi, Rwanda, Somalia and Uganda. Restrictions on trading such as CITES (Convention on International Trade in Endangered Species)

could do much to prevent this decline and money is now being spent on anti-poaching methods, new reserves and making improvements to existing ones.

Kenya has banned all trade in game products. If other countries followed her example gruesome scenes like this gin-trap for catching rhinos and shelves full of horns could become a thing of the past. The alternative is that they will instead become our only reminders of a once magnificent creature. As with the elephant, the major task must be to show African and Asian peoples the long-term economic arguments of tourism and sustainable populations for keeping their rhinos rather than destroying them. As Kenya hopes that tourism will soon become its greatest foreign exchange earner, the arguments are not unpersuasive.

and are declining over most of Africa, including Kenya. The ivory trade begun by the Arab sailors centuries before, continues to flourish. A kilogram of ivory worth $7.25 in the 1960s sold for $74 in 1979. Between 1976 and 1979 the price of rhino horn rose by 2,000 per cent. Poachers now use anything from poison to automatic weapons to secure their quarry and a week's work to obtain a pair of 10 kilogram elephant tusks can earn them the equivalent of eight to seventeen months' wages. Fortunately, poaching is a rare event in the Mara and the fifty-four rhino which survive there enjoy a good measure of protection. For the foreseeable future, the wildebeest too will remain relatively undisturbed by man and continue their 480 kilometre journey around their ecosystem.

Six hundred kilometres north of Nairobi at the town of Kargi, a trek of a very different kind was about to begin. It was 2.00 a.m. in the morning and, huddled around the camp fire beside a lone *Acacia* tree, sat the members of the camel trek team, licking the last of the rice pudding from their mess tins. Richard Davis, our photographer, was there along with four YEs, two members of the support team and Hussein Adan, an ornithologist from the National Museums of Kenya. Hussein had joined the team to make collections of the animals and plants specially adapted for living in this arid area of Kenya. For him there would be the added interest of visiting the local settlements of the region, for he was himself a Gabbra tribesman and knew the region well.

Their journey was to take them westwards across the Koroli desert towards the southern end of Lake Turkana. The lake is sometimes known as the Jade Sea due to the changing colour of the algal blooms in its waters. In 1888 Count Teleki von Szek and Ludwig von Höhnel discovered the 256 kilometre-long lake then known as Basso Narok. They named it Lake Rudolf after Prince Rudolf of Austria. It is the largest alkaline lake in the world and supports the world's greatest concentration of crocodiles which flourish on the abundant fish. Less than 13 centimetres of rain usually falls each year although once it was much wetter and the lake waters lapped the shore over 70 metres higher than they do today. A second lake covered much of what is now the Chalbi desert on its eastern shore and occasionally, after exceptionally heavy rain, the salt flats of the Chalbi are once again converted into a shimmering lake.

Having reached the southern part of the lake, the camel trek was to follow Teleki's route up the eastern shore to Alia Bay in the Sibiloi National Park. Here Ian Gardiner, a Captain in the Royal Marines, was running the Northern Group Camp and Sandy Evans, who had joined Operation Drake in Papua New Guinea and somehow could not bring himself to leave it, was organising the boundary marking project. For Sue, Margaret, Wesley and Rusty, the YEs on the journey, the challenge was not one of avoiding the scorpions that were scurrying back and forth around their feet by the camp fire, but of withstanding the environment. The Northern Frontier District, as it used to be called, covers 40 per cent of Kenya's total area and has one of the smallest population densities in the world, about 2 per square kilometre. Most of the region is semi-desert and long periods of drought are common. The sun beats down out of a clear sky raising shade temperatures to over 40 degrees Centigrade. The land is barren and in the area the team were to travel through, strewn with boulders of dark, polished lava.

Teleki had marched across East Africa with three Swahilis, six guides, eight Somalis, fifteen Askaris and over 200 porters. Our camel trek, with seven expedition members, eight Rendille tribesmen and fifteen camels, was somewhat less impressive but no less exciting for those taking part. As the YEs loaded their groaning beasts, hundreds upon hundreds of camels belonging to the men of Kargi began sedately marching from their enclosures after the morning's milking and headed for the grazing areas. Behind them walked the herdsmen, dressed in bright red cloth, each carrying a spear and a stick and surrounded by sheep and goats. One question was uppermost in everyone's mind as they set off from Kargi towards the lake. How do these people survive in such a hostile and waterless environment? As the trek progressed Hussein and the YEs were able to study this and they quickly gained an immense respect for the remarkable ways in which the people, animals and plants of the region have adapted to life in the desert.

Moving westward from Kargi and into the Koroli desert, lack of drinking water, the intense heat and clinging 'wait-a-bit' thorn, another *Acacia*, made progress slow and extremely difficult. By night strong winds, cold temperatures and the sneaking feeling that a scorpion or perhaps a snake was about to crawl into the sleeping bag with you did not make for relaxing nights.

The scorpions of the Koroli desert deserve some admiration for the way in which they adapt themselves to their harsh surroundings. During the day they hide themselves in holes underground dug with their claws, so avoiding the intense heat of the surface and minimising water loss. At night they emerge and forage for insect prey which they seize and paralyse with a powerful neurotoxin in their tail. They obtain most of the water they need from the prey they catch. At night they shine brightly in ultraviolet light and in this way Hussein and the YEs were able to catch fifty-eight in just one hour around the camp.

Water was a constant problem for those on the camel trek. Water holes were often several days distant from each other and sufficient had to be carried on the camels along with stores and food to cover everyday needs as well as emergencies. Camels are ideally suited to the arid desert conditions. They have excellent resistance to desiccation and very high temperatures and can survive without water for over a fortnight, feeding on the succulents and thorny desert bushes which no other domestic animal will eat. To the local people of the area the camel provides meat and hides from which sandals, bags and covering for their huts are made. Even in the dry season they produce copious amounts of milk. They are used for transport in migrations to search for water and when it is found, regularly carry it over 25 kilometres back from the waterhole to the village. For our purposes they were ideal, capable of transporting with ease 90 kilograms of baggage or 70 litres of water in jerrycans strapped to their backs over the difficult terrain.

Anyone who had expected to ride the camels was quickly disappointed and found themselves having to walk beside the tall, skinny, Rendille tribesmen leading the bellowing animals. Having collected water at Kurkum well they climbed 513 metres to the summit of Mount Kobatal. From here, as the sun was setting, they could see their target, Mount Kulal, on the other side of the desert.

After 10.00 a.m. it was necessary to stop every hour for water and by 3.00 p.m. it

The camel trek moves slowly across the desert under the leadership of Charles Weston-Baker.

Hussein Adan examining desert plants with two YEs on the camel trek.

was too hot to continue. The afternoons were spent gasping under tall *Acacia* trees. Dehydration is the desert creature's most dangerous enemy and to avoid it everything is done to minimise water loss. Camels eliminate panting and oryx *Oryx beisa* have no need to drink at all. Whilst walking through the desert Hussein came across a beautiful, almost white, tree frog sitting on the completely bare stem of a euphorbia shrub, apparently quite at home in the full glare of the sun. There was no sign of water anywhere nearby, at least not within a radius of 16 kilometres. Yet far from being burnt to parchment, the frog's pale skin was cold and even felt damp. This was *Chiromantis petersii* one of the very rare species of amphibian that performs the miracle of desert adaptation. Unlike other frogs, it excretes uric acid (a very efficient way of reducing water loss) and can soak up night time dew directly into its body through porous skin on its belly. The females lay their eggs in balls of froth which hang on branches over pools in the wet season, moist and safe from aquatic predators. On hatching, the tadpoles drop down into the water and quickly develop into adult frogs which lead a completely terrestrial existence.

Sue and Margaret helped to keep a careful record of the birds seen along the route. In 720 kilometres they saw 145 species. Dry river beds and gorges had the greatest abundance of species including white-bellied go-away birds *Corythaixoides leucogaster,* blue-naped mousebirds *Colius macrourus* and yellow-vented bulbuls *Pycnonotus barbatus.* Beautifully camouflaged sandgrouse were the most common birds in the open desert and one species, the yellow-throated sandgrouse *Pterocles guttaralis,* was nesting. Incubating eggs in the intense heat presents severe problems for the birds. Not only is the air temperature hot but the ground progressively heats up during the day. Studies of these birds have shown them to be remarkable geologists. Before nesting they search the ground and choose an area of porous rocks on which to nest. These are poor conductors of heat and hence remain cooler than the surrounding dense rocks. The sandgrouse also has unusually thick plumage which not only provides protection against solar radiation during the day but also insulation against the cold at night. The feathers are also used for transporting water. In the morning and evening, the male bird flies to a source of water that may be several kilometres away. There he drinks and then soaks his thick belly feathers with water by walking about in the pool. On returning to the nest the chicks drink from the feathers.

Picking his way across the desert, Hussein collected cuttings from shrubs and plants for the National Museum in Nairobi. The land was dominated by thorny *Acacia* trees, *A.senegal* and *A.reficiens* in particular. Most plants had neither leaves nor flowers except for the parasitic epiphyte *Agelanthus zizyphifolia* which, despite its host appearing almost dead, was in full blossom. Its bright red flowers provide a plentiful supply of nectar for various species of sunbird. Digging below the soil surface revealed the tubers and bulbs of the plants that are responsible for transforming the desert into a green and flower-strewn landscape immediately after rain. Plants such as the *Acacia* trees, send deep tap roots down to the water table far beneath the surface whilst others have an extensive root system near the surface to obtain moisture from any rain that might fall. Sweet grewia berries provided succulent snacks as the camel trekkers continued on their march. Brown-naped ravens *Corvus corax ruficollis* followed the camel caravan for hours at a time, stopping only occasionally to feed on the blue-black berries of *Salvadora persica*. The reason for this soon became apparent when the camels stopped to rest. Groups of ravens would immediately descend upon them to clean off ticks and chase *Hippoboscid* flies that attempted to escape. Even the animal hides which formed cushions under the camel packs were voraciously torn to pieces and consumed.

From Kobatal the trek moved along the Balessa Kulal lugger, a main highway for the desert people of the area. From the El Kajarta Gorge they were forced to walk around the southern shoulder of Mount Kulal to avoid jagged lava and thick wait-a-bit thorn. On moving into another dried-up river bed, the Sirrima lugger, they came across a huge pool of blue bubbling water coming out of the ground. The water hole was unmarked on the map but there were thousands of cattle and goats being watered by their Turkana owners. Water holes such as this are carefully policed by warriors to ensure that nobody jumps the queue. A careful system has developed amongst the tribes of the area to ensure all receive water according to their needs. Later, when the camel trek was returning to Kargi along the edge of the Chalbi desert, they passed through land occupied by the Gabbra tribe and were able to experience the system at first hand.

Every water hole is named after the person who first excavated it. Though it belongs to him, he has no direct control over its use so that monopolisation of this vital resource by a family or clan is avoided. Nonetheless, he is responsible for the upkeep of the water hole. Whenever it is in need of repair, such as after heavy rain when it may need to be re-excavated, everyone who uses it must assist. A special supervisor or Jars Herrega, (literally 'the accounting elder') holds overall responsibility for the organisation at watering points. At the height of the dry season thousands of animals will congregate around a particular cluster of water holes. Differences in tolerance to desiccation means that cattle, sheep and goats require water every second or third day, while camels need water every sixth to sixteenth day depending on the season and whether they are lactating. A large meeting is held during which the Jars Herrega designates which day a particular herd is to be watered and the order of precedence. Anyone who repeatedly refuses to conform to the watering schedule may have his watering rights refused. Etiquette at the water hole is also important. It is a great offence for anyone who has watered his stock to walk off and leave a fellow herdsman to get out of a deep well unaided; everyone must remain at the water hole to assist others until all have finished. Such measures ensure that families short of manpower do not suffer.

Most water holes are dug in dry river beds. At the start of the dry season the water table is just below the surface and only a shallow hole is needed to reach it. As the dry season progresses, the wells have to be widened and deepened, sometimes to a depth of more than 10 metres. Under these circumstances a wooden ladder is constructed and placed in the well. Then, accompanied by rhythmic chanting, a chain of men pass water-filled containers up with one hand and empty ones down with the other. At Wanno water hole the YEs timed them. In one minute, four men could raise fifty-five containers from the bottom of the well and pour some 100 litres of water into troughs for the animals to drink. Only about ten to fifteen animals could drink at any one time and the remainder have to be prevented from stampeding forward. The water holes are fenced with thorn bushes to prevent the animals from falling in or fouling them.

To sustain milk production, lactating animals are given watering priority. To maintain this the Gabbra have a grazing strategy involving the use of core villages and

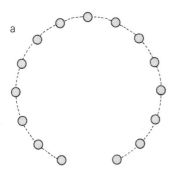

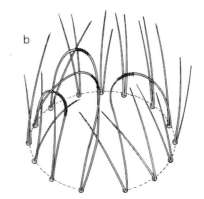

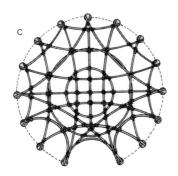

A house for a camel to carry

The Gabbra huts are skilfully constructed so that they can be easily dismantled and taken on migration. The circular shape is first marked out by a series of holes dug in the ground (a). When planning the size of the hut, the beds are placed inside the circle area to ensure that it is big enough. The hut will also contain a fire and a sitting room. Thin sticks, 3 to 4 metres long, are then planted, two in each hole, and the protruding ends are bent and wrapped together with fibre ropes to form the dome-shaped structure. To reinforce the hut framework some sticks are planted with both ends in the ground forming a semi-circle and others are shaped round the standing sticks and tied on with ropes (b) and (c). Once the framework is ready, the thatches are tied on with string. About forty pieces of thatch are needed for each hut (d). On migration the Gabbra take down this standard thatch and fold and roll it up ready for loading onto the camels together with the framework.

satellite camps. In the core villages, the principal inhabitants are elders, women and children and they try to avoid frequent and unnecessary long-distance migrations. The length of time that such a core village can spend on a particular site is largely governed by the availability of water and pasture. To reduce pressure on pasture land near to the core village the stock is organised into two herds – the lactating herd and the dry. The dry animals, bulls, bullocks and heifers are of no immediate use and require less water. They are therefore driven far away from the core village into the more waterless tracts of the desert where they are looked after by herdboys and girls. They may be away from the core village for over a year. Being very mobile they become grazing opportunists, using whatever pasture they find. Temporary fences are made at night and the herdboys sleep at the entrance to ward off any intruding lions or hyaenas. The heat and thirst of the day make for a hard life. Water is carried in a gourd hung from a docile animal's neck. When this supply is exhausted, the herdboys will dig up tubers of certain plants such as 'gaabe' *Vatovaea pseudolablab* and 'hammess' *Commiphora* sp. which contain considerable amounts of water. At the time the camel trek was passing through the Gabbra grazing lands everyone was trying to predict one thing – when was it going to rain?

Ceremonies to promote rainfall are common amongst the nomads of the area. In many cases it involves the sacrifice of an animal but the Rendille herdsmen with the expedition explained a different form of sacrifice performed by their own tribe. If water is becoming short, women from surrounding villages are contacted and congregate in the centre of the village where the ceremony is held. A song called 'Lalo-imeyle' is sung in which 'Wakh' (God) is praised and asked for rain. Alternatively, a male camel may be sacrificed and all the meat is allowed to burn, rising as smoke into the heavens where it is believed to change into rain clouds. If these methods fail a boy from a sacred clan known as 'Galdeylan' is chosen and made to sit in the centre of the village dressed in his traditional clothes. Then all the lactating camels of the village are milked and the milk fed to the boy. When he can drink no more the remainder is poured all over his body and he bathes in it; this at a time when milk is in short supply. There he remains in the scorching sun for the whole day until evening when the animals return and he is allowed to go home. The rain will then be expected within two or three days.

For people who have struggled through the dry season, the appearance of dark clouds and subsequent rain is their greatest source of hope and excitement. Every possible means is used to try and predict the onset of rain. Abdim's stork *Sphenorynchus abdimii*, swallows *Hirundo rustica*, and yellow wagtails *Motacilla flava*, are believed by the Rendille to indicate rain and, as they generally migrate into Kenya in October at the start of the short rains, they are a reliable sign. When it does come the landscape is transformed within hours. Giant velvet mites, *Dinothrombium* sp., the most conspicuous animals seen after rain, are believed to descend to the earth on raindrops. In fact, they emerge from small burrows in the ground. The Gabbra call them 'Ilmaan Waqa' the children of God. Plants respond almost as fast as the animals. *Commiphora* bushes suddenly sprout leaves and shoots and the hitherto dormant tubers and bulbs carpet the desert in green. Myriads of small creatures appear in the abundant pools.

As soon as the rain arrives, the Gabbra send out 'Aburu' (scouts) who cover long distances surveying the land for standing water and pasture. When a suitable area is found, the core village area which has served as a dry season refuge is abandoned and the entire village migrates to the rainy season pasture. The whole of the rainy season is spent away from areas of permanent water so that these may recover from dry season over-grazing in time for their return as the rains disappear.

Whilst passing through the region, the YEs were able to take a close look at the Gabbra's huts which are specially designed to be taken on these long migrations. They are made of intricately woven light thatch supported on a delicate framework of bent sticks. The raw material for the thatch is obtained from a sisal-like plant *Sansivieria guineensis,* which only grows in sufficient quantities on isolated and inaccessible volcanic hills. When in need of thatch, the Gabbra organise a large party which travels to these hills, sometimes over 150 kilometres away. There, they cut the fleshy leaves of *Sansivieria*, burn and bury them before returning home. After waiting fifty days they return with a camel caravan, by which time the fleshy leaves have decayed, leaving only very strong fibres from which the thatch is made. The fibres are beaten and then carried back to the village where they are woven into roofing material for the huts. A good thatch will last up to fifteen years. When it is necessary to move the huts, all their contents can be dismantled, packed and loaded onto camels in hours.

With Mount Kulal behind them the camel trek team spent three exhausting days marching up the eastern side of the lake, Count Teleki's 'silver pearl in the desert' and arrived at Loyangalani. Here they treated themselves to a roasted goat for supper. Unable to find any wood near the lakeside they ended up sacrificing a few tent poles for the fire. Charles Weston-Baker read the next episode from Count Teleki's journal

A Gabbra tribesman
reading sheep entrails
for signs of rain.

written by his 'faithful dull-witted biographer', von Höhnel. In his day each of three
islands opposite Loyangalani had been inhabited by a different tribe. Today crocodiles
are the only residents, the nearest settlement belonging to the Elmolo further north up
the lake shore. The Elmolo have the distinction of being one of the smallest tribes in the
world, their numbers dropping to below 100 a few years ago. Now they intermarry
with the Turkana and have taken on the ways of cattle herdsmen. Count Teleki had
noted that they existed entirely on fish, crocodiles and hippo meat. The lake water has
a high soda content making it taste soapy and fishy. It also has a purgative effect which
caused Teleki's men and animals much discomfort. Moving north towards the
Jarigoli lava flow, the vegetation began to thicken and the amount of game increased
including gazelles, oryx, the occasional giraffe and Grevy's zebra. Count Teleki had
relied heavily on wild game to feed his men but his accounts of herds of antelope and
large numbers of rhinoceros have, along with his journey, become a figment of the
past. After camping at the foot of Mount Moiti, the way north was blocked by the
Jarigoli lava flow and, as Teleki had done, the camels and weary band of explorers were
forced to move inland away from the lake. After two days they came across a small
spring in a ravine, very possibly the same one mentioned by Teleki and still unmapped.
Early the next day they arrived at the Northern Group Camp to be welcomed by

Captain Ian Gardiner and end their twenty days of marching through the desert.

The boundary marking of the Sibiloi National Park was going well and gradually a line upon a map was transformed into a line of brick cairns across hills in the desert The location of the cairns had been decided after discussions with Richard Leakey and the park warden. The warden kindly allowed the YEs to use his cement brick making machine to make the eleven bricks needed for each cairn. They were positioned by line of sight around the boundary, the bricks being moved in over the boulder-strewn terrain by Land Rover and then backpacked up the hills on which they were to be built. It was exhausting work in the crippling heat but the physical boundary will make it easier to protect the fascinating archaeological remains which lie inside the park. At Kobi Fora, about 300 metres of accumulated sediment lies exposed in several large areas, dating back as far as four million years. In 1972 the skull of *Homo habilis*, between two and three million years old, was discovered here. Sibiloi contains some of the earliest evidence of the origins of man. Underneath a small protective hut are the remains of a mammoth which once must have roamed the petrified forest of the lake's eastern shore. In 1979 the research project, directed by Richard Leakey, uncovered footprints left by man's ancestor *Homo erectus*, one-and-a-half-million years old.

Out on the lake itself the *Halcyon* was conducting her survey of the lake shore zone. This was an immense task, not least because of the powerful winds which could suddenly appear transforming the lake surface into a tempestuous sea. No comprehensive survey of the shore zone had been attempted before and the series of collecting sites around the perimeter and on the lake's three volcanic islands were already producing exciting results. The *Halcyon's* voyage had been split into two phases, the first covering the south of the lake and the second the northern area. Having arrived off a chosen site the YEs rowed ashore laden with tentage and stores and squelched through the mud to set up a temporary camp. 'Chum' Van Someren, complete with deer-stalker and long flowing beard, would instruct Carlos Avilia from Panama in the art of setting mist nets in a howling gale, while Alec MacKay would explain to

Sandy Evans lines up one of the cairns which now mark the boundary of Sibiloi National Park. These had to be strong enough to withstand elephants using them as scratching posts.

Elizabeth Sutcliffe from England how to search for molluscs beneath the mud or lizards and spiders amongst the rocks. Billy Chong collected grasshoppers amidst Chinese threats and incantations whilst Victor Mtasa fished both for the Museum and the table. At the end of the day bird specimens had been skinned and stuffed by museum skinners, fish were preserved in formalin, insects were carefully pinned and the last of the soil and water samples recorded and stored. After a few days at each site all stores were loaded aboard and the *Halcyon* moved on to the next site.

Over the two-month survey period, 149 bird species were recorded, almost 40 per cent of the total known for the area. Perhaps because of the time of year, very few of these were migrants. Lake Turkana is an important flyway for northbound migratory birds, many of which use the volcanic Central Island as a staging post at which to rest and feed. Its shores provide important breeding grounds for the lake's vast population of crocodiles as well as the African skimmer *Rhynchops flavirostris,* some unusual rodents and even an undescribed species of toad. The survey team aboard the *Halcyon* discovered that the island is now under severe threat from fishermen who use the beaches for smoking and drying their fish, the breeding grounds for their camps and the vegetation for fires. The berries and insects upon which the migrating birds depend in this harsh, desert-like environment are fast disappearing.

The survey was pronounced a great success, despite the burning sun and occasional storms, one of which destroyed the *Halcyon's* dinghy forcing a return to base. Meanwhile, back in Nairobi, stores and equipment were being loaded onto 4 tonne trucks and prepared for a journey to one of the most unexplored parts of Kenya. Surprisingly it is only about 45 kilometres north-west of Nairobi in the Rift valley. Thousands of people drive past it each year and some even climb the hills that surround it, gazing down on the extraordinary world within the huge crater of Susua volcano. Eleven kilometres across, the crater is impressive by any standards. Situated in its centre is a raised 'raft' or plug some 3 kilometres wide and covered in scrubby vegetation. A deep 'moat', in places almost 300 metres deep, separates the outer crater rim from the 'raft'. Thick with massive lava, boulders and thorn bushes, this alone is quite an obstacle to reaching the 'raft' but the main reason for its isolation is the total lack of water. The 'raft' has received a small number of visitors in its history, the most notable being the geologists and botanists, Spink, Richard and Bally in 1943. Owing to the lack of water, however, none had remained on it for more than a day or penetrated its interior.

Daniel Sindyo, chief of the Wildlife Conservation Management Department (WCMD) was interested in developing the crater as a wilderness area for more adventurous visitors, so diversifying Kenya's attractions in what is fast becoming its greatest foreign exchange earner – tourism. Dr Gordon Davies, the Canadian head of Kenya's Wildlife Planning Unit, suggested we survey the interior and John Blashford-Snell agreed to implement the scheme. Under the direction of Warrant Officer John Leach, a 300 metre steel wire ropeway was heaved down into the moat and up the other side by the sweating YEs. Then John Blashford-Snell engaged himself in one of his favourite occupations – blowing things up. Having laid a series of demolition charges on the edge of the 'raft' all retired to a safe distance. Two huge plumes of lava dust sprouted from the 'raft' edge, soon followed by the roar of the explosion. The far end of the ropeway was fixed, buried with rubble in the blasted holes and tensioned with Tirfor jacks. Slowly water in jerrycans and equipment were ferried from the crater rim to the 'raft' and after seven days when all was across, the YEs prepared to journey into the interior.

A group of twelve YEs led by Charles Langat from Kenya and John Bland from Zimbabwe, set out to cross the 'raft' whilst others began collecting animal and plant specimens directed by Ian Redmond who had joined us from studying mountain gorillas in Rwanda. Huge lava boulders and heat from steam vents made the work extremely tough and challenging. Groups of baboons, initially curious, became somewhat aggressive and on one occasion a YE found himself being followed by a leopard, apparently unconcerned at his presence. It is likely that these animals had never seen

Valleys and ridges make intricate patterns in the outer rim of Susua crater. It is possible to drive to the moat surrounding the inner plateau; beyond that the land had surprisingly never been explored before.

All hands on the cable to haul it across the gorge at Susua crater.

human beings before. An Army Air Corps Beaver aircraft which had been flown all the way out to Kenya by Colonel Mike Badger and Major Mike Sommerton-Rayner, who were affectionately christened 'Biggles and Biggles' by the expedition, parachuted in water supplies to the YEs crossing the 'raft' enabling the study groups to remain there for two weeks. The results are now being examined by the Nairobi Museum. The presence of large animals and also amphibians suggests that there is water available somewhere although we did not find it. Rock hyraxes *Procavia capensis* crept up to steam vents at night to lap water condensing on the stones nearby, so perhaps some creatures survive in this way. In the mornings the hissing spirals of steam and huge jagged, black boulders presented an eerie spectacle. Little wonder that the Masai who lived near to the volcano called it the 'lost world'.

The volcanic eruption that threw up the 'raft' also created Susua's highest point at 2,357 metres. Inside this peak, called 'Ol Doinyo Onyoke', lies an almost perfect conical pit crater covered in forest and still unvisited as far as records show. On the north-east side of the caldera, where the lava once flowed over its rim, is a complex of lava caves, perhaps some of the strangest and most extensive in the world. Eight kilometres of tubes, not fully mapped and rarely visited since the 1960s, permeate the volcanic crust. They are believed to have been created by outer layers of lava cooling, forming a solid tube through which the still molten lava flows, leaving a gradually solidifying cave behind it. These extraordinary tubes, up to 11 metres in diameter, run as the lava did, from the centre of the volcano in a west to east direction. They are only evident from the fifty or sixty places where the roof has fallen in. Guano from the myriads of bats which inhabit the caves was once used as fertiliser and the caves were also used as a refuge for Mau Mau raiders. Walking through the caves proved a remarkable experience and groups of YEs spent some time mapping the most accessible tunnels.

Kitum Cave, 2,320 metres up, concealed amongst the forested slopes of Mount Elgon on Kenya's border with Uganda is interesting for a very different reason. It is here that elephants go underground to 'mine' salt. Many animals regularly visit salt licks but Kitum is believed to be the only place in the world where elephants enter caves and in total darkness dig at the soft rocks inside with their tusks to obtain the mineral salt, mirabilite, they contain. The salt has a mild purgative effect which may help their digestion. As another WCMD project, the YEs were asked to construct a viewing platform inside the cave entrance and record the frequency of visits by the elephants. The YEs including Fin Davey from Kenya and Bjargey Ingolfsdottir from

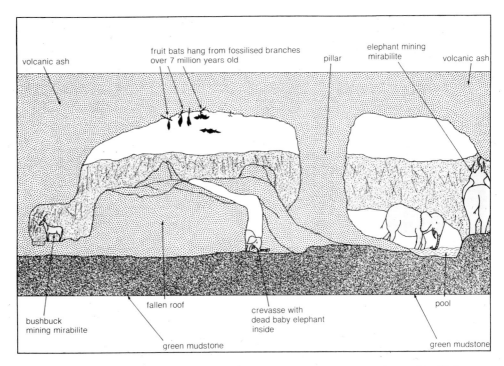

A diagram of elephants mining salt in Kitum cave. As they gradually erode the central pillar holding up the roof, will the cave collapse?

Labels in diagram: volcanic ash; fruit bats hang from fossilised branches over 7 million years old; pillar; elephant mining mirabilite; volcanic ash; bushbuck mining mirabilite; fallen roof; crevasse with dead baby elephant inside; pool; green mudstone; green mudstone

Iceland waited in the caves for several days when only the occasional bushbuck *Tragelaphus scriptus* paid them a visit. Then the elephants came. It was night time and the YEs huddled on the ledge above the cave floor listening to the sounds of the slowly approaching group. With hearts pounding and a mixture of fear and excitement they heard the elephants move slowly past them in the darkness and enter the cave. In the darkness it was impossible to tell how many there were, but their rumbles and grunts reverberated around the cavern, filling it with sound. Later photographic evidence showed the group to number over thirteen elephants. Marks from their tusks were found 4 metres up the cave walls indicating that the elephants probably stand on their hind legs to reach up to the cave roof. It seems possible that the action of not only elephants but also other animals which use the caves has in fact helped form its present structure. Years of scraping with horns and tusks have created a series of semi-circular depressions around the edge with a few pillars holding up the roof. When these pillars are scraped thin, the roof may collapse as has happened in the centre of the cave. A deep cleft in the cave floor in which two carcases of young elephants were found, clearly provides other hazards for the elephants but this has not prevented them from 'mining' the salt, probably for centuries past.

By September 18th the archaeological work on Pate Island near Lamu had ended and the teams returned from Susua four days later. Two other camel treks had followed the first. One was led by Dick Snailham, veteran of many expeditions to remote corners of the world. On the other Fiona Alexander discovered a new archaeological site, including tools, amongst the rocks of the Chalbi desert. The YEs completed a new path up Mount Kenya from Teleki Rock to Klarwill's Hut to prevent further vegetation damage that had occurred in the valley bottom. The mass of stores at Kahawa Barracks was labelled, manifested, packed and banded for its final journey back to Britain. The last of Operation Drake's major land projects was complete. A thousand kilometres away, *Eye of the Wind* was already sailing up the east coast of Somalia heading for Egypt. On board were Mwinyi Japan and Barack Wasuna, two Kenyans who had been chosen to represent their country on the final phase of the voyage and the return home to England.

The journey home

Mwinyi was a ship's officer and Barack was a student from Nairobi, sponsored by Plessey. Neither had ever imagined they would be sailing a square-rigged ship. Following their selection outside Nairobi, they had joined *Eye of the Wind* in Mombasa along with the twenty-two other international YEs on the ninth and last phase of Operation Drake. Like the others they were going as ambassadors of their countries and were looking forward to the final moment of excitement as *Eye of the Wind* sailed under Tower Bridge in London. Now all they could think of was clinging to the yards high above the heaving deck that seemed so far below and watching spume flicking from wave crests as the ship sped northwards to the Horn of Africa.

Eye of the Wind had left Mombasa on August 8th and immediately ran into steep seas and 40 knot squalls, making progress slow. After four days, however, she began to pick up the strong south-westerlies that had carried the mediaeval Arab traders, some perhaps having exchanged goods at Shanga, towards their homeland in the Gulf. She crossed the equator, entering the northern hemisphere for the first time since leaving it a year and a half before near the Galapagos Islands. His Aquatic Majesty, King Neptune, once again honoured the ship with his presence in the form of Trish Holdway and twenty-five souls were initiated into the Most Noble Order of the Deep, baptised in shaving foam and porridge.

With force 7 south-westerlies, the ship was averaging 10.5 knots and made her best day's run of the voyage, 251 miles. The Indian Ocean off the Horn of Africa is renowned for its strong wind at this time of year and sailing *Eye of the Wind* was suddenly a challenging business, with storm boards in and green water pouring over the gunwales. The ship was moving so fast that it was almost impossible to make any neuston collections. The net sprang from wave top to wave top, fishing the spray-filled air rather than the sea. The watch routine meant that groups of YEs rarely met each other except during changeovers, as the oncoming watch scrambled up the spiral companion way from their cabins below whilst the offgoing watch gathered in the galley for a hot cup of tea. In the daylight hours the eternal maintenance, chipping, scraping, painting metal work and polishing brass, whipping ropes and mending sails, occupied everybody who was not already busy.

After covering the 2,400 miles to Port Sudan in record time, *Eye of the Wind* moored off Coal Quay for two days to take on fuel and stores before sailing on towards Suez on August 29th. It was then that everything started to go wrong.

Fortunate though it often was, it seemed impossible for *Eye of the Wind* to visit any country without the red carpet being rolled out. This sometimes gave the impression that she was sailing a tight schedule between celebratory departures and enthusiastic welcomes often involving anyone from a local mayor to a head of state. The importance of such events should not be underestimated. Operation Drake was viewed as much more than an adventure for young people or a scientific research opportunity; it was a small but nonetheless important experiment in international cooperation between nations. The success or failure of a visit to a particular country rested on the support which the host government and local community were prepared to provide. The idea of an international group of young people under the patronage of HRH Prince Charles arriving in a country to lend worthwhile assistance was usually attractive to most governments and the response was often overwhelming. The arrival of the ship was therefore good reason for speeches to be made and receptions given, during which the crew would yet again recount the highlights of the voyage and the harrowed

'Crossing the line', a ritual as old as the sea itself. Diane Beer from New Zealand is initiated by Neptune and Davey Jones into the 'Most Noble Order of the Deep' as the equator is crossed.

organisers of the expedition could seek discreet support for any outstanding difficulties. Alas, a brigantine's movements are largely determined by the elements and despite Mike Kichenside's brilliant seamanship, important guests eager to see the ship were occasionally left with an empty horizon.

Colonel John Hines, who in the latter stages of Operation Drake, had become one of its most active supporters, paced the seafront at Port Suez in a not very clement mood. The Governor of Suez had kindly organised a reception for the ship and seventy influential Egyptian guests. His Excellency the Australian Ambassador had also arranged to visit the ship. Unfortunately, after leaving Sudan, *Eye of the Wind* started having engine trouble and the reception had to be cancelled. Now, a week later, there was still no sign of the ship although there was every sign of a second reception with guests preparing themselves for the imminent arrival, supposedly the following day. Being a Friday, the Moslem sabbath, it was impossible to inform the Governor of a second delay. What was more embarrasing was that no one could reliably report where the ship was. The only way to communicate with London was to drive 220 kilometres to Cairo as neither the phone nor the telex was working in Port Suez. The press started asking awkward questions.

Two hundred and sixty miles to the south of Port Suez the ship's rigging was as taut as bowstrings. She was taking heavy water for'ard as she struggled to make headway into gale force winds. The bowsprit was frequently buried in a cloud of spray as huge waves crashed against the side of the ship. Later the jolly boat was partly smashed as it hung from the stern davits. The main engines had to be stopped repeatedly to enable the good natured ship's engineer, Chief Petty Officer Brian Holmes, to change the fuel filters. The Gardener diesel could push the ship along at 8 knots under calm conditions but now it was only managing 2 and fuel reserves were getting low. Thirty-five miles south of Ras Shauliz and with enough fuel for thirty hours motoring left, she anchored to wait for the storm to abate. The YEs set to repairing the storm damage. On the fourth day they heard the sound of a helicopter approaching.

John Hines had managed to persuade the Egyptian airforce to lend him a Mig. 21 fighter to search for the ship and having located her after some difficulty, he borrowed a helicopter from Mobil Oil to fly out to her. Now, hovering above the deck, he lowered a message attached to a nut and bolt suspended on a wire. The rotors whirled unnervingly close to the mainmast and then the helicopter was gone. The message stated that it was not possible to convey the YEs to the shore nearby as it had been mined following the 1973 Middle East War, but that transport was on its way though the YEs had no idea what.

The *Alex Tide*, an oil rig supply vessel appeared later, courtesy of Aramco. Having resupplied the ship with fuel, water, carrots and potatoes it took off twenty-four YEs and powered its way through the waves to the oil station at Ras Shuakir. In a bus loaned from Tarmac Ltd, the YEs sped up the coast to Port Suez to the much delayed official welcome and the next day moved on to Sheik Zeid Camp outside Ismailia. The camp had been built by the United Nations for refugees left homeless following the Middle East hostilities and the refugees were still in residence. Working with Egyptian cadets from the Military Training College at Cairo, the YEs planted 1,500 trees in the shape of a Maltese cross at the camp and dug irrigation channels for vegetation plots. The work took several days after which they moved to Port Said and later Cairo. Here they took a camel trek to the Pyramids, two spending the night on top of one of them. After a final reception at the British Embassy and a presentation by the Egyptian cadets, the YEs re-embarked aboard *Eye of the Wind*. The ship with her skeleton crew had sailed through more storms and then the Suez canal and on September 25th, with a full complement, she began her voyage across the Mediterranean.

Though the Mediterranean covers only 1 per cent of the world's ocean surface it contains 50 per cent of its floating oil and tar. Around its shores are some of the world's most famous holiday resorts together with massive industrial complexes. It is now one of our most polluted seas. This has been so widely publicised that few of the 100

The storms over, *Eye of the Wind* **heads for the Suez Canal.**

million tourists that visit it each year can be wholly unaware of the threat to their holiday playground. A combination of two factors has produced the present situation; the large human population, both resident and seasonal, who use the sea as a convenient receptacle for their domestic, industrial and agricultural waste, and the slow rate of flushing and consequent renewal of its enclosed waters. Recycling takes about eighty years.

Eighty-five per cent of all pollution entering the Mediterranean originates on land. Coastal zone discharges include sewage from some 120 cities, 90 per cent of which is inadequately treated or not even treated at all. Poisonous effluents from factories and oil refineries are pumped or dumped into the sea. Thousands of tonnes of chemical pollutants, notably pesticides, are carried over the Mediterranean by the wind falling into the sea as rain. Hundreds of tonnes of oil are discharged from the tankers, liners, and freighters using its busy waterways. Rivers carrying pollutants from far inland deposit them in the sea at a rate which exceeds that of the coastal zone. However, the pollution of the Mediterranean is not new. The early cultures which flourished upon its shores recorded large scale die-offs of fish and shellfish following lethal plankton blooms, possibly caused by the enrichment of the sea from sewage. The difference now is that the sheer quantity of material entering the Mediterranean has been vastly increased and in addition, new synthetic chemicals, such as the chlorinated hydro-carbons in pesticides, are totally foreign to the marine environment and can have catastrophic effects.

Most sinister of all perhaps is the steady rise in the level of heavy metal pollution. Mercury, lead, copper and zinc all occur naturally in the waters of the Mediterranean but in some areas, notably near estuaries and outfalls, their concentration is enormously increased. As they can accumulate in our body tissues, the question naturally arises as to the effects this could have on the population of the Mediterranean. Following the notorious disaster at Minamata in Japan in which many fisher folk died from eating mercury-contaminated fish, levels of this element have been closely monitored. And nowhere more closely than in the Mediterranean. The world's major source of mercury is derived from natural degassing of the earth's crust which releases up to 125,000 tonnes per year. Man adds about another 20,000 tonnes. In man mercury poisoning causes damage to the central nervous system and can result in painful death. Food provides the main pathway of mercury to man. Micro-organisms in the sea can convert mercury into its more dangerous methyl-mercury compound which can be concen-trated by edible fish when they consume them so reaching man at the top of the food chain.

In May 1980 the United Nations Environment Programme (UNEP) persuaded all but one of the eighteen nations bordering the Mediterranean to sign a treaty designed to help clean up the sea and limit the emission of pollutants into it. Now eighty-four different institutions are cooperating in UNEP's MED POL programme, co-ordinated by Dr Stjepan Keckes at the Regional Seas Activity Centre in Geneva. This provided the background for an unlikely partnership between a helium filled airship and *Eye of the Wind*.

Airships, or 'blimps' as they are called, have come a long way since the leviathans of the 1900s. They have been used for anything from luxury passenger transport to long distance military patrols. Goodyear has built 300 airships since 1917. They agreed to let Operation Drake have the use of *Europa* for a four-day period to conduct a pollution monitoring experiment in the Ligurian Sea to the south of Genoa in northern Italy. *Europa* was built in 1972 and is one of four airships operated by the company in various parts of the world on a regular year-round basis. Of all the flying machines man has yet devised, blimps are perhaps the most enchanting. Craft heavier than air are all commotion and bluster next to a blimp. Even from a distance the sight of *Europa*'s silver, shining form floating effortlessly transfixed the senses as it appeared out of the sky like a harbinger from some futuristic age. *Europa*'s 60-metre-long neoprene-dacron envelope is filled with inert helium gas which could never ignite with the same

Inside the airship Herr Breder explains the pollution monitoring experiment to Barbara Martinelli, an executive with Pan American Airways.

disastrous consequences as the ill-fated *Hindenberg* which crashed in flames in 1937. Suspended below is a 'car' capable of carrying six passengers and the pilot. Attached to this are two aircraft engines providing thrust to drive the blimp through the air at a cruising speed of 56 kph. The advantage of using the airship and sailing ship was that both were relatively pollution-free vehicles from which samples could be taken; also the blimp could remain stable and airborne for up to twenty-three hours and float motionless over specific sites.

Having crossed the Mediterranean, *Eye of the Wind* called at La Spezia to collect scientists and equipment before sailing across the Gulf of Genoa to Alassio where the airship was waiting at a nearby airfield. The Italian Riviera was a remarkable contrast to the isolation and wildness of other areas in which we had been operating but with the summer gone the tourists had also leaving the delightful Italian hospitality and excellent food. British Caledonian kindly flew in John Blashford-Snell with a small team from the London HQ to co-ordinate the operation and the next day work began.

Eye of the Wind sailed out of Alassio looking magnificent, her white sails standing out brightly against the dark blue of the sea. On board Trish Holdway and the YEs began collecting neuston samples for Professor Aristeo Renzoni from the University of Sienna, a Principal Investigator in two of MED POL's projects. He supervised the work and was principally interested in determining the mercury levels of surface-living plankton. Herr Flucht, a German oceanographer from La Spezia, extended an enormous aluminium pole from the bowsprit to collect samples of sea water. By examining the mercury and other heavy metal levels in the sea it would be possible to calculate the uptake by marine biota caught in the nets. Dr Brian Wannamaker, an oceanographic scientist from the SACLANT Research Centre at La Spezia was also aboard gathering data on temperature profiles (thermoclines) beneath the ocean surface. An impressive bazooka-shaped launcher was positioned near the stern of the ship from which small expendable bathythermographs (XBTs) were dropped into the sea. A small thermistor probe on the XBT measured the temperature through which it was passing and relayed the information along fine copper wire to instruments in the ship's laboratory on the surface. This data helps in understanding the process of water mixing in the Mediterranean and consequently the movement of pollutants.

The *Europa* hovered above *Eye of the Wind,* its silvery bulk dominating the ship. Inside the car were Professor Wolfgang Nürnberg, Director of the Institute of Applied

Herr Flucht prepares to scramble out along the bowsprit to collect water samples ahead of the ship off the Ligurian coast.

Water samples are filtered in the ship's laboratory into contamination-free bottles before being transported to analytical laboratories in Italy and Germany.

Eye of the Wind **and
Europa team up off
Alassio.**

**Rosemary Black from
England with Mwinyi
Japan examining an
XBT. The spool of
copper wire pays out
as the thermograph
sinks into the sea.**

Physical Chemistry at the Nuclear Research Centre in Julich, West Germany, and his assistant Herr Breder. A special device had been fitted to the car which sucked air from its leading edge along tubes and into a thin glass section containing silver wool. Any mercury in the air would deposit on the silver which could then be analysed so providing data on atmospheric mercury levels. Professor Nürnberg, who ·is also a Principal Investigator in MED POL, was able to examine samples from fifty different localities collected by the airship ranging from far out to sea to just above factory chimneys in Genoa. Results showed that mercury levels were 280 times higher over Genoa than in the non-industrialised areas of the coast.

Part of the aim of the project was to draw the public's attention to the disturbing state of the Mediterranean. It is the home of the rarest seal in the world, the monk seal *Monachus monachus*, only a few hundred of which survive in the Aegean, on Sardinia, and the island of La Galite off the Tunisian coast. As a top predator in the marine food chain the seals are particularly at risk from toxic metal build-up. *Europa* carries around a form of Piccadilly Circus-in-the-sky consisting of 7,560 computer-controlled lights. Attached to the exterior of its envelope, these are capable of depicting words, sentences and even animations in a multitude of colours and designs. Floating in the twilight off the Ligurian coastline she enthralled onlookers with a light show in support of the UNEP campaign to clean up the Mediterranean.

Almost all the YEs who stayed with the ship had a chance to fly in the blimp, an experience they are unlikely to forget. 'Biggles and Biggles' had flown up all the way through the Sudan from Kenya in the Beaver aircraft to assist in the project and Mike Badger realised one of his dreams by actually piloting the blimp over Alassio. The sluggish controls were quite different from the highly manoeuvrable Beaver, but the enjoyment of being able to float in a circle or hover on the spot and wave to the crew aboard *Eye of the Wind* just 60 metres below was as much an experience for him as for any of the YEs.

The Riviera lived up to its reputation of beautiful weather and all the experiments were completed on time. The blimp headed off to Milan for a well earned winter rest, the Beaver flew north towards England, and *Eye of the Wind* sailed on to Gibralter. Just before breakfast one morning an excited cry from the masthead brought everyone on deck. There, not far from the ship, oblique fountains of spray could be seen bursting from the surface of the sea: sperm whales, a whole school of them. Captain Mike Kichenside ordered sail to be shortened and altered course to have a look.

The sperm whale *Physeter catodon* or cachalot is a member of the Odontoceti or toothed whales. The lower jaw is armed with forty impressive teeth, each about 20 centimetres long. These are specially designed to grip the giant squid *Architeuthis* on which it principally feeds. Sperm whales are capable of diving to enormous depths using their form of sonar to seek out their quarry which is itself a capable adversary. As the sperm whale rushes in to attack its prey, the squid, whose tentacles may be anything up to 10 metres long, grips the whale's huge blunt snout, perhaps seeking to cover its eyes. Scars from the powerful suction pads on the squid's tentacles are sometimes seen on the whale's thick skin. The squid has a well-developed nervous system, excellent eyes and salivary glands that secrete a poison as well as a savage beak. But the whale's strength and large teeth are more than a match for it and pieces of squid can occasionally be found floating on the sea surface as evidence of subterranean battles.

Cruising parallel to *Eye of the Wind* the whales made an impressive sight. Their huge squared snouts burst through the surface sending a characteristic angled spout from one of their paired blowholes. Moving effortlessly, their bodies arched in rhythm, they slid silently beneath the waves. It was not our first encounter with sperm whales. Months before, off the northern coast of Papua New Guinea, *Eye of the Wind* had encountered another large school. John Blashford-Snell was aboard and instantly despatched an inflatable boat in pursuit to film them. It was a family group of about thirty animals. Large males can weigh 50 tonnes and be 18 metres long so it was with some trepidation that they motored close to them and switched the outboard off.

Now it was quiet, save for the lapping water and the sound of the whales' approaching breaths. Twelve metres away a tail fluke rose majestically from the water. John had forgotten how large they were and beneath the boat, the blue grey form of the whale's head was rising to the surface. With not a little haste, Major Frank Esson started the outboard and moved the boat quickly out of its way as the whale went on, unconcerned at their presence.

Within the cachalot's head is a cavity which contains a thin, colourless oil. On contact with air, this solidifies and is known as spermaceti. It was used to light lamps before paraffin mercifully took over. The whales were also hunted for ambergris, an intestinal concretion possibly derived from the cephalopods upon which the whales feed. With time ambergris acquired properties which have made it highly prized as a

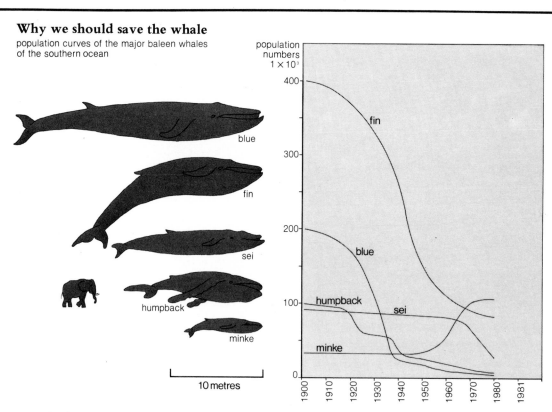

Why we should save the whale
population curves of the major baleen whales of the southern ocean

The figures speak for themselves. It seems unbelievable that the largest creatures the world has ever known could have been brought to the very brink of extinction and continue to be hunted, even in the 1980s. West Germany is one of the world's major traders in whale products importing 7,000 tonnes of whale oil in 1978 and 115 tonnes of spermaceti. The largest commercial whaling operations are run by Russia, Japan and Chile. Whale oil is largely used in the leather industry as a lubricant and in cosmetics. In Japan the meat is a popular food both for the pet industry and the human population. Substitutes for every kind of whale product are available, often superior to the original. The trade continues however as the cost of redistributing the capital tied up in whaling fleets is considered prohibitive. International pressure is having some effect and many countries now ban trade in whaling products. The European Economic Community's ban comes into effect in January 1982 but some species are already so low in numbers that even if there were a complete moratorium on whaling they would continue to decline for decades until their populations could recover their full breeding capability. The future prospect of harvesting krill, on which the largest whales feed, will need careful study if it is not to be the final blow for the whales of the world.

base for the most precious perfumes. Today the sperm whale is being virtually hunted to extinction and the plight of other whales is either worse or at least severely threatened. Almost everything obtained from them can, however, be provided more cheaply from synthetic or other sources. Many simply end up as dog meat. Owing to their remote aquatic habits, little is known of their ecology making their protection more difficult. The International Whaling Commission (IWC) is beset by the national and political interests of the countries involved and attempts to produce a moratorium on sperm whale killing died in a storm of confusion in 1980. Instead the Commission agreed to permit 3,523 sperm whales to be taken between 1980 and 1982 and this makes no account of those killed by pirate whalers owing no allegiance to the IWC. Perhaps it is already too late.

A curious sperm whale *Physeter catodon* **inspects** *Eye of the Wind* **off Papua New Guinea.**

Early in the morning on September 26th, *Eye of the Wind* arrived in Gibralter to be welcomed by General Sir William Jackson, a member of the Scientific Exploration Society. It was noticeably cooler now compared to the tropical climes the YEs had left behind them in Kenya but soon it would get much colder as the next project was to take them to the snows of the Atlas Mountains in Morocco. There was much excitement as the YEs boarded the hydrofoil with rucksacks and oilskins clutching camping gear and climbing ropes. Speeding across the Straits of Gibralter they arrived in Tangier and the following day took the long train journey south to Marrakech. It was not until the next morning that they got their first sight of the thousand-year-old mud ramparts of the city, outlined against the distant peaks of the Atlas Mountains. As the morning progressed the *medina* in the centre of the ancient city gradually came to life and the YEs were able to explore its minute alleyways, colourful bazaars and stalls. Metal workers tapped out intricate designs in brass, leather workers stitched hides from nearby tanneries, there were kaftan makers, wood carvers, carpet traders and jewellers, spice sellers and story tellers and Mauretanian dancers. Sharon Crockett and Joanna Hood, an inseparable pair since leaving England, bargained furiously whilst others went to watch the snake charmers in the main square. All around was a kaleidoscope of colour and sound.

In the morning a hired bus took the party into the mountains, 50 kilometres across the plains, up through forested foothills and finally onto a dirt road to the village of Imil where an alpine hut was used as a base. Hamish Brown, author and climber, knew Morocco intimately and organised the trek as a last piece of adventure for the YEs. The first snows of winter had brushed the peaks and the walnut leaves were sun yellow with fresh autumn colours. The following day, packs were loaded and everyone moved past the kasbah nearby up into the mountains. By the time they reached 3,150 metres it was snowing. A bitter change from the searing heat of the Red Sea.

Not everyone had been able to come prepared. Some with only plimsoles on their feet had to stop at Nelter hut while the others carried on. The new snow drifted over boulders and ravines. Progress was slow. Some YEs wrapped plastic around their boots to stop the snow getting in. At last they reached Tizi-n-Ougane at 3,750 metres and gazed out over a cloud sea stretching eastwards to the Sahara desert. The cold was forgotten in the warmth of achievement. The following day five YEs made the summit of Toubkal, the highest peak north of Kenya in Africa. On their way back to the ship they traded every piece of clothing possible for carpets, kaftans or drums and sailed from Gibralter on the final leg back to England.

When Sir Francis Drake arrived in Plymouth after his momentous voyage around the world he was a worried man. Had the monarch who had discreetly supported him no longer occupied the throne, his enemies would almost certainly have turned against him. He had set sail three years before with a fleet of five ships and 164 men and boys. The *Christopher* and the *Swan* had been abandoned on the coast of South America as had the prize *Santa Maria* wrested from its brilliant navigator, Nuño da Silva. The bones of the executed Thomas Doughty also lay in South America. The *Marigold* had sunk with all hands on board south of Magellan's strait and Drake had not seen the *Elizabeth* since she had turned back for England. Now he was returning alone

It was an odd feeling to be climbing waist deep through the snow in oilskins in Morocco.

with just under sixty men. The *Golden Hind* appeared out of the sea mists off Plymouth and drifted slowly towards some fishing boats outside the port. 'Does the Queen live?' Drake called across the water. 'In health!' replied the fishermen. Relieved, Drake steered his ship into the lee of St Nicholas's Island in Plymouth Sound and so ended his epic circumnavigation. Surprisingly, few people came out to welcome him. The black death was ravaging the town and most were at church praying for deliverance.

The Bay of Biscay had done its traditional worst in attempting to delay *Eye of the Wind*'s northward passage but on November 19th she arrived at Guernsey in the Channel Islands where she was slipped and cleaned before sailing to Jersey and a rapturous welcome from the islanders, the Bailiff, the Constable of St Helier and Adrian Troy who had done so much to raise sponsorship for the island's YEs. The granite shield she had carried all round the world bearing the town's coat of arms was returned to take pride of place in the Town Hall, and the Constable, Peter Baker, said he hoped that more would follow, carried by future expeditions in which young Jerseymen would take part. On passage to Plymouth she ran into the worst storm of the voyage and was forced to remain at sea for twenty-four hours, unable to enter the port. Then on December 9th *Eye of the Wind* moored alongside the Barbican in Plymouth Sound, opposite a pub called the Three Crowns. The green hills of the Devonshire countryside told the crew they were once again in England.

One last journey remained. The final ending of the expedition was due to take place in London where George Thurstan, now Director of Administration of Operation Drake, had planned the return home like a military exercise. The brown waters of the Thames flicked into small waves as thousands of people braved the blustery, winter's day to line the river banks near Tower Bridge. It was a Saturday and December 13th. Ships' sirens could be heard all the way down river as *Eye of the Wind* made her passage up from Greenwich and eager spectators strained to see who could catch sight of her first. Traffic halted and the ancient spans of Tower Bridge lifted slowly towards the sky. Just as she appeared around the final bend Biggles and Biggles in the Army Air Corps Beaver flew overhead chased by an enormous RAF Hercules transport. The YEs lined the yards and a great cheer went up from 10,000 people who had followed the expedition's progress around the world. A fleet of barges and river craft swept around the bend and followed *Eye of the Wind* towards Tower Bridge. And as she passed slowly beneath its raised arms and into the pool of London to a welcome from the Lord Mayor, tears trickled down cheeks in a mixture of joy, pride and sadness. Surely it could not all be over?

A traditional welcome home as *Eye of the Wind* **sails under Tower Bridge to enter the pool of London.**

Reflections

W hen Drake returned to England he commanded the richest treasure ship the world had ever seen. His sponsors, the Earl of Leicester, Sir Francis Walsingham, Sir Christopher Hatton and Queen Elizabeth I each received approximately £47 for every pound they had invested in the project, a return of 4,700 per cent. Drake had expanded the world's knowledge of geography and brought about significant changes in the Spanish attitude to Britain. In his message of support at the launching of Operation Drake 400 years later, HRH The Prince of Wales remarked:

> From my historical studies I seem to remember Francis Drake managed to elicit some discreet Royal support for his expedition, but only if the rewards from a little well planned piracy were forthcoming! Times have changed!

They certainly have, for the riches that we returned with were very different and, unlike the previous voyage, we were only too happy to reveal to the world the fruits of our enterprise.

Eye of the Wind became the centrepiece of an exhibition at St Katharine's Dock in London immediately after her return and many thousands of curious visitors scrambled over her decks, meeting crew members and YEs. In an exhibition hall nearby, displays depicting the projects on the expedition were on view including a simulated aerial walkway which proved a great favourite with the many children and their parents who clambered through it. On the last day Prince Charles came to meet the Young Explorers who had journeyed from all over the world to join in the final celebrations. Over half of them, 215 in all, were there. Charles Langat had travelled from Kenya, Bryce Bathe from New Zealand, Ernie Jones from America, Freddy Siu from Hong Kong, Jane Southey from Australia; all had raised the money to come themselves. This

HRH The Prince of Wales maintained an enthusiastic interest in Operation Drake throughout the voyage. With General Sir John Mogg, Chairman of the expedition, he visited *Eye of the Wind* at St Katharine's Dock.

was measure enough of the tremendous bond that had developed between the YEs on each phase and of their immense enthusiasm for the expedition in which they had played such an important part. The atmosphere of the occasion clearly captivated Prince Charles as he moved amongst them, listening attentively to their tales of adventure so far removed from the comfortable surroundings of the Tower Hotel in which they stood. When the last of the reunion parties was over there was time to reflect on what had been achieved in two years of exploration around the world.

How can one measure the success of a venture such as this? There are so many aspects involved that it is difficult to know where to begin one's examination. Four hundred and fourteen Young Explorers seems a tiny number when set against the world's unemployed and discontented youth. Scientific results will take years to emerge and even then are unlikely to change the course of international events. The real secret of Operation Drake's success was that it affected a great many more people than merely those who went on it. It provided an imaginative inspiration to thousands of people who, whilst knowing they could not sail aboard *Eye of the Wind* across some far off tropical sea, could still be involved, feel a part of it and so, learn from it.

The flood of applications to join the expedition from all over the world made us realise what a pitifully small number of people we could take, despite the fact that the expedition was larger than any previous venture of this kind. When Capital Radio, London's largest commercial radio station, agreed to sponsor ten people from the city, the expedition was provided with a voice through which some five million people could be reached. Capital became one of our most valuable supporters. John Whitney, Managing Director of the station, was keen to involve some of the many thousands of young people from schools who had applied unsuccessfully. Professor Brian Groombridge, Director of the Department of Extra Mural Studies at the University of London, was asked to advise on setting up an education project based on Operation Drake. John Baker laid plans with the Inner London Education Authority (ILEA) with Tim O'Mara, Capital's education officer, feeding him information as it came in from Operation Drake's headquarters. On each phase of the expedition the radio station had its own reporter aboard *Eye of the Wind*. David Briggs joined in Plymouth complete with silver jacket and mirrored sunglasses and quickly proved that he was as adept as any YE at furling sails in the Atlantic storms. Pam Armstrong crossed the Pacific Ocean

**HRH The Prince of Wales talking to YEs;
the memories of their experiences will
remain with them for ever.**

to Papua New Guinea where Linda Batt-Rawden, Capital's YE on Phase III, took over and stayed with the expedition all the way back to Britain acting in a new role as a radio producer. Tapes containing interviews were flown back to the radio station from the most distant expedition camps and relayed across the air waves to enthrall the London audience twice a week. This provided the spark of interest which allowed us to reach into London's schools.

A Cuna girl getting the message across to David Briggs, Capital's radio reporter in Panama. Her voice could then be heard all over London.

In all, 220 schools took part in the education project, each receiving a weekly news-letter, charts, photographs and slide packs depicting the expedition's progress and findings. Returning Young Explorers visited the schools giving first-hand accounts of their exploits. The response was remarkable. An estimated 25,000 school children took part in the programme, eagerly following the expedition and so feeling in a small way a part of it. It was not restricted to London schools alone. Linda Batt-Rawden visited many schools in Papua New Guinea and some in Indonesia. They too received material and pupils struck up correspondence with others in England on the same scheme so exchanging experiences from very different backgrounds. Some produced collages depicting the structure of a tropical rainforest or compared the navigational aids used by Francis Drake with those aboard *Eye of the Wind*. Papuan headdresses were made, songs written, plays performed and sculptures fashioned following tribal designs. Learning about projects in progress brought new life to old textbooks. Communication was central to its success. Questions asked in lessons were relayed out to the relevant person in the field and the answers later heard through the radio in the boy's or girl's home. The chance of hearing their name or that of someone they knew helped keep the spirit of the project alive so that instead of it being something happening to other people it was in some way happening to them. Here was a way in which so many young people who would perhaps never have the opportunities offered to the YEs, could take part and open their eyes to subjects they might otherwise never have thought about.

The expedition reaped a rich harvest of scientific and historical information. The remarkable archaeological discoveries in Panama were not just about the disastrous Scottish colony of New Caledonia nor the uncovering of the 'lost city' of Acla but of

**Schoolchildren in England at work on an
Operation Drake education project.**

the whole palimpsest over 600 years of human occupation. The realisation that we had also discovered, in the *Olive Branch*, one of the most significant wreck sites on the Caribbean coast of Panama was the crowning achievement of this phase. But for the YEs, facing down into the muddy slime of the moat or endlessly brushing carefully at the soil and dust within Fort St Andrew, the value of what they were doing was sometimes lost on them, as Hazel Preston, a secretary from Yorkshire, recalls:

> *Trowelling for hidden 'treasure' in the hot sand was not everybody's idea of fun, especially with the sandflies biting and the heat at 90 degrees in the shade. It tended to become monotonous and I fell into a semi-trance which could only be broken by Mark Horton whooping with excitement when I found an interesting artifact, like a piece of broken pottery or a nail! It was a relief when he waved his arms about and dragged me off to dig test pits across the headland. When I became involved in the surveying I did begin to understand how the fort had been put together, but how I longed for the 'Jungle Juice' break and the taste of lukewarm orange to wash away the sand.*

In work of this kind the historical context is all important in order to understand what is being revealed archaeologically. This necessitates a painstaking and laborious attention to detail as Mark Horton concludes in his Caledonia Bay report:

> Our historical judgements are clouded because our documents are so biased. The local population have had to live with their temporary neighbours, friendly or hostile, but have left no documents and few traditions. If justifications are needed to investigate historical sites, then it is the need to understand the background to the very complex network of relationships; to forget the drama and analyse the mundane.

Few YEs will now deny the admiration they have for the Scots who came to inhabit the inhospitable Darien shore and all feel pride at having helped to uncover a fascinating piece of history.

The mediaeval town of Shanga in Kenya provided another challenge. The initiative created by the expedition fulfilled the Nairobi National Museum's long-standing wish to survey the ruins. In a short space of time the whole site was mapped and many interesting discoveries made. Virtually no references to Shanga exist in surviving historical documents and the work has given historians a new appreciation of the town's significance in the early development of the East African Swahili culture.

Another of Operation Drake's major concerns was tropical rainforests. We could not solve the problem of the world's disappearing forests but we could add another important piece to the complicated jigsaw. The life of the upper canopy is still little understood but the walkway project opened up a new method of examining it which

The pursuit of scientific solutions to environmental problems requires understanding and assistance from every possible source.

can be repeated. Plans are now in progress to implement a three-year canopy study programme using the walkway in conjunction with other methods of reaching into the tops of these huge trees. It is only by understanding the complex ecological relationships within the forest that sound judgements can be made to ensure their survival in perpetuity. It is unfortunate that the demands of economic development continue to be given precedence over those of concerned environmentalists.

The biggest single obstacle in tackling the world's conservation problems is that of communication. As science becomes increasingly specialised it is removed further and further from the layman and often the development practitioner as well. Universities continue to produce large numbers of academics eager to study aspects of species, sometimes already oversubscribed with researchers, producing arguments which may appear abstract and of little immediate benefit. The Young Explorers responded well to those scientists who took the time to explain and involve them in their subjects and less well to those who did not. The World Conservation Strategy, launched in March 1980 by the International Union for the Conservation of Nature and Natural Resources (IUCN), the United Nations Environment Programme (UNEP) and the World Wildlife Fund (WWF) identifies three priorities for conservation:

1 **To maintain essential ecological processes and life support systems.**
2 **To preserve genetic diversity.**
3 **To ensure sustainable utilisation of species and ecosystems.**

This attempt to integrate conservation and development is vital for the two are indivisible. The loss of individual species is merely symptomatic of an underlying deterioration in the environment. The confrontation of the past must now develop into co-operation for the future. It will increasingly affect all our lives.

The work carried out in the tropical forests on Operation Drake impinged on all these priorities. The resources of the expedition enabled our botanists and zoologists to reach areas of the world which they would not have done on their own. This can reveal new information of great importance but it will not change the situation overnight. Perhaps one of the most surprising aspects to emerge was how little we know of the magnificent tropical forest ecosystems. Surprising also is the rate at which new things are being discovered and the realisation of how much we have to gain from them.

Working in them proved both rigorous and enchanting as Claire Bertschinger, the nurse who helped build the walkway in Panama recalls:

The hike up to the walkway camp was pretty tough, with 30lb packs on our backs. Up steep hills, through ankle-deep mud and thigh-deep water, wearing jungle boots, long trousers and long-sleeved shirts. I carry round my neck my whistle, my compass and an ampoule of omnopon just in case. One of the party collapsed with heat exhaustion but I managed to bring him round fairly quickly and he finished the march. The jungle is really quite beautiful around here. Small rushing torrents with lots of little waterfalls – lovely orchids hanging from the trees on the river banks, but if you stand still too long, dozens of ants will be running up your legs and biting you! There are enormous butterflies with wings that are black underneath and turquoise blue on top so that you keep seeing this flash of bright blue gliding through the air. And then there are the hummingbirds. If you wear red and stand quite still you will hear this humming sound getting louder and louder. You turn around slowly and see this tiny bird hovering beside you with its wings spinning round.

The walkway and forest research in which the YEs played such an important part is in the front line of enquiry into the rainforest system and the duties of the scientist to observe, record and elucidate were well rewarded. But scientific research moves slowly and for each answer a host of new questions arises. There will be little point in providing a solution to the 'rainforest problem' unless it can be done quickly before they disappear completely. Action not indecision has to follow on findings.

The survey of Morowali in Sulawesi illustrated this well. Here the YEs were able to

Claire Bertschinger, nurse, pilot and walkway builder.

see the dilemma facing governments requiring both economic development and conservation of the earth's resources. The needs of economic development at Morowali have been put aside temporarily but cannot be ignored. Timber is still required and thus an alternative concession had to be issued elsewhere to the logging company hoping to exploit Morowali's forests. Java, with 1,500 people per square kilometre, is still grossly overcrowded and families need land elsewhere in Indonesia. However, this does not have to be at the expense of Sulawesi's forests. There is much land already free of forest which is lying exhausted and useless through over intensive agricultural use following clearance. It is just that in the short term, rehabilitation of this already cleared land is often more expensive than cutting down virgin forest.

The work at Morowali showed us that the original shape of the reserve was inadequate to serve its needs. The Management Plan, drawn up from information supplied by the scientific team, the Young Explorers and supporting logistic groups, proposed changes and developments to the original plan which are now being implemented. Even so was the Morowali reserve big enough? The Sunda Islands, including much of the Indonesian Archipelago, seem to exhibit an interesting phenomenon and to demonstrate a basic rule which may also apply to nature reserves. The larger the island, the greater the species diversity of animals and plants within it. Thus the huge island of Borneo has some 1,000 bird species whilst Sulawesi has about 200. The forests of Barro Colorado in Panama became isolated into an island when Gatun Lake was formed as part of the

Panama Canal. Since then the number of bird species inhabiting the island has declined though its forests have remained untouched. When recommending the size of a nature reserve this aspect has to be considered, as in the future they may well become islands surrounded by development, agriculture or at worst, devastation. Morowali also showed that such theoretical considerations are rarely a part of the decision making process. Nature reserves are more often created on land unwanted for anything else. At Morowali the valuable chromite in its soils was contaminated and so uneconomic to extract, the infertile soils rendered agriculture unfeasible and the timber, whilst of great biological interest, was of poor quality to the logging company. Wibisono, an Indonesian YE, whilst examining the coral reefs on the coast heard of a black ooze in the soil near a village inland. On examining it he found he had discovered oil. Had analysis not shown it to be of a low grade the future of Morowali's forests may well have been very different.

And what of the people who live there? One could not help feeling that their brief encounter with the expedition somehow changed their lives for ever. Beneath the kindness and friendship there was concern on their faces. Our presence was an omen of change for them. Trade in forest products, which has made some coastal people rich, may now be restricted. The Wana's forest homes have now been protected from a much more devastating change had either logging or mining taken over. The change to their lives will prove inevitable as the modern pioneers of western civilisation, the cassette recorder, coca-cola can and quartz crystal watch, advance. Many isolated tribes have tasted the fruits they can bring and often want more. However, the change does not have to be immediate and need not be catastrophic.

Dimo, a Wana child from Sulawesi. What future does the exploitation of his forest home leave open to him?

The YEs were fortunate in coming into contact with so many different peoples around the world learning much from them and allowing them to reassess completely their own standards and attitudes to life. Eighteen-year-old Philip Beale was sponsored from Drake's own country of Devon. He was one of the YEs taking part in the hurricane relief project on the Fijian island of Moala:

> We found ourselves much to our surprise, in the tender hands of a very loving people whose hospitality knew no bounds. Whenever we thanked them for anything all they could do was echo those very same thanks, 'venaka, venaka'. I was invited to have lunch with one of the villagers. I was slightly taken aback by the invitation and he was bewildered when I rushed to get my knife and fork; Fijians all eat with their fingers. I could feel he was embarrassed to show me his house, knowing that I probably had seen many far more impressive than his own. It was his hospitality and kindness that meant much more to me. The house consisted of a few wooden pillars which provided the framework and these were sparsely covered with corrugated iron and cardboard. His household did not even have its own lavatory. With all his pride he offered me a piece of Fiji pudding consisting of crushed tapioca, mixed with coconut oil, brown sugar and spices. It was delicious, far superior to a poor substitute I had once in Soho.

Philip is now organising his own expedition to complete the first north–south crossing of Papua New Guinea.

The tall, thin Gabbra tribesmen of northern Kenya demonstrated how the co-operation between families and clans enabled them to survive in their virtually waterless world. Their houses, their camels and their bodies were tuned to the harsh environment as was the animal and plant life around them. The Masai to the south lead a totally different life centering on their cattle. From them they obtain food in the form of blood and milk, clothing from hides and fuel and mortar from the cattle dung. Masai teenagers learning geography and mathematics at school sometimes run away to become Moran warriors living in their round, all-male 'manyatta' settlements. Education in their eyes is a poor substitute for the spirit of valour and adventure of a Moran's life. The YEs met them at Kilgoris near the Mara Game Reserve and watched a magnificent ceremony as those who had completed seven years of service graduated to eldership. The YEs had something in common with them; they too were looking for a spirit of adventure.

The people of Papua New Guinea provided yet another contrast. Some lived on the scooped out pith of a sago palm whilst others farmed pigs and cultivated sweet potatoes. They had no need for jewellery, finding all their decorations from the forest around them producing a blaze of colour unmatched anywhere in the world. The comparative medical project was most successful in Papua, not only carrying out projects as an extension of our own survey of health in Panama and Sulawesi, but also assisting the government health department in West Sepik Province. It was a revealing experience for the YEs to encounter people living under the most primitive conditions and suffering appalling levels of malnutrition and disease. A new five-year health plan is now being implemented in the area which will greatly improve facilities and take into account the results of those first surveys along the border with West Irian. Even for the local Papuan YEs the opportunity to get around their own country was enlightening as was meeting the YEs from overseas, Seth Jupuc, a YE from Lae on the northern coast of Papua New Guinea gives his personal view:

> I found that there were many things that I heard and learned that were new to me. I felt very proud I had the opportunity to see new places outside Lae and had the chance to act as an ambassador for Papua New Guinea, live amongst people who do not know our customs and traditions, and who have less opportunity to see places like Papua New Guinea which is not known to many countries in the world and who still think that it is uncivilised. These people will go back to their countries and will tell their people about Papua New Guinea.

Caroline Buxton, a YE from Jersey in the Channel Islands, summed up her feelings on leaving Papua New Guinea in a poem:

Tell me friend how long you'll keep these moments in your mind?
The blood and sweat and compo trash and bugs of every kind.
Was that true life? The basic way in which man's fight began,
The fertile soil, abundant growth, where timeless rivers ran,
The hissing jungle, drowsy heat, burning grasses, throbbing feet,
Fatal sunlight, fiercest foe, cowards perish – have to go.
We struggled on so many times, surpassed our former best,
Falling over every root and fighting every crest.
We tumbled on in burning line, bearing silent cry:
'Exchange an English autumn for this scorching searing sky'.
I wonder which worked harder, my body or my mind?
My mind forced out the orders, my body following blind.
And yes, my friend, I loved it – I need another go.
The beauty of the people shone bright as any flare,
We talked and laughed and loved as one and made onlookers stare.
For when these super-tough YEs were saying their goodbyes,
We cried and wept with no restraint and left with swollen eyes.

Moving backwards across the Pacific through Fiji and Galapagos we come to Panama and the Cuna Indians. They have been in contact with successive waves of colonial occupation for centuries, yet their lives have remained largely unchanged. They seemed unimpressed with the expedition's apparently superior technology and gave careful judgement to our activities. Here was another valuable insight for the YEs. Perhaps because of their very strong social and political organisation the Cuna have resisted pressures from outside, absorbing into their lives only what they need without destroying the traditional fabric of their society. Also the changes to which they have been subjected have occurred over a very much longer time than is often the case now.

Operation Drake therefore encompassed many things. It was about science and research, the results of which are now beginning to appear in journals of biology, medicine, archaeology and geography around the world so that other specialists may have access to the knowledge that was gained. It was about international co-operation between institutions, between the Armed Services of many nations, between corporations and governments. For most of the YEs it was about exploration, adventure, challenge and discovery. Prince Charles speaking in the House of Commons said:

Many young people, I believe long to have the chance of tasting adventure, of achieving something through personal endeavour, or simply giving service where it is needed. Today, however, there seem to be few opportunities available to satisfy these aspirations . . .

The fact that so many young people applied to join Operation Drake is proof of how true these words are. For the YEs who went on the expedition the experience was sometimes unsettling, making it difficult to return to their former way of life. For others it proved inspirational:

The time I spent in the jungles of Sulawesi has got to be the most exciting experience of my life so far. I still find it hard to believe that they picked me.

wrote Ann Melville from Bristol, Pennsylvania.

It was like a dream come true. How can I explain to you all the things I learned from that wonderful adventure? I think about it constantly and when I close my eyes I can remember everything in vivid detail. I learned to adapt and feel at home in my surroundings, to love both the hardships and the good times. I learned to have

'I still find it hard to believe they picked me.' Ann Melville.

**Masai women at
Kilgoris watching
Moran dancers.**

Cathy Hignell cutting her way through the
jungle in Papua New Guinea. 'Putney
Heath was never like this!'

confidence in myself and the things I could do. I could never fully describe to you what it was like, it is something you just have to live through to understand. It is something that many people need but rarely experience.

Eye of the Wind provided a romantic link with the past as well as being a sail training ship and a focus for the land phases. The long Pacific crossing provided Gillian Rice, a medical student from Britain, with something new – time to think:

The weeks at sea brought me closer in contact with nature and the elements than at any other time in my life. Never before have I had the opportunity to ponder over wind and waves, stars and sky, the clouds and the moon, and rising and setting sun, but for two months they were my constant companions, whose beauty thrills me over and over again as if a veil has been lifted from my eyes, blessing me with an increased awareness and appreciation of nature.

Other YEs, such as those on the Balboa trail, met their mental and physical limits and on returning to their local communities, have begun to convey the excitement and value of what they saw and to organise expeditions of their own, gathering new people around them.

Papua New Guinea now has a fully fledged Drake Fellowship, with a growing membership based on the original Papuan YEs. A continuing range of community projects is in progress into which future YEs from Australia and other countries will be placed. The magnificence of the country is challenge enough for those hoping to take part. In Britain, under the Chairmanship of General Sir John Mogg, a new and impressive Council has been formed to advise on the future of the international Operation Drake Fellowship launched in 1981. Links are being carefully maintained with supporting organisations overseas. It is planned to operate on three levels. The first seeks to provide new opportunity and incentive to young people from under-privileged backgrounds in Britain, using the Operation Drake YEs as focal points within their communities. The second level will be to advise and encourage YEs to organise their own expeditions and other projects incorporating some of those people on level one. The third will be to organise a further large international expedition to produce the same kind of unique possibilities Operation Drake offered for science, exploration and adventure.

Around the world in museums and universities, the work of collating and cataloguing the data and specimens continues. Elsewhere new maps are being pinned to walls and fingers point to blue lines and mountain ranges. The experiment, far from being over, is just beginning again and it must, for in this diminishing world of ours, we still have so much to learn.

'Being at sea gave me something different – time to think.' Gillian Rice.

How the expedition worked

The atmosphere two floors below ground in the Whitehall basement was not unlike that of a tropical forest: hot, humid and vibrant with activity. Spread between five poster-clad offices were the people who occupied the power house which kept Operation Drake going twenty-four hours a day. It was known simply as Room 5B.

Aptly seated in the central office was Val Roberts, the Chief Registrar, one of those people without whom the entire organisation would have been unable to function. At her fingertips and in her files she held the names and details of every YE and project on the expedition. To the left was John Blashford-Snell, or JBS as he was known, in an office wallpapered with numerous maps depicting the areas we were to visit and a huge world map upon which *Eye of the Wind*'s daily position was plotted by his faithful aide Major Peter Marret another Royal Engineer. Here the land phases were planned.

In any expedition careful planning is crucial and also one of the most exciting stages in its development. Having decided on the basic idea of following Drake's route around the world and working in Panama, Papua New Guinea and originally the Sudan, it was merely necessary to fill in the bits in between. Here, the Scientific Exploration Society (SES), under whose auspices Operation Drake was organised, proved very helpful. Freddy Rodger a council member of SES, brought together a Scientific sub-committee and with Professor Geoffrey Haslewood, a biochemist and also a member of the SES council, he devised the comparative medical survey in Panama, Papua New Guinea and Sulawesi. Frank Whatley, Professor of Botany at Oxford University, screened botanical projects and in particular supported the aerial walkway studies. Dr Stephen Sutton from Leeds University provided expertise on tropical ecology. Professor John Alexander from Cambridge joined to represent archaeology and Dr Keith McLachlan from the School of Oriental and African Studies helped initiate the geographical projects. An accomplished marine biologist, Dr Andrew Campbell, agreed to suggest research work that could be carried out as *Eye of the Wind* crossed the world's oceans or approached coral reefs. Major General Griff Caldwell, who founded the Army Bird Watching Society during his distinguished military career, sought out contacts in the ornithological world and funds from the commercial sector in support of the research. Educational aspects were covered by Kitson Smith from the University of Bristol and I liased between this committee and the rest of the expedition, also co-ordinating the research programme in the field.

The SES has a network of contacts all over the world, many of whom have taken part in previous SES expeditions including the navigation of the Zaire River and the Blue Nile and crossing the Darien Gap in Panama. Letters streamed out to them requesting ideas and help. Slowly, the remaining pieces were fitted together to include Galapagos, Fiji, Sulawesi and the Seychelles. It was then necessary to seek the approval of the governments in the countries selected and to request them to suggest projects in which we could assist, as well as implementing our own. Now was the time for overseas committees to be formed.

Panama knew SES well from the Darien Gap expedition which had taken place eight years before. General Omar Torrijos, now commanding the armed forces, gave much support to our plans there as did His Excellency Mr John Sanders the British Ambassador, Eric Brewis of BAT and Billy St Malo, now Panama's representative on the Council of the International Drake Fellowship. In Papua New Guinea, Colonel Ken Noga of the Papua New Guinea Defence Force chaired the steering committee, assisted by Nigel Porteous, an old school friend of John Blashford-Snell's from Jersey. John Girling provided much needed advice and his wife Ida counselled the expedition over likely health problems. Later they were to form the PNG Drake Fellowship. Support also came from many others in the commercial and trading community.

Next it was Indonesia's turn. John Blower, head of the FAO National Parks Development Project there, suggested the survey of Morowali and brought in the support of the World Wildlife Fund. The Director of the Indonesian Institute of Sciences, Dr Didin Sastrapradja, agreed to chair the committee. Dr Julius Tahija, President of Caltex in Indonesia also served on the committee providing immense assistance as did Robin Leonard, Director of BAT Indonesia, who raised sufficient funds locally to sponsor Indonesian scientists and students to take part. His Excellency Mr Terence O'Brien, the British Ambassador, gave unstinting support and later found himself perched high on our aerial walkway watching his wife learning to absail down a rope from a tree platform 2,000 kilometres away from his embassy in Jakarta.

With the cancellation of the Sudan phase John Sutton, after some gentle persuasion from the Prince of Wales whom he knew well, agreed to chair the Kenyan committee with Daniel Sindiyo, Director of the WCMD and Richard Leakey to advise on projects. Plans steadily crystallised prior to each phase and underground in Room 5B we peered excitedly at the maps and blue lines that were rivers along which the YEs would soon be travelling.

Further down the dingy passage was Jim Masters with the job of selecting the Young Explorers from the thousands of applicants. Friends and contacts in Britain agreed to be county representatives and helped to organise the selection weekends. Britain was only one of the twenty-seven countries involved, however, and funds then had to be raised to sponsor all the YEs selected, under the direction of George Thurstan. Following the initial generous donation made by Mr Walter Annenberg, which effectively launched Operation Drake, thousands of letters were sent and visits made to potential sponsors. Donations rapidly came in, ranging from £50,000 to £5 from a Sunday School class. Frank Taylor, Financial Controller at Esso Petroleum in London, acting as Honorary Treasurer maintained a critical eye on the accounts.

Outside Britain, Sir Gordon White of the Hanson Trust formed the American Committee with Sir Gordon Booth, at the time British Consul General in New York. In Canada Outward Bound began raising funds and selecting the YEs later followed by the Canadian Committee chaired by Douglas Murray. Dennis Cordner, Managing Director of ICI in Melbourne energetically chaired the Australian Committee setting up a complete network in the country whilst John Chapman-Smith, a former medical officer on the Zaire River Expedition, organised New Zealand. In each country mini Room 5Bs emerged as the net spread further.

Though almost £900,000 in cash was raised, much more was needed in terms of goods and help in kind. This came under the department of dulcet-toned Ruth Mindel, which she ran from offices kindly provided by the Gestetner Corporation. Her persuasiveness was enough to send any sponsor reaching for his catalogue to see what could be donated. The range of goods provided was immense. Batchelors kept us well fed with lightweight dried foods, ideal for an expedition on the move. BP fuelled *Eye of the Wind*'s engines around the world, Halls Barton provided ropes for the rigging, Gallenkamp fitted out the laboratory, Avon helped with inflatable boats, Swartz gave spices and Ansul fire prevention gear for the ship, Silva donated compasses and Tri Wall, containers for us to put everything in, Calor gave us gas and Husqvarna provided chainsaws with which to build our camps. An ever changing collection of attractive 'Charlie's Angels' assisted Ruth and JBS in this global search. The most enduring 'Angel' of them all must have been Barbara Martinelli, who with her husband Vince netted many a New York sponsor.

At an army training depot on England's south coast enormous, barrel-chested Lieutenant Colonel Ernie Durey presided as expedition Quartermaster over the 60 tonnes of stores that were needed for each land phase. His boundless good humour

The man behind the camera one never normally sees, Chris Sainsbury. He sailed right round the world on *Eye of the Wind* recording as much of the voyage as possible on ciné film and stills.

enabled him and his men to carry out the laborious task of manifesting, packing and labelling the countless boxes destined for some of the most inaccessible places in the world. Everything had to arrive in perfect condition whether it was an outboard motor or a delicate balance. Somehow these boxes had to be moved from the Dorset country-side to an airstrip at Caledonia Bay or the jungles of Papua New Guinea. This was back to Jim's department.

Jim, himself a retired army Quartermaster, had the extraordinary knack of seeking the impossible and working forward from there. When the answer 'no' came back he simply carried on with his request as though nothing had happened. Such was the case with the RAF who provided incalculable support, moving tonnes of stores to remote airstrips in their Hercules C130 transports. These were during routine training flights and provided the pilots with challenging new opportunities to test their skills. When they had seats available the RAF's VC10 aircraft carried scientists and support groups along their normal route to Hong Kong where the 7th Gurkah Transport Regiment kindly allowed us to use their barracks as a staging post to the East. The most expensive part of an expedition's budget is often the airfare component. Here the world's airlines came to our aid. British Caledonian helped to fly people to Panama and the American YEs flew all over the world with Pan Am. Cathay Pacific took the teams on from Hong Kong to Papua and Indonesia whilst Kenya Airways helped with flights to Nairobi and Quantas and Air New Zealand also assisted. Local airlines such as Tal Air in New Guinea moved doctors to tiny villages in Twin Otters and Garuda carried scientists across the vastness of Indonesia.

Most stores could not be moved by air and Jim had to approach the shipping lines.

'I was just an ordinary camel handler until I discovered that anything could and did happen on Operation Drake.' Dick Snailham.

They responded generously. Pacific Steam Navigation Company sent hundreds of boxes to Colon in Panama, Bank Line helped us to Papua New Guinea, Ben Line took 80 tonnes of stores to Java and Clan Ellerman sailed with Land Rovers and stores to Kenya. In all, 300 tonnes of stores were transported by sea to the expedition areas and the number of passenger miles flown equated to journeying to the moon and back seven and a half times!

The complicated nature of such an expedition is hard to imagine. At any one time there may have been 120 scientists, YEs and support groups scattered across Papua's inhospitable mountains, while YE selection weekends were being arranged in Canada or New Zealand, a reconnaissance trip was in progress in Sulawesi, *Eye of the Wind* needed fuel in the Bismarck Archipelago and funds had to be raised in Britain. The whole basis of the expedition relied upon accurate information as to what was going on where and that required instant and reliable communications.

In most of the areas we were operating in, either the telephones were hopelessly unreliable or they simply did not exist. Therefore we had to use radios. The days of complicated tuning and Donald Duck voices are over in the field of advanced radio communications. Plessey's 320 and MEL's 321 radios, with expert operators from the Royal Corps of Signals, enabled us to talk clearly from beneath a Papuan palm tree direct to 30 Signals Regiment base at Blandford in England and thence to Jim Masters or George Thurstan in Room 5B. The signals bouncing off the ionosphere from the other side of the world were as clear as a telephone call from across the street. Marconi's no less efficient sets allowed us to keep in regular contact with the ship anywhere in the world whilst the RACAL and Drake 7 Ham radios provided other links. Behind John Blashford-Snell's desk in Room 5B all incoming and outgoing communications were pinned to boards, our eyes on projects in progress at the tips of the expedition's fingers. Press-worthy pieces of information were fed to the Public Relations Committee under

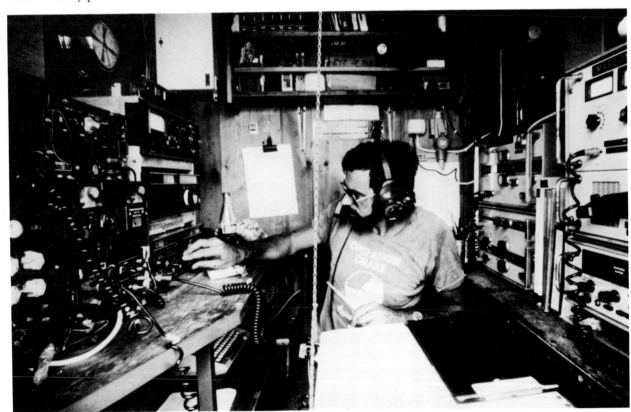

From *Eye of the Wind's* **radio room, Signaller Bill Martin could talk to the rest of the world.**

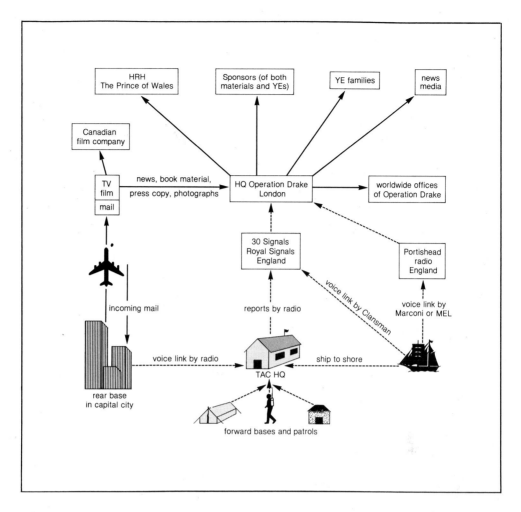

Operation Drake could only succeed with instant and reliable communication. This enabled the expedition teams to send news of events deep in the jungle back to the HQ in London and so to the rest of the world.

Sir David Checketts, formerly the Private Secretary to Prince Charles. Photographs were continually added to the ever growing collection at Room 5B having been sorted by Nigel Lang, a former Phase I YE sponsored by Kodak. Most of them were taken on Kodak film by the expedition members or our professional photographers, Chris Sainsbury, Rupert Ridgeway and Richard Davis. The stories were then channelled, through the tireless Beth Barrington-Haynes at Nielson McCarthy in London, to television, radio and the newspapers and so to the rest of the world.

Around the globe roughly 2,000 people became involved in the process of running the expedition and supporting the 800 expedition members and over 400 YEs that took part. The Armies, Navies, and Airforces of Panama, Papua New Guinea, Australia, Indonesia, Kenya, Fiji and the United States all played a vital role in the success of the expedition as did the many signallers, mechanics, engineers and administrators from the British Armed Forces. To mention everyone is of course impossible. But no expedition of this size would have survived or even begun without the constant support of its sponsors. It is to them that we owe our greatest thanks for, without them, not a single insect would have been collected and not one YE would have climbed a mountain to gaze on the land of his dreams.

The organisers
and the projects

Patron: HRH The Prince of Wales KG KT GCB
President: Walter H Annenberg KBE

Executive
Chairman: General Sir John Mogg GCB CBE DSO DL
Director of Operations: Lt. Col. J N Blashford-Snell
MBE RE
Director of Logistics and Personnel: Jim Masters
Chairman of Publicity Committee: Sir David Checketts
KCVO
Chairman of Scientific Committee: Freddy Rodger
MD MCh FRCS DOMS
Director of Administration: George Thurstan
Chairman of Ship's Committee: Maldwin Drummond
DL JP
Foreign Affairs: George Baker CBE VRD
Treasurer: Frank Taylor BA CA JDip MA
Procurement and Public Relations: Ruth Mindel
Scientific Co-ordinator: Andrew Mitchell BSc
Chief Registrar: Val Roberts

Eye of the Wind
Master: Captain Michael Kichenside, Captain Patrick
Collis
Mate: Tiger Timbs
Purser/Nurse: Leslie Reiter
Bosun: Bruce Phillips, Guy Clarkson
Watchkeepers: Spider Anderson, Steven Glenn, Maj.
Frank Esson, Robert Clinton, Capt. Keith Jolly, Borkur
Arnvidarson, Ulfar Danielsson
Engineers: Cpl. Steve Merritt, CMEMN(P) Brian
Holmes, CMEMN(P) Bob Coupland, CPO Richard
Shrimpton
Signallers: Cpl. Roger Secker, WOI Graham
Widdowson, Cpl. Bill Martin, Capt. James Heck
Doctors: Dr Nigel Pearce, Dr Hugh Savill, Dr Jonathan
Haig, Dr David Nixon
Capital Radio Reporters: David Briggs, Pam
Armstrong, Linda Batt-Rawden
Marine Biologist: Dr Patricia Holdway
Photographer/Watchkeeper: Christopher Sainsbury

Atlantic Crossing
1 Distribution of neuston and pollution at the ocean
surface: Dr Patricia Holdway (This project was carried
out on all ocean voyages of *Eye of the Wind*.)
2 Thermometric survey of crater lake of the volcano La
Soufrière, St Vincent Island: Dr Patricia Holdway

Panama
Director of Operations: Lt. Col. J N Blashford-Snell
HQ Staff: Kim Batty, Sara Everett, Lilly Dawson
Field Leaders: Maj. Jeremy Groves, Maj. Alan Westcob,
George Thurstan
Quartermaster: Lt. Col. Larry Batty, Capt. Jim Winter
Engineer: Sgt. Mike Christy
Boat Officer: Sgt. Ben Cartwright
Signals: S. Sgt. Steve Gair

1 Survey and excavation of the Scottish colony of New
Caledonia and the Spanish settlement of Acla: Mark
Horton, Andrew Hunter, Maria Mabee, Debbie
Fulford
2 Discovery of wreck of the *Olive Branch*. Diving
leaders: Flt. Lt. Mike Cameron, Cpl. Brian Ranner
Marine archaeologist: Meredith Sassoon
3 Aerial walkway project: Dr Andrew Sugden, Dr
William Wint, Dr Peter Hudson, Cathy Mackenzie,
Caroline Ash
4 Medical research project: Dr Nigel Pearce
5 Ecology of Geoffroy's tamarin *Saguinus oedipus
geoffroyi*: Nick Lindsay
6 Balboa Patrol: George Thurstan
7 Gold Mines of Cana: Lt. Col. J N Blashford-Snell

Pacific Crossing
1 Coastal biological survey, Corcovado National Park,
Costa Rica: Dr Patricia Holdway
2 Botanical and zoological collections, Cocos Island:
Dr Patricia Holdway
3 Galapagos:
Ecology of *Geochelone elephantopus*: Dr Ian Swingland
Behaviour of *Halobates robustus*: Dr John Treherne
and Dr William Foster
Assistance to Charles Darwin Research Station
4 Fiji: Hurricane relief work on Moala Island: Rupert
Grey, Maj. Frank Esson

Papua New Guinea

Director of Operations: Lt. Col. J N Blashford-Snell
Field Leaders: Maj. Roger Chapman, Capt. Anthony Evans, Mike Gambier, Lt. Col. Robin Jordan, Robert Roethenmund
TAC HQ Staff: Capt. Mike Knox (Ops Officer), 3rd Officer Clare Downham, Cathryn Barker, Sara Spicer-Few
Quartermasters: Lt. Nick Ray, WOl Len Chandler
Signals: Sgt. Peter Lavers
Engineer/Workshops: Sgt. Louis Gallagher, WOll Les Winterburn

Scientific Projects at Buso

1 Aerial walkway project: Dr Michael Swain, Dr Angela Wilkins, Dr William Wint, Estelle van der Watt, Benjamin Gaskell
2 Physiology of the leaf in its environment and nitrogen fixation in lowland rainforest leaves: Dr David Lamb, Dr David Yates, Stephen Goosem
3 Ion regulatory physiology of freshwater invertebrates: Dr Roger Stobbart
4 Blood-sucking insects associated with arboreal animal reservoirs of human disease: Dr Robert Domrow, Dr Ian Fanning
5 Collections of plant-parasitic and sap-sucking bugs (Homoptera): Jon Martin
6 Ecology of intertidal snails: Dr Laurence Cook
7 Ornithological survey: Dr Peter Driscoll

Medical research

8 Comparative medical research project at Buso and Vanimo: Dr Hugh Savill, Dr Valerie Robson, Dr David Roberts, Sister Sheila Kerr, Nurse Claire Bertschinger
9 Medical Survey in West Sepik Province: Dr David Bowdler

Strickland and Fly River Survey

10 Exploration of the Strickland Gorge: Maj. Roger Chapman, Jim Masters
11 Numbers and distribution of crocodiles, *C. porosus* and *C. novaguinea*: Jerome Montague
12 Botanical collections: Jim Croft, Osia Gideon
13 Collections of amphibians and reptiles: Ian Redmond

Offshore projects

14 Collections of medicinal plants from the Bismarck Archipelago: Dr David Holdsworth
15 Survey of wartime ship and aircraft wrecks, Diving leader: Capt. Tony Molony

Other projects

16 Search for *Varanus salvadorii*, Salvador's monitor lizard: Lt. Col. J N Blashford-Snell, Ian Redmond
17 Search for wartime aircraft wrecks and marking of wartime trails for Ministry of Tourism: Lt. Col. Robin Jordan, Lt. Desmond Monteith

Sulawesi

Director of Operations: Maj. Derek Jackson (retd.)
Field Leaders: Wandy Swales, Lt. Kol. John Prasanto
Quartermasters: WOl Keith Crawford, Sgt. John Cornish, Maj. Ted Carradus
Engineers: Bob Powell, Cpl. Mike Prior, Cpl. John Rimmer
Signals: Capt. Ray Lloyd-Jones, Sgt. Bob Hooper, Sgt. Narjang Gurung, Sgt. Kelvin Cunningham
Diving team: Robbie Williamson, Lt. Robin Bacon, Peter Dury, LAC Gary Brindle
Support Groups: Sgt. Ben Cartwright, David Smith, Eddie McGee, Bernadine Holmes, Chris Owen, Chal Shute, Charles Bailey, Sandy Evans

1 Topographic survey, Morowali nature reserve: Sgt. Phil Maye, L/Cpl. Alan Bretherton
2 Vegetation mapping and evaluation of satellite imagery applications: Arie Budiman, Dedy Darnaedi, Robert Warwick-Smith, M H Halim
3 Collections of small mammals from lowland forest and Gn. Tambusisi: Dr Christopher Watts (rodents), Benjamin Gaskell (bats)
4 Inventory survey of different bird species: Bill Timmis
5 Entomological collections: Maj. Anthony Bedford-Russell (Rhopalocera), Martin Brendell (Coleoptera)
6 Botanical collections and studies of pollination biology: Dr Peter Kevan, Dr Andrew Lack, Geoff Grimes
7 Geological and soil survey: Dr Luckman Effendi
8 Aerial walkway project: Dr Stephen Sutton, Dr Christopher Rees, Jan Morton, Dr Andrew Lack
9 Production of World Wildlife Fund Management Plan: Dr Andrew Laurie, Andrew Mitchell, Dr Richard Watling
10 Comparative medical research project: Dr Ian Gauntlett, Dr Margaret Long, Dr Ferdy Limengka, Nurse Mary Garner, Nurse Claire Bertschinger, Nurse Fiona Muat
11 Socio-economic survey: in addition to the above projects the Young Explorers made a major contribution to the collection of information about local people living in Morowali nature reserve and its environs. This included mapping settlements, recording population, place names, trade and lines of communication.

Offshore projects

12 Coastal coral reef survey of Morowali nature reserve: Prapto Darsono
13 Zoological and botanical collections from the Banggai Islands: Dr Patricia Holdway
14 Survey of Vesuvius reef and search for Drake's cannons: Dr Patricia Holdway, Lt. Robin Bacon

15 Coral reef surveys in the Banggai Islands and Tomori Bay in association with the Indonesian research vessel *Samudera*: Dr Kastoro, Operation Drake diving team, Dr Patricia Holdway, Fiona Muat
16 Search for dugongs *Dugong dugon* and survey of sea grass beds: John Blower

Indian Ocean Crossing

1 Community projects on Cocos Keeling Islands: Tony Wildgoose
2 Collections of some of the world's rarest plants, *Toxocarpus schimperianus* and *Medusagyne oppositifolia* in the Seychelles: Dr Ian Swingland
3 Census of giant tortoise *Geochelone gigantea* populations of Frigate and Curieuse Islands, Seychelles: Dr Ian Swingland
4 Census of breeding populations of sooty terns *Sterna fuscata* on African Banks: Dr Ian Swingland, Dr Patricia Holdway
5 Mapping and coral survey of Curieuse Bay, Seychelles: Dr Patricia Holdway

Kenya

Director of Operations: Lt. Col. J N Blashford-Snell
Operations Officers: Capt. Mark Mans, Maj. Peter Marett
Quartermasters: Lt. Col. Ernie Dury, Lt. Col. Stan Huggett
TAC HQ Staff: Cathryn Barker, Andrew Laidlaw, Carolyn Longhurst, Jennifer Stephens
Group Leaders: Capt. Ian Gardiner, Capt. Charles Weston-Baker, Richard Snailham, Lt. Nick Ray, Charles Bailey, Ken Norman
Signals: Sgt. John Topping, Cpl. Neil Davie, Cpl. John Lathbury
Engineers and transport: Lt. Hugh Brown, WO2 John Leach, Cpl. Ray Thomas, Peter Dury

1 Survey and excavation of the mediaeval town of Shanga: Mark Horton, Athman Lali, Maria Mabee, Kate Clark, Mike Carter, Janet Brooke
2 Study of the reef intertidal zone and assessment of tourist damage to reefs off Casuarina point: James Dumont. Diving leader: Sgt. Ian MacDonald
3 Counts of large herbivores in Masai Mara Game Reserve: Mworia Mugambe, Andrew Mitchell
4 Construction of cattle dips in Masai Mara Game Reserve: Lt. Peter Cosgrove
5 Peripheral survey of Lake Turkana: Alec Duff MacKay, Cunningham van Someren
6 Boundary marking of Sibiloi National Park: Capt. Ian Gardiner, Sandy Evans
7 Camel treks through Chalbi desert region: Capt. Charles Weston-Baker, Fiona Alexander, Richard Snailham
8 Construction of entrance walkway to Ark Lodge: Lt. Nick Ray, Charles Bailey
9 Exploration and collection of zoological and botanical specimens from Susua crater: Lt. Col. J N Blashford-Snell, Ian Redmond

The Journey Home

1 Community projects in Egypt: Col. John Hines
2 Pollution monitoring experiment in association with UNEP and the Goodyear airship *Europa*: Prof. Wolfgang Nürnberg, Prof. Aristeo Renzoni, Dr Brian Wannamaker
3 Ascent of Tizi-n-Ougane, Atlas Mountains, Morocco: Hamish Brown

Unfortunately it is not possible to include here a complete list of those who took part or of the projects carried out. This information can be found in the expedition reports available through the Scientific Exploration Society.

The Young Explorers

PHASE I G. Arngrimsson (Iceland), E. Van Asbeck (NZ), A. Bonnick (UK), M. Browne (UK), R. Burke (Canada), S. Campbell (UK), S. Chadwick (UK), J. Denny (UK), K. Henderson (UK), M. Henrys (UK), N. Hopkins (UK), R. Jackleman (UK), N. Kean-Hammerson (UK), N. Lang (UK), D. Limbu (Nepal), M. Limbu (Nepal), C. McHugh (UK), M. Newman (UK), D. Newton (NZ), R. O'Connor (UK), P. Shea (UK), B. Shopland (Canada), J. Wright (UK).

PHASE II S. Arthur (UK), S. Barrow (UK), I. Bennett (Panama), R. Bennett (Panama), T. Burns (Canal Zone), J. Bracewell (UK), J. Calland (UK), M. Clark (UK), A. Courtney (UK), C. Davies (UK), K. Drinkwater (UK), M. Fong (Panama), D. French (UK), T. Grey (Canada), E. Guardia (Panama), I. Hillier (UK), H. Mallinson (UK), D. McAlpine (Canada), S. McCallum (UK), J. McGregor (UK), E. McMillan (Panama), D. Meechan (UK), R. Murray (Canada), C. Ong (UK), R. Pascoe (Panama), N. Peberdy (UK), H. Preston (UK), A. Richards (Canada), N. Simpson (Canada), A. Smith (Canada), F. Welstead (UK), P. Whitehouse (UK), J. Wiggins (UK), C. Willis (UK), M. Wright (UK).

PHASE III R. Adrian (Canada), J. Barlow (Australia), L. Batt-Rawden (UK), A. Beresford Foster (Australia), S. Brown (Australia), B. Buckley (UK), G. Combes (Canada), M. Creer (Canada), C. Downes (USA), J. Flavell (NZ), C. Goy (Australia), W. Hargroves (USA), A. Houiellebecq (UK), J. Howard (USA), C. Lawrence (Canada), D. Mills (UK), D. Patterson (NZ), N. Person (USA), G. Rice (UK), D. Rickleen (USA), T. Spence (UK), S. Turton (UK), J. Wall (USA), I. Murray White (UK), G. Whitelaw (S. Africa).

PHASE IV P. Beale (UK), S. Budibent (UK), J. Catt (UK), R. Chandler (Australia), P. Cosgrove-McGuirk (UK), S. Davis (NZ), K. Ditges (Germany), S. Gambier (UK), A. Gay (UK), L. Gibbons (UK), W. Goodwin (USA), C. Hale (UK), G. Harch (Australia), P. Harrison (Australia), D. Huber (UK), R. Hunter (UK), A. Keller (Australia), T. Linehan (USA), M. McKee (NZ), P. Oakes (Australia), R. Paterson (NZ), A. Penney (UK), A. Poole (Australia), C. Richardson (UK), M. Stockdale (Australia), J. Suchy (Canada), N. Waghorn (USA), G. Watson (UK), P. Wesley (UK).

PHASE V T. Akivi (Papua New Guinea), B. Bathe (NZ), B. Boloti (Papua New Guinea), D. Brough (UK), C. Buxton (UK), C. Chapon (UK), R. Charette (USA), M. Clough (UK), S. Collins (Australia), P. Daur (Papua New Guinea), S. Elisha (Papua New Guinea), F. Elly (Papua New Guinea), A. Fila (USA), K. Foellmer (Canada), E. Francis (Papua New Guinea), S. Gibson (NZ), S. Glass (USA), C. Greham (Australia), G. Griffiths (Australia), M. Grosze (USA), C. Hall (UK), M. Heinrich (USA), J. Henderson (Australia), C. Hignell (UK), C. Hobden (Australia), M. Holt (Australia), J. Hulo (Papua New Guinea), R. Jacques (USA), J. Johns (Papua New Guinea), S. Jupuc (Papua New Guinea), S. Kamia (Papua New Guinea), D. Keeley (Australia), W. Kepelei (Papua New Guinea), B. Koiti (Papua New Guinea), G. Kunlong (Papua New Guinea), J. Kupul (Papua New Guinea), A. Lakamanga (Papua New Guinea), B. Laker (Papua New Guinea), F. Lewis (Australia), H. Lufa (Papua New Guinea), S. Lulupa (Papua New Guinea), P. Mann (Australia), D. Mansell (UK), B. McDonald (Canada), F. Mingen (Papua New Guinea), K. Morobe (Papua New Guinea), S. Mountford (NZ), T. Mouvaira (Papua New Guinea), C. Munagun (Papua New Guinea), I. Munei (Papua New Guinea), Q. Narampan (Papua New Guinea), O. Nimita (Papua New Guinea), P. Om (Korea), B. Pilokos (Papua New Guinea), B. Rhind (Australia), P. Sharpen (Papua New Guinea), H. Sigurdardottir (Iceland), S. Sinsick (Papua New Guinea), T. Sipo (Papua New Guinea), M. Steven (Papua New Guinea), D. Tarnas (USA), L. Thompson (UK), F. Tomangana (Papua New Guinea), M. Turnbull (UK), J. Varagi (Papua New Guinea), P. Vakaloloma (Fiji), J. Violaris (Papua New Guinea), B. Wamoi (Papua New Guinea), T. Wanzing (Papua New Guinea), J. Wemin (Papua New Guinea), A. Wilcox (UK), V. Wohinga (Papua New Guinea), W. Yamuna (Papua New Guinea).

PHASE VI R. Baldock (Australia), A. Beavis (Australia), M. Brookes (Australia), W. Bygrave (UK), D. Coleman (Australia), H. Erf (USA), T. Du-Feu (UK), L. Fogarty (Australia), K. Gurung (Nepal), B. Jackson (Canada), N. Johnson (UK), C. Kaczmarek (Australia), S. Mattson (Australia), A. McPherson (UK), C. Merryweather (UK), A. Miller (Australia), S. Rice (Australia), S. Rigley (UK), A. Roberts (Australia), T. Roberts (UK), A. Savage (UK), A. Short (Australia), R. Tarlov (USA), L. Wakefield (Australia), J. Warne (UK), I. Westlake (Australia), P. Wright (Australia), S. Young (UK).

PHASE VII N. Adwin (Indonesia), I. Ain (Indonesia), T. Alamsyah (Indonesia), B. Atkinson (Australia), Atmaji (Indonesia), A. Cannon (UK), L. Carter (USA), E. Cecil (USA), C. Cheung (Hong Kong), C. Cotton (USA), P. Ellison (UK), N. English (UK), D. Etter (USA), C. Flather (USA), R. Hakim (Indonesia), J. Hardjono (Indonesia), B. Harris (USA), D. Hudson (Australia), E. Jones (USA), A. Latief (Indonesia), P. Lau (Hong Kong), C. Leung (Hong Kong), J. Levens (USA), Puspa Liman (Indonesia), L. Lumingas (Indonesia), A. Lyall (Australia), M. Mahamit (Indonesia), S. Manning (UK), A. Melville (USA), J. Milbank (USA), D. Moffat (Australia, B. Om (Indonesia), T. Parenghuam (Indonesia), E. Reppie (Indonesia), S. Richardson (UK), Z. Ridayah (Indonesia), A. Sabarung (Indonesia), E. Setiawan (Indonesia), F. Siu (Hong Kong), J. Southey (Australia), Sularto (Indonesia), R. Tantu (Indonesia), E. Wardhana (Indonesia), M. Wibisono (Indonesia), C. Wong (Hong Kong).

PHASE VIII B. Arnvidarson (Iceland), W. Bird (UK), D. Burroughs (Canada), J. Byrne (UK), J. Dank (USA), C. Darrah (UK), E. Dolan (USA), G. De Francis (USA), T. Hood (UK), C. James (USA), S. Llewelyn (UK), W. Lowdon (UK), D. Macleod (USA), E. Marquis (UK), P. Morris (USA), H. Nisenbaum (Canada), H. Pettigrew (UK), R. Poskus (UK), M. Schnitger (USA), M. Smart (UK), R. Titmarsh (UK), P. Ward (UK).

PHASE VIIIA R. Araujo (Panama), C. Avila (Panama), O. Ayim (Kenya), S. Ballantyne (UK), J. Barnley (Kenya), J. Bell (Kenya), F. Brancato (Gibraltar), A. Bridger (Zimbabwe), A. Campbell (UK), T. Catton (UK), B. Chong (Hong Kong), F. Davey (Kenya), P. Dobbs (UK), D.

Elliot (UK), I. Ellman-Brown (Zimbabwe), N. Galma (Kenya), G. George (Zimbabwe), A. Gibson (UK), R. Hopkins (UK), B. Ingolfsdottir (Iceland), G. Johnstone (UK), B. Jude (UK), P. Kamau (Kenya), K. Kassam (Kenya), D. King (Zimbabwe), B. Kisilu (Kenya), R. Knight (Kenya), K. Kuck (Kenya), C. Langat (Kenya), P. Lawton (UK), A. Maara (Kenya), H. Madyavanhu (Zimbabwe), P. Mangla (Kenya), R. Mangoka (Kenya), A. Mar (Fiji), A. Marshall (Zimbabwe), C. Mason (Zimbabwe), A. Mazvidzo (Zimbabwe), S. Mbuguah (Kenya), C. Moscrop (Hong Kong), B. Moss (UK), T. Moss (UK), G. Moyo (Zimbabwe), A. Musiiwa (Zimbabwe), V. Mutasa (Zimbabwe), S. Ndegwa (Kenya), W. Ndongi (Kenya), M. Ngundo (Kenya), A. Niemandt (Zimbabwe), K. Njururi (Kenya), S. Odonga (Kenya), W. Oduor (Kenya), B. Okatch (Kenya), P. Onyando (Kenya), D. Osu (UK), R. Rioga (Zimbabwe), E. Rugoiyo (Kenya), M. Shah (Kenya), V. Sikuku (Kenya), A. Smithdorf (Zimbabwe), E. Sutcliffe (UK), I. Tapiwa (Zimbabwe), P. Todd (UK), S. Vincent (Zimbabwe), S. Walton (UK), N. Watson (Zimbabwe), B. Williams (UK), T. Williams (UK), W. Yamuna (Papua New Guinea).

PHASE IX S. Abbott (USA), R. Boalch (UK), B. Burns (USA), M. Cohen (USA), S. Crockett (UK), G. Dade (UK), C. Evans (UK), B. Finnie (Canada), D. Hackett (USA), J. Hood (UK), C. Jackman (UK), M. Japan (Kenya), R. Johnson (UK), K. Jones (UK), A. McBrine (UK), C. Mead (UK), G. Morgan (UK), A. Pearson (USA), A. Rawson (USA), P. Ryan (Australia), S. Thomas (UK), M. Totton (UK), B. Wasuna (Kenya), A. Wotton (UK), D. Yates (UK).

In addition a total of 38 cadets from B.P. Tanker Co. Ltd. joined the expedition during Phases II and V.

Further reading

Allen, R. *How to Save the World. World Conservation Strategy.* Kogan Page, 1980.

Ayensu, E. S. *Jungles.* Jonathan Cape, 1980. (World Wildlife Fund recommended)

Baker, Robin (ed.). *Mystery of Migration.* Macdonald and Janes, 1980.

Bellamy, D. *Botanic Man.* Hamlyn, 1978.

Blashford-Snell, J. and Ballantine, A. *Expeditions: The Experts' Way.* Faber & Faber, 1977.

Blashford-Snell, J. and Cable, M. *Operation Drake.* W. H. Allen, 1981.

Brandt, W. *North South – A Programme for Survival.* Report of the Independent Commission on International Development Issues. Pan Books, 1980.

Chittick, H. N. 'Discoveries in the Lamu Archipelago'. *Azania, Vol. II,* 1967.

Cott, H. B. *Looking at Animals: A Zoologist in Africa.* Collins, 1975.

d'Albertis, L. M. *New Guinea: What I Did and What I Saw.* Low, 1880.

Dousset, R. and Taillemite, E. *The Great Book of the Pacific.* Chartwell Books, 1979.

Eltringham, S. K. *The Ecology and Conservation of Large African Mammals.* Macmillan, 1979.

Gash, N. and Whittaker, J. *A Pictorial History of Papua New Guinea.* Jacaranda Press, 1975.

George, D. and J. *Marine Life: An Illustrated Encyclopaedia of Invertebrates in the Sea.* Harrap, 1979.

Hardy, A. *Open Sea: Its Natural History Vol. 1 The World of Plankton.* Collins, 1971.

Hillaby, J. *Journey to the Jade Sea.* Constable, 1964.

Höhnel, L. R. von. *Lakes Rudolf and Stefanie. Teleki's expedition 1887–1888.* Longman, 1894.

Jensen, A. C. *Wildlife of the Oceans.* Harry N. Abrams, 1979.

Kirkman, J. S. *Men and Monuments on the East African Coast.* Lutterworth Press, 1964.

Knox-Johnston, R. *The Twilight of Sail.* Sidgwick & Jackson, 1978.

Leakey, R. E. *The Illustrated Origin of Species by Charles Darwin.* (Abridged) Faber & Faber, 1979.

MacGregor, D. R. *Square rigged sailing ships.* Argus Books, 1977.

McKee, A. *The Queen's Corsair, Drake's journey of circumnavigation.* Souvenir Press, 1978.

Marsh, R. O. *White Indians of Darien.* G. P. Putnam's Sons, 1934.

Myers, N. *The Sinking Ark.* Pergamon Press, 1979.

Newby, E. *The World Atlas of Exploration.* Mitchell Beazley, 1975.

Osterberg, C. and Keckes, S. 'The State of Pollution in the Mediterranean Sea'. *Ambio 6,* 1977.

Prebble, J. *The Darien Disaster.* Secker & Warburg, 1968.

Richards, C. G. *Count Teleki and the Discovery of Lakes Rudolf and Stefanie.* Macmillan, 1960.

Richards, P. W. *The Tropical Rainforest.* Cambridge University Press, 1952.

Simon, N. and Geroudet, P. *Last Survivors.* Edita Lausanne, 1970.

UNEP. *Experts meeting on Tropical Forests. Overview Document.* UNEP/WG/35/4, United Nations Environment Programme, Nairobi, 1980.

Vaux, W. S. W. *The World Encompassed.* Hakluyt, Burt Franklin, 1854. Originally published by the Drake family, 1628.

Wallace, A. R. *The Malay Archipelago.* Dover Publications, 1962. Originally published by Macmillan, 1869.

Whitmore, T. C. *Tropical Rain Forests of the Far East.* Clarendon Press, Oxford, 1975.

Wilson, D. *The World Encompassed. Drake's Great Voyage 1577–1580.* Hamish Hamilton, 1977.

World Conservation Strategy. Published jointly by IUCN, WWF and UNEP. Gland, 1980.

Index

Acknowledgements

Colour
Hussein Adan 175, 179; Aquila Photographics: Gary R. Jones 87; John Blashford-Snell, 202; Hamish Brown 194; Mike Christy 67; Ben Gaskell 103, 114, 126, 131; Mark Horton 158; Bill Johnstone, Magic Lantern Ltd. 190 (top); Andrew Mitchell 50, 70, 102, 166, 190 (bottom), 206; A. van den Nieuwenhuizen 71; Ian Redmond 106; Rupert Ridgeway 127, 138, 143; Ray Pringle-Scott 55; Christopher Sainsbury, title spread, 19, 22, 26, 31, 35, 47, 62, 91, 94, 98, 146, 150, 170, 186, 210, endpaper.

Black-and-white
Hussein Adan 177; Borkur Arnvidarson 152 (bottom); John Blashford-Snell 56, 79 (top), 120; British Museum 154 (bottom); Philip Coffey 79; Richard J. Davis 169 (top), 174, 180, 196, 197; Lawrence Ford 32; R. Grey 121; J. Harris 104 (bottom); Mark Horton 157 (top), 159, 160; ILEA 199; Hakan Lagergren 36 (right); Nigel Lang 111, 167, 168; Maria Mabeé 49; Mansell Collection 9, 10, 89 (left), 142, 154 (top); Ministry of Information, Fiji 93; Ministry of Information, Kenya 182 (left); Andrew Mitchell 44, 73 (top), 76 (right and left), 108, 112, 113, 128, 129, 135, 137, 140, 165, 169 (bottom), 189 (left and right), 198, 212; National Library of Scotland 48 (right); Bill Neumeister 116, 118, 193; Adrian Penny 104 (top); Rupert Ridgeway 124 (bottom), 125, 133 (top and bottom), 136, 145 (top and bottom), 200, 203, 205, 214; Toby Roberts 195; Christopher Sainsbury 11, 13, 16, 17, 18, 24, 25 (left and right), 28, 29, 36 (left), 37, 42, 43, 48 (left), 52, 59, 65, 73 (bottom), 74 (top and bottom), 75, 80, 82, 86, 89 (right), 96, 97, 130, 148, 152 (top), 153, 157 (bottom), 182 (right), 184, 188, 208, 213; Ian Swingland 83; World Wildlife Fund: Marcus Borner 60 (left), Mark Boulton 172, Glyn Davies 60 (right).

Fact boxes: text contributions
Hussein Adan 177; Ben Gaskell 130; Mark Horton 46, 160; Ian S. Menzies 110; Andrew Mitchell 21, 33, 68, 92, 102, 119, 123, 144, 149, 172, 192; Ian Redmond 120; Christopher Rees 76; Andrew Sugden 70; Ian Swingland 84.